10169

D1233383

RADIATIVE HEAT TRANSFER

Consulting Editor

RICHARD J. GROSH

Purdue University

RADIATIVE HEAT TRANSFER

TOM J. LOVE

University of Oklahoma

CHARLES E. MERRILL PUBLISHING COMPANY, COLUMBUS, OHIO

A Bell & Howell Company

Library of Congress Catalog Card Number: 68-18876

PRINTED IN THE UNITED STATES OF AMERICA

1 2 3 4 5—72 71 70 69 68

Preface

The study of radiative heat transfer is concerned with the prediction of the net rate at which electromagnetic energy of thermal origin flows through a thermodynamic control surface of interest. In general, the purpose of such a study is to contribute a quantitative prediction of the thermal radiation exchange in an energy balance of a system. Almost invariably, conduction and convection modes of heat transfer are present either at the boundary of the system of interest or within the system. Some simple examples of approaches to problems involving the analysis of these combined effects are presented in Chapter 7. However, the analysis of the radiative mode of heat transfer itself presents a rather complicated problem and requires a type of mathematics and visualization which is somewhat different from that encountered in most undergraduate engineering programs. For this reason, this book is primarily concerned with the development of a model for visualizing thermal radiation, and with ways of simplifying this general model by making assumptions which permit solutions useable as engineering approximations.

The wave model of electromagnetic radiation is helpful in predicting the reflection characteristics for smooth surfaces, visualizing the effects of diffraction, and dealing with other problems associated with the relative size of a particle of matter and the wavelength of the interacting radiation. However, to visualize most radiative heat transfer analyses, the "particle-like" photon model may be used. Although, with the exception of Monte Carlo techniques, we do not attempt literally to trace and count the photons streaming between the elements of our system, the mental picture

v

of these energy packets streaming between surfaces and bouncing away or being absorbed is often helpful.

To appreciate the complexity of precise prediction of radiative heat transfer, one may observe the room about him and attempt to formulate a mathematical expression which will predict the amount of light falling on any area of the room as several light sources are moved about the room or varied in magnitude. This is the problem of radiative heat transfer—with one additional major complication. Every bit of matter in the room is a source of thermal radiation which varies in magnitude as its temperature changes. Because each surface contributes both emitted and reflected radiation which varies in a complicated way with direction depending on its roughness configuration, its composition, and its state of contamination, precise prediction becomes almost a hopeless task. Available precision will improve only with increased utilization of large-scale high-speed computers, not only for computational purposes, but for the recording, storage and retrieval of the properties of matter. Because the era of the computer is just beginning, this book includes the discussion of some concepts which are not yet useful in obtaining numbers for general usage. It is hoped that some of these models will prove helpful to persons involved in the development of more precise analytical predictions and experimental determinations.

Simplified models for radiative exchange predictions are not slighted. The solutions for the lumped system approximation to enclosures bounded by diffuse opaque surfaces are presented in matrix notation for both evacuated enclosures and those containing a non-scattering participating media. This presentation differs slightly from Hottel's or Gebhardt's notation, but is essentially equivalent and is more adaptable for current digital computer methods.

Although only a limited number of practical problems may be solved utilizing the solutions for integral equations, I feel that it is important for persons working in the field to be familiar with this approach, which emphasizes the fact that radiosity varies as a function of geometrical coordinates.

I would like to caution teachers who use this book as a text against spending too much time on Chapter 2. The subject matter has been included to give some insight into the electromagnetic nature of thermal radiation and, if properly developed, could form the subject of several courses. My own tendency and that of those colleagues who have used the manuscript is to become engrossed in this chapter and not have sufficient time to cover later topics which are more directly involved in heat transfer predictions.

I am deeply indebted to many persons who have contributed and assisted in the development of this book. It started with a very excellent course taught by Professor R. J. Grosh at Purdue University and has evolved through courses taught by the author at the University of Oklahoma. The inspiration, encouragement and foundation provided by Dr. Grosh are sincerely appreciated. Although there have been too many to mention by name, I am grateful to the students in my courses whose frank comments and criticisms were particularly helpful. I do wish to recognize gratefully some of my colleagues who have utilized various versions of the notes and manuscripts in their classes, and who have made valuable comments and suggestions: Dr. C. A. Fritsch of the Bell Laboratories, Professor D. C. Hamilton and Professor Robert Watts of Tulane University, Professor J. H. Lawrence of Texas Technological College, Professor W. A. Beckman of the University of Wisconsin, Professor Maurice Wildin of the University of New Mexico, and Professor J. E. Francis of the University of Oklahoma.

The patience and care with which the secretaries of the School of Aerospace and Mechanical Engineering typed the various sets of class notes are particularly appreciated. Special thanks are due Wanda Sharpton, Lynda Nolen and Joann Wilkes for their work on the various versions of the book.

TOM J. LOVE

Norman, Oklahoma

March 1, 1968

Table of Contents

Chapter **6**

ABSORBING, EMITTING AND SCATTERING MEDIA   **139**

Chapter **7**

COMBINED RADIATION, CONDUCTION AND CONVECTION   **163**

Chapter **8**

EXPERIMENTAL METHODS   **174**

RADIATIVE HEAT TRANSFER

1   Introduction

It is the purpose of the ensuing chapters to provide a logical foundation for the development of methods for the prediction of energy transport by thermal radiation. It is well known that thermal radiation is electromagnetic energy propagation and is characterized by a frequency range which includes the visible portion of the electromagnetic spectrum and extends through the infrared. It is distinguished as "thermal" radiation by virtue of its origin. Because of this origin, which is the thermal agitation of microscopic matter, there exists a type of statistical distribution of the energy with respect to frequency. It was the study of this distribution that led to the development of the quantum mechanics, which provides man's best current model for the microscopic behavior of matter.

The engineer concerned with improving methods of predicting radiative heat transfer should study current literature in such fields as optics, illumination, radio and microwave propagation, astrophysics, plasma physics, spectroscopy, colloid chemistry, and meteorology. It should be noted that the objective of a heat transfer analysis or design is usually somewhat different from the objectives of other disciplines. However, the laws of the interaction of electromagnetic energy and matter are quite general.

The problems of radiative heat transfer that concern the engineer may normally be categorized as radiant energy exchanges between surfaces that emit and reflect radiant energy separated by (1) free space, (2) homogeneous, absorbing and emitting, but partially transmitting, media, and (3) clouds of particulate media which scatter the radiation as well as absorb and emit energy. Computational methods and the approximations involved with such methods will be discussed in detail in separate chapters. Because the interaction of electromagnetic energy and matter is dependent on the frequency of the radiation and its direction of propagation, it is desirable that we begin our discussion with some of the theories of the nature of thermal radiation. These discussions will include some implications of classical thermodynamic reasoning, quantum statistical explanation of energy distribution with frequency, and the elements of electromagnetic wave theory.

It is important that the reader have certain definitions clearly in mind. This is particularly necessary since there has been considerable variation in nomenclature with little standardization. The principal quantity that describes a radiation field is the intensity.* In order to describe the intensity of a radiation field, it may be helpful to visualize an imaginary plane with a differential element of area through which radiant energy streams just as a beam of light from a flashlight lens. The magnitude of the intensity is the rate at which the electromagnetic energy (thermal radiation) streams through the differential area in any direction contained within a differential solid angle about the normal to the imaginary plane. The symbol I will be utilized to denote the intensity function. The definition for intensity (I) is given as the *radiating electromagnetic energy leaving or approaching a differential element of area of an imaginary plane within the time interval t and t + dt and having a direction of propagation contained in a differential solid angle $d\omega$ whose central direction is normal to the imaginary plane.*

It should be noted that the dimensions of intensity are

$$I = \frac{\text{Energy}}{\text{Area} \times \text{Time} \times \text{Stearadian}} \qquad \text{(1-1)}$$

It can be seen that intensity is a vector quantity and that, as the imaginary plane is rotated in space, the intensity will vary with the direction of the plane.

In defining intensity in terms of differential elements, it is important to note that the implication is that it is described by a limiting process in each of the differential variables. This gives rise to a very important property of the intensity of radiation. *The intensity is invariant along its propagation path in free space.* That is, the radiation leaving a surface

---

*Intensity as defined here agrees with the nomenclature generally used in engineering and astrophysics literature. The term *stearadiancy* is used in most optics literature.

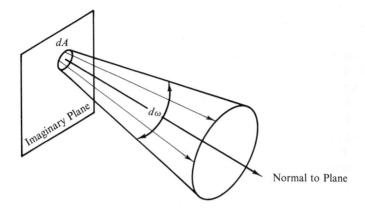

Figure 1-1.

will be characterized by the same value of intensity at any distance from its origin along a straight line in free space. This property becomes very important in formulating the radiative exchange between surfaces.

A quantity closely associated, and sometimes confused with, intensity is *flux.** In this work, it will be denoted by the symbol q. Flux is also a vector quantity. It is defined as the *radiant energy leaving or approaching a differential element of area of an imaginary plane within a time interval $t + dt$ in all directions in the hemispherical solid angle bounded by the imaginary plane*. The flux (q) is thus the total rate of radiant energy flow and has the dimensions

$$q = \frac{\text{Energy}}{\text{Area} \times \text{Time}} \tag{1-2}$$

The relationship between intensity and flux is of particular importance. The intensity vector actually describes the flux in any direction. It can be readily seen that integration of the intensity over the hemisphere will give the flux if a suitable correction is included to account for the projected area. Thus, the intensity may be termed a generating function for the flux. Note that the differential element of area associated with intensity is normal to the central direction of the propagation.

In Figure 1-2, dA refers to the differential element of area pertaining to the flux and dA' pertains to the intensity. Note that $dA' = \cos \theta \, dA$.

The differential solid angle including the energy flow defined by the

---

*Flux is called *radiancy* in optics literature.

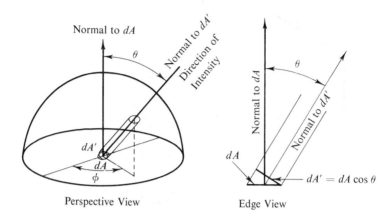

Perspective View   Edge View

Figure 1-2. Geometry relating intensity and flux.

magnitude of the intensity may be written as

$$d\omega = \sin \theta \, d\theta \, d\phi \qquad (1\text{-}3)$$

where θ is the polar angle between the direction of the intensity and the normal to the plane at which the flux is desired, and ϕ is the azimuthal angle measured from any convenient reference. The relationship between intensity and flux is then expressed by

$$q = \int_0^{2\pi} \int_0^{\pi/2} I \cos \theta \, \sin \theta \, d\theta \, d\phi \qquad (1\text{-}4)$$

It is more convenient to utilize the notation $\mu = \cos \theta$.

$$q = \int_0^{2\pi} \int_0^1 I \mu \, d\mu \, d\phi \qquad (1\text{-}5)$$

It can readily be seen that Equation (1-5) gives a result $q = \pi I$ for an isotropic intensity field. If the intensity of the thermal radiation emitted from a surface does not vary with direction, it is sometimes referred to as a *Lambertonian surface*. In this book, such a surface will be designated as a *diffusely-emitting surface*.

It should be noted that the flux defines the energy flow only in a positive direction as referred to the normal of the differential area. Normally, a net flux is the ultimate objective of engineering computation. The net flux will be designated Q and defined as *the difference between the radiant flux in the directions referred to the positive normal to the imaginary plane and the radiant flux in the directions referred to the negative direction.* In terms of the intensity, Q may be determined by the following integration, where μ is measured from the positive normal.

$$Q = \int_0^{2\pi} \int_{-1}^{+1} I\mu \, d\mu \, d\phi \qquad (1\text{-}6)$$

It can be readily shown that this is equivalent to

$$Q = q^+ - q^- \qquad (1\text{-}7)$$

where q^+ refers to the flux in the positive direction and q^- refers to the flux in the negative direction.

Many fluxes encountered in engineering practice may be considered monodirectional. Solar radiation is an example. It should be noted, however, that it is impossible for a flux to be absolutely monodirectional. Consider Figure 1-3 where the sun irradiates a surface at some distance approximating the radius of the earth's orbit. The intensity of the flux incident on the surface is zero for all angles not included in the solid angle subtended by the sun at the surface. Within the solid angle, the intensity of solar radiation may be assumed constant.

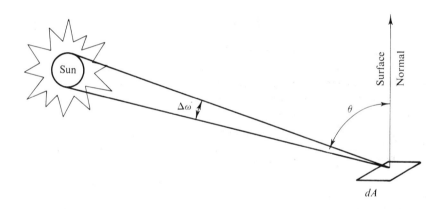

Figure 1-3. An example of a monodirectional flux.

The flux incident would then be determined by Equation 1-5 to be

$$q_{\text{solar}} = I_{\text{solar}} \cos \theta \, \Delta\omega \qquad (1\text{-}8)$$

The dimensions of the flux would be energy per unit of time and per unit of surface area. The solid angle $\Delta\omega$ may be readily determined by dividing the projected area of the sun by the square of the distance from the sun. In a similar manner, the flux from any distant object may be computed. The more complicated problem of accounting for and predicting intensity variations will be the main object of later chapters.

The results of the interaction of radiant energy and matter depends in part on the frequency characterizing the radiant energy. For example, the eye distinguishes frequency in the visible portion of the spectrum as color. For this reason, a beam of electromagnetic radiation consisting of a very narrow range of frequency is called a *monochromatic beam*. The monochromatic intensity will be designated as I_v and defined as the *radiating electromagnetic energy characterized by a frequency within the differential interval v and $v + dv$, leaving a differential element of area of an imaginary plane within the time interval t and $t + dt$ and having a direction of propagation contained in a differential solid angle $d\omega$ whose central direction is normal to the imaginary plane.*

The dimensions of monochromatic intensity are

$$I_v = \frac{\text{Energy}}{\text{Area} \times \text{Time} \times \text{Stearadian} \times (1/\text{Time})} = \frac{\text{Energy}}{\text{Area} \times \text{Stearadian}}$$

(1-9)

The relationship between intensity and monochromatic intensity can be seen to be

$$I = \int_0^\infty I_v \, dv$$

(1-10)

Similarly, the monochromatic flux q_v and the monochromatic net flux Q_v may be defined as *that part of a flux or net flux that is characterized by a frequency in the interval between v and $v + dv$.*

Frequency has been purposely chosen to designate the monochromatic field properties. The reason for this choice is that the energy of a photon is proportional to the frequency and is conserved as the photon traverses different media. It is well known, however, that the speed of propagation of light varies with different media. Thus, the wavelength corresponding to a fixed frequency will vary with the media through which the energy propagates.

The definitions presented in this chapter serve as a basis for the development of a vocabulary to be utilized in understanding and predicting radiative heat transfer. Several exercises are provided to give practice in visualization of these definitions and to assist in the familiarization process. In later chapters, this familiarity will help the reader to understand the complicated geometrical relationships that must be utilized in the analysis of radiative transfer.

PROBLEMS

1. Using an energy balance, show that the intensity of solar radiation is not a function of distance from the sun.

2. If the solar flux is 420 (Btu)(hr^{-1})(ft^{-2}) at one mean earth distance from the sun, what is the solar intensity?

3. A diffusely-emitting plane surface, A_1, having an area of 1 ft^2 and intensity of I is parallel to and directly opposite a small plane of equal area, A_2. The distance separating the surfaces is 20 ft. Compute the fraction of the flux emitted by A_1 that is incident on A_2.

4. A flux with an intensity that is axially symmetric with respect to a surface normal is incident on the surface. If the intensity is described as

$$I(\mu) \equiv I \qquad 1 \geq \mu \geq \tfrac{1}{2}$$
$$I(\mu) \equiv 0 \qquad \tfrac{1}{2} > \mu \geq 0$$

Determine the incident flux in terms of I.

5. Compute the flux incident on an elemental plane area parallel to a semi-infinite plane slab that emits radiant energy in a uniform diffuse manner. The intensity of the emission is I. The area element is located opposite the edge of the semi-infinite surface. See Figure P.1-5.

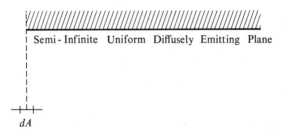

Semi-Infinite Uniform Diffusely Emitting Plane

dA

Figure P.1-5.

6. A surface emits thermal radiation such that the intensity of emission varies in accord with the relationship

$$I = I_0(\cos \theta)^{0.2}$$

Compute the emitted flux in terms of I_0.

7. The intensity of a flux reflected from a surface varies in accord with the following relationship:

$$I \equiv I_0 \cos \theta \cos \phi \qquad -\frac{\pi}{2} \leq \phi \leq +\frac{\pi}{2}$$
$$I \equiv 0 \qquad \text{all other } \phi$$

Determine the reflected flux.

8. A surface emits thermal radiation in a diffuse manner with an intensity of magnitude ϵI_1. A diffuse flux having an intensity I_2 is incident on the

surface. A reflected flux leaves the surface with a uniform intensity ρI_2. Compute the net flux Q.

9. A beam of thermal radiation composed of energy characterized by a range of frequencies is incident on a perfectly smooth surface. A beam of thermal radiation is reflected by the surface from the original beam. The fraction of the energy reflected by the surface is known to vary with the frequency in accord with the function ρ_ν. In other words,

$$I_{\nu(\text{reflected})} = \rho_\nu I_{\nu(\text{incident})}$$

Find an integral expression which relates ρ_ν to ρ, if ρ is a constant such that

$$I_{\text{reflected}} = \rho I_{\text{incident}}$$

2   The Nature of
Thermal Radiation

Before proceeding to the development of methods for the prediction of radiative heat transfer, it is desirable to review some of the physics of thermal radiation.

This review will be very brief and of an elementary nature inasmuch as there are a number of excellent treatises in print that devote entire volumes to subjects mentioned in this chapter. Our purpose will therefore be to recall some of the implications of classical thermodynamics, statistical quantum mechanics, electromagnetic theory, and classical optics which apply to thermal radiation transfer.

For further study the interested reader is referred to the classical works of Planck, Lorentz, Stratton, Landau and Lifshitz, Drude, Jenkins and White, as well as numerous other texts in heat transfer, classical and statistical thermodynamics, electromagnetic theory, and optics.

2-1.   Some Implications of Classical Thermodynamics

Consider an isolated, evacuated isothermal enclosure with walls having a finite temperature T. Assume that the enclosure is completely isolated so that there is no exchange of energy with the surroundings. The enclosure will then approach thermodynamic equilibrium. The evacuated container must contain thermal radiation since the matter in the walls has a finite constant temperature. For the condition of thermal equilibrium, the walls must be emitting and absorbing energy with equal rates and the radiation field within the vacuum of the enclosure must have certain characteristics. In particular, the net flux across any imaginary plane must be identically zero for any location and orientation within the enclosure. This may be reasoned to be a direct consequence of the second law of thermodynamics. Should there be a nonzero net flux, this would mean a directed flow of energy, which is impossible in a system that is in thermodynamic equilibrium.

A further consequence is that the monochromatic net flux must be zero for all locations and orientations within the enclosure. Otherwise, a static frequency-selective device might be utilized to produce a directed flow of energy. It can also be reasoned that the *monochromatic intensity of thermal radiation within an isolated, evacuated enclosure in thermodynamic equilibrium must be homogeneous and isotropic.* It will be shown later that this condition may be utilized in the development of important relationships regarding the manner in which surfaces emit and reflect radiant energy.

At first inspection of the variables involved in the radiant field within this enclosure it might be expected that the character of the radiation would depend on both the temperature and the surface characteristics of the enclosure. The following reasoning, however, shows the radiation within the enclosure to be a function of temperature alone and independent of the surfaces of the enclosure.

Consider an opaque body to be located within the enclosure. The flux leaving the surface must be equal to the flux incident, in order to satisfy the zero net flux condition of the enclosure. Let

q_e = emitted flux

q_i = incident flux

q_r = reflected flux

ρ = the fraction of the incident flux that is reflected

Thus,

$$q_e + q_r = q_i \tag{2-1a}$$

and

$$q_e + \rho q_i = q_i \tag{2-1b}$$

or

$$q_e = (1 - \rho)q_i \tag{2-1c}$$

This relationship is an expression of Kirchhoff's law and must hold for all surfaces within the enclosure. By inserting a surface which does not reflect radiant energy (i.e., $\rho \equiv 0$), it can be seen that $q_{e,b} \equiv q_i$. In other words, the radiant energy within the enclosure must correspond to the energy emitted by a surface that does not reflect thermal radiation. Since such a surface would appear black to the eye when viewed in a reflected light, it is called a *black surface* or a *black body*. This is the reason for the subscript b in the preceeding expression. Thus, any isolated, evacuated isothermal enclosure will be filled with thermal radiation, which has a character dependent only on temperature. The monochromatic intensity of the radiation within enclosure and its dependence on temperature and frequency is a subject of considerable interest. Cavities have been constructed with small apertures that have negligible effect on the radiation within the cavity. Experimental measurements verify the fact that the field within such an enclosure does indeed depend only on the temperature. In Chapter 8, on experimental techniques, the construction and accuracy of these cavities will be discussed. The experiments also show a definite relationship in the dependence of monochromatic intensity on the frequency characterizing the radiant energy. Planck developed a theoretical model for the relationship of monochromatic intensity with frequency and temperature. This will be discussed in detail later in this chapter.

It will be noted from Expression (2-1c) that the thermal emission from an ideal black body represents a limiting maximum for the emission from any real surface at a given temperature. For this reason, the black surface, or black body, serves as a reference standard for radiative characteristics of materials and computations. For experimental purposes, the cavities of the type mentioned above are carefully constructed for use as reference sources. Construction of these will be discussed in the chapter on experimental methods.

2-2. Radiant Energy Density

Since energy is transported in the propagation of electromagnetic waves, it follows that a volume of space through which the radiation propagates must at any instant contain a quantity of energy. Here the symbol u will be utilized to designate the *radiant energy density*. This is defined as the radiant energy per unit volume of free space. A relationship between the intensity of radiation and the radiant energy density in an evacuated, isolated isothermal enclosure may be readily developed following an analysis similar to that presented by Planck (1).

In order to compute the radiant energy density, select a small element of volume located at a large distance from the walls of the enclosure. Surround the element of volume with an imaginary spherical surface, the center of which is in the designated element of volume. The radius of the spherical surface is at least an order of magnitude larger than L, the characteristic length of the volume element.

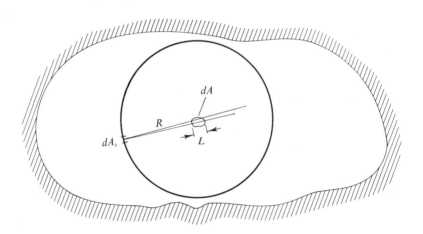

Figure 2-1.

An expression for the radiant energy leaving a differential element of the surface of the sphere and incident on the element of volume is

$$dA\,(q_{dA_s \to dA}) = \frac{I_b(T)\,dA_s\,dA}{R^2} \tag{2-2}$$

Here, $I_b(T)$ is the intensity of black-body radiation at the temperature T; dA_s is a differential area element on the surface of the imaginary sphere in Figure 2-1; R is the radius of the imaginary sphere, and dA represents a differential area projection of the elemental volume under consideration at the center of the sphere. Thus dA/R^2 is a differential solid angle and since the direction of the ray of interest is normal to the spherical surface ($\cos\theta \cong 1$) and $q_{dA_s \to dA}$ is then the radiant flux leaving a differential element of the sphere's surface and passing through the volume element.

Since radiant energy propagates at a single velocity c (the speed of light) in a vacuum, the energy within the volume element and traveling along the ray will be

$$d^2U = \left(\frac{I_b(T)\,dA_s\,dA}{R^2}\right)\!\left(\frac{L}{c}\right) \tag{2-3}$$

Integrating over the elemental volume gives Expression (2-4) for the energy within the volume resulting from radiation passing inwardly through the differential area element of our imaginary spherical surface.

$$dU = \frac{VI_b(T) \, dA_s}{cR^2} \tag{2-4}$$

where V is the volume of the element chosen. Integrating this expression over the surface of the sphere and noting that the integrand is constant gives

$$U = \frac{4\pi VI_b(T)}{c} \tag{2-5}$$

where U is the radiant energy within the volume. Therefore,

$$u = \frac{U}{V} = \frac{4\pi I_b(T)}{c} \tag{2-6}$$

It is also convenient to compare the energy density to the emissive power of a black body (surface). The symbol used here to designate emissive power is q_e, and the quantity is defined as the rate at which radiant energy is emitted by a surface. It can be readily seen that for a black surface the emissive power $q_{e,b}$ is related to the intensity in the following manner.

$$q_{e\,b} = \int_0^{2\pi} \int_0^1 I_b(T)\mu \, d\mu \, d\phi = \pi I_b(T) \tag{2-7}$$

The expression for energy density in terms of the emissive power of a black body at the temperature of the enclosure becomes

$$u = \frac{4q_{e,b}}{c} \tag{2-8}$$

2-3.   Radiation Pressure

The recognition that this energy density exists in "free" space within a cavity allows several important characteristics of thermal radiation to be deduced by classical thermodynamic reasoning. The first of these is called *Bartoli's proof of the existance of radiation pressure*. Bartoli visualized the hypothetical device pictured in Figure 2-2, where two parallel

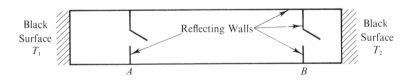

Figure 2-2.

black surfaces maintained at temperatures T_1 and T_2, respectively, are connected by a hollow cylinder having interior walls that are perfectly reflecting. Two movable partitions of perfectly-reflecting material are mounted in the cylinder. Each partition has a shuttered opening that may be opened or closed.

Assume that $T_1 < T_2$ and preform the following sequence of operations.

1. Move partition A close to wall 1 and partition B close to wall 2.
2. Close the aperture in B and open the aperture in A. This allows the space between A and B to fill with black-body radiation characterized by the temperature of Body 1. The energy within this volume is the product of the radiant energy density and the volume.
3. Now close the aperture in A and open the aperture in B.
4. Move partition A over until it contacts partition B. The energy trapped between partitions A and B is then transferred into the space between partition B and Surface 2. But the radiation density in this space corresponds to black-body radiation at temperature 2. Therefore, Body 2 must have absorbed the energy taken originally from Body 1.

This operation could be repeated an indefinite number of times and thus energy would be transferred in a cyclic fashion from a body of lower temperature to a body of higher temperature. The second law of thermodynamics demands that work must be applied to the system in order to accomplish this. That is, a force must be exerted in Step 4 in order to move partition A over to B. This force must represent the pressure of the radiant energy acting on the partition. Thus, the radiation must exert a pressure. It can be argued that the greater the temperature, the greater the pressure.

Experiment, as well as electromagnetic theory, indicates that for a perfectly reflecting surface

$$p \cong \frac{u}{3} \qquad (2\text{-}9)$$

while for a black surface

$$p \cong \frac{u}{6} \qquad (2\text{-}10)$$

2-4.   Stefan-Boltzmann's Law

Stefan first reported the results that the radiant emissive power of a black surface is proportional to the fourth power of the absolute temperature. His conclusion was based on measurements of radiation from wires. Boltzmann, in 1884, derived the relationship on the basis of thermo-dynamic reasoning. His method utilizes a hypothetical engine that operates on a field of thermal radiation as the working substance.

Consider the cylinder in Figure 2-3 that is assumed to be enclosed in a perfect vacuum and in complete isolation. The end of the cylinder is a black surface. The temperature of this surface may be controlled. The walls of the cylinder are perfectly reflecting and a perfectly-reflecting frictionless piston completes the enclosure. The cross-section area of the cylinder is assumed to have a unit dimension and is uniform. The radiant energy within the cylinder is thus

$$U = ux \tag{2-11}$$

The differential change in energy becomes

$$dU = x\,du + u\,dx \tag{2-12}$$

The energy conservation equation gives

$$dQ = dU + p\,dV = x\,du + u\,dx + p\,dx \tag{2-13}$$

where p is the radiation pressure exerted against the piston.

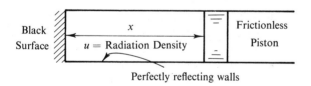

Figure 2-3.

If the piston is moved in a slow quasi-reversible fashion while energy is supplied to maintain a constant temperature, the differential change in entropy may be expressed as

$$ds = \frac{dQ}{T} = \frac{1}{T}\,(x\,du + u\,dx + p\,dx) \tag{2-14}$$

Substituting Relation (2-9) for the radiation pressure and collecting terms gives

$$ds = \frac{x}{T}\,du + \frac{4u}{3T}\,du = \left(\frac{x}{T}\frac{du}{dT}\right)dT + \left(\frac{4u}{3T}\right)dx \tag{2-15}$$

However, ds is an exact differential, and therefore the following relationship must hold:

$$ds = \frac{\partial s}{\partial T}\,dT + \frac{\partial s}{\partial x}\,dx \tag{2-16}$$

Therefore,

$$\frac{\partial s}{\partial T} = \frac{x}{T}\frac{du}{dT}, \qquad \frac{\partial s}{\partial x} = \frac{4u}{3T} \qquad \text{(2-17)}$$

Utilizing the fact that the order of differentiation does not change the value for a properly behaved function, the first expression in (2-17) is differentiated with respect to x and the second with respect to T.

$$\frac{\partial^2 s}{\partial x\,\partial T} = \frac{1}{T}\frac{du}{dT} = \frac{4}{3T}\frac{du}{dT} - \frac{4u}{3T^2} \qquad \text{(2-18)}$$

Simplification gives

$$\frac{du}{dT} = \frac{4u}{T} \qquad \text{(2-19)}$$

Integrating (2-19) results in

$$\ln u = 4 \ln T + \ln B \qquad \text{(2-20)}$$

where B is a constant of integration; it follows directly that

$$u = BT^4 \qquad \text{(2-21)}$$

Substituting the relationship (2-8) for U in (2-21) gives

$$q_{e,b}(T) = \sigma T^4 \qquad \text{(2-22)}$$

where σ is a constant and is called *Stefan-Boltzmann's constant.* The value of this constant is not determined by this analysis; however, it will be determined in later analyses based on statistical reasoning.

2-5.   *Frequency Distribution of Thermal Radiation*

The Stefan-Boltzmann constant σ was first evaluated by experimental means. The theoretical development followed when Planck developed the concept of the quantization of radiant energy. Prior to the work of Planck, Lummer and Pringsheim had experimentally measured the frequency distribution of thermal radiation. Rayleigh and Jeans partially explained the distribution with a theoretical model which conformed to the experimental results for long wavelength or low frequency, but predicted infinite amounts of energy at short wavelengths. This deviation was called the *ultraviolet catastrophe.*

Figure 2-4 gives a qualitative sketch of the monochromatic radiant energy density of a field of black thermal radiation plotted as a function of frequency.

The model used in the Rayleigh-Jeans analysis may be discussed by considering a radiation field within a cubical container of dimension a. It is assumed that the constant field density of the radiant energy is

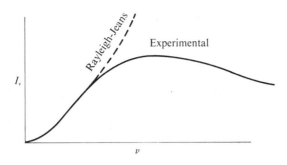

Figure 2-4.

composed of a field of stationary waves. The allowable frequency of the waves is obtained on the basis of simple resonance theory and an analogy to the kinetic theory of gases. It was assumed that an energy of kT would be associated with each allowable stationary wave, where k is Boltzmann's constant and T is the temperature characteristic of the radiation. The monochromatic energy density is thus the number of standing waves having the prescribed frequency multiplied by the energy kT and divided by the volume of the enclosure. The following represents a mathematical development of this.

The solution for the three-dimensional wave equation, using separation of variables technique, is accomplished as follows, where Ψ represents the displacement function.

$$\frac{1}{c^2}\frac{\partial^2 \Psi}{\partial t^2} = \frac{\partial^2 \Psi}{\partial x^2} + \frac{\partial^2 \Psi}{\partial y^2} + \frac{\partial^2 \Psi}{\partial z^2} \tag{2-23}$$

Assume a product solution as follows:

$$\Psi = T(t) \cdot X(x) \cdot Y(y) \cdot Z(z) \tag{2-24}$$

The boundary conditions required for stationary waves in the cubical container are

$$\begin{aligned}\Psi &= 0 \quad \text{for} \quad x = 0,\ x = a \\ \Psi &= 0 \quad \text{for} \quad y = 0,\ y = a \\ \Psi &= 0 \quad \text{for} \quad z = 0,\ z = a\end{aligned} \tag{2-25}$$

These result in a solution of the form

$$\Psi_n = (A_n \cos \omega_n t + B_n \sin \omega_n t) \sin \frac{n_1 \pi x}{a} \sin \frac{n_2 \pi y}{a} \sin \frac{n_3 \pi z}{a} \tag{2-26}$$

where

$$\omega_n^2 = \frac{\pi^2 c^2}{a^2}(n_1^2 + n_2^2 + n_3^2) \tag{2-27}$$

and n_1, n_2, n_3 are arbitrary integers. Sometimes ω_n is called the *circular frequency*, and is related to ν by the relation $2\pi\nu = \omega$. Thus,

$$\nu_n = \frac{c}{2a}\sqrt{n_1^2 + n_2^2 + n_3^2} \qquad (2\text{-}28)$$

The problem now arises to devise an expression for the number of these discrete frequency modes that are allowed in the frequency interval $\nu, \nu + d\nu$ where $\nu \gg 1$. In order to devise this expression, it is convenient to think of these discrete frequencies in terms of a space lattice having unit dimensions.

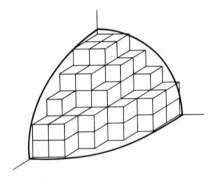

Figure 2-5.

The similarity of this geometrical representation becomes apparent when you notice that the radius r to any point n can be expressed as

$$r_n = \sqrt{n_1^2 + n_2^2 + n_3^2} \qquad (2\text{-}29)$$

The number of points having a distance between r and $r + dr$ from the axis may be shown in the expression

$$dN = \frac{4\pi r^2}{8}\, dr \qquad (2\text{-}30)$$

when $r \gg 1$, this may be visualized as the number of lattice cells in the volume of an octant of a spherical surface having a differential thickness, since the number of lattice intersections correspond to the number of unit cells.

By analogy, the number of allowable frequencies N, may be computed by

$$dN_\nu = \frac{4\pi a^3}{c^3}\, \nu^2\, d\nu \qquad (2\text{-}31)$$

Since the volume containing these frequencies is a^3, the monochromatic energy density may be expressed as

$$u_\nu = \frac{8\pi\nu^2}{c^3} kT \qquad (2\text{-}32)$$

The 8 results from the fact that there are two possible directions to be considered for each transverse vibrational mode. It can readily be seen that the energy associated with frequencies such as those encountered in the visible spectrum would become tremendous.

Planck postulated that this deviation must result from a failure to consider the statistical nature of the "elemental chaos" of the natural radiation. He assumed the radiation to be the result of a field of ideal linear oscillators. The energy of such oscillators is the sum of the potential and kinetic energy at any given instant. He visualized a "phase plane" in which the microscopic state of an oscillator could be described in terms of a plot of displacement versus momentum. Planck concluded, on the basis of his study of the thermodynamic characteristics of thermal radiation, that the area of the phase plane enclosed by the curve describing the possible microstate of the ideal oscillator would be a universal constant h (now known as *Planck's constant*). He called this an "element of action." This essentially limited the energy associated with a given frequency and a single oscillator to a multiple of $h\nu$.

Although Planck's approach involved much more detail, it is possible to develop some physical insight from the following somewhat simplified illustration. This model assumes that a single oscillator may contribute energy to the radiation field only in multiples of $h\nu$. The number of oscillators contributing the energy would be proportional to the base of the natural logarithm raised to a negative power proportional to the energy of the oscillators. The following illustrates this distribution:

Energy of oscillator	Number of oscillators
0	A
$h\nu$	$Ae^{-\beta h\nu}$
$2h\nu$	$Ae^{-2\beta h\nu}$
$3h\nu$	$Ae^{-3\beta h\nu}$
.	.
.	.
.	.

The total number of oscillators in the assumed system may be found by evaluating the infinite sum

$$N = A + Ae^{-\beta h\nu} + Ae^{-2\beta h\nu} + Ae^{-3\beta h\nu} + \cdots \qquad (2\text{-}33a)$$

$$= \frac{A}{1 - e^{-\beta h\nu}} \qquad (2\text{-}33b)$$

The total energy of the system of oscillators is then expressed by the infinite series

$$E = 0 \cdot A + h\nu A e^{-\beta h\nu} + 2h\nu A e^{-2\beta h\nu} + 3h\nu A e^{-3\beta h\nu} + \cdots \quad \text{(2-34a)}$$

$$= \frac{h\nu A e^{-\beta h\nu}}{(1 - e^{-\beta h\nu})^2} \quad \text{(2-34b)}$$

Thus, the average energy associated with an oscillator may be found by dividing the total energy by the number of oscillators in the system.

$$\text{average energy of oscillators} = \bar{\epsilon} = \frac{h\nu e^{-\beta h\nu}}{1 - e^{-\beta h\nu}} \quad \text{(2-35a)}$$

$$= \frac{h\nu}{e^{\beta h\nu} - 1} \quad \text{(2-35b)}$$

Recall that the number of stationary electromagnetic waves per unit volume of the radiation field derived in the Rayleigh-Jeans approach is expressed as

$$dN_\nu = \frac{8\pi\nu^2}{c^3} d\nu \quad \text{(2-35c)}$$

Multiplying the total number of possible standing waves characteristic of a given frequency by the average energy possessed by the waves or ideal oscillators at that frequency gives the following expression for the radiant energy density.

$$u_\nu = \frac{8\pi\nu^2}{c^3} \frac{h\nu}{e^{\beta h\nu} - 1} = \frac{8\pi h\nu^3}{c^3} \frac{1}{e^{\beta h\nu} - 1} \quad \text{(2-36)}$$

Notice that

$$\underset{h\nu \to 0}{\text{Limit}} \, u_\nu = \frac{8\pi\nu^2}{c^3} \frac{1}{\beta} \quad \text{(2-37)}$$

It can be readily seen that for the Planck expression to coincide with the Rayleigh-Jeans expression in the region of low frequency where it agreed with experimental results, the following relation must hold.

$$\beta = \frac{1}{kT}$$

Therefore,

$$u_\nu = \frac{8\pi h\nu^3}{c^3} \frac{1}{h\nu/e^{h\nu/\kappa T} - 1} \quad \text{(2-38)}$$

This, then, is the expression which Planck developed for the frequency distribution of energy in black radiation.

The type of statistical probability which Planck used is now called the *Einstein-Bose statistics*. It perhaps will be of some benefit to mention other types of statistics encountered in the study of statistical mechanics and the distinguishing features of the systems that they describe.

1. *Maxwell-Boltzmann* statistics apply to the energy distribution of a group of particles when
   a. the particles are distinguishable.
   b. a number of particles with the same energy level may occupy the same region of "phase space."
   EXAMPLE: molecular gas.
2. *Fermi-Dirac* statistics apply when
   a. the particles are indistinguishable.
   b. only one particle of a given energy may occupy the same region of "phase space."
   EXAMPLE: electrons of an atom.
3. *Einstein-Bose* statistics apply when
   a. the particles are indistinguishable.
   b. a number of particles may occupy the same cell of "phase space."
   EXAMPLE: photon gas.

The expression for monochromatic intensity of radiation from a black body becomes

$$I_{b,\,\nu} = \frac{2h\nu^3}{c^2}\,\frac{1}{h\nu/e^{h\nu/\kappa T} - 1} \qquad (2\text{-}39)$$

In defining the monochromatic intensity, the frequency characterization has been utilized because the frequency of a photon remains constant regardless of the medium through which the energy propagates. However, it is often convenient to discuss monochromatic radiation in terms of the characteristic wavelength of the radiation. The wavelength characterization is often important when discussing the interaction of radiation and matter. This is of special interest when the concern is with surface roughnesses or particulate matter with physical dimensions of the same order of magnitude as the wavelength of the radiation.

In this book, the term *spectral* will be utilized to designate properties that apply to the wavelength interval λ, $\lambda + d\lambda$. Spectral intensity will be designated I_λ, spectral flux q_λ, and net spectral flux Q_λ. The reader should be cautioned, however, that this difference between the definition of monochromatic and spectral is not standardized in the literature and these terms are often used interchangeably.

The relationship between I_ν and I_λ can be demonstrated readily by noting that these refer to the same energy so that

$$|\,I_\nu d\nu\,| \equiv |\,I_\lambda d\lambda\,| \qquad (2\text{-}40)$$

The well-known relationship between wavelength and frequency also must apply so that

$$\lambda = \frac{c}{\nu} \tag{2-41}$$

The reason for the absolute value signs in Equation (2-40) can be seen from the differential of (2-41)

$$d\lambda = -\frac{c}{\nu^2}\, d\nu \tag{2-42}$$

Planck's relationship for spectral intensity becomes

$$I_{b,\,\lambda} = \frac{2h\nu^5}{c^3}\,\frac{1}{h\nu/e^{h\nu/\kappa T} - 1} \tag{2-43a}$$

$$= \frac{2hc^2}{\lambda^5}\,\frac{1}{hc/e^{hc/\kappa\lambda T} - 1} \tag{2-43b}$$

Snyder (10), utilizing the following values for h, c, and k, has computed the information in Table 2-1 for use in evaluating Planck's and Stefan-Boltzmann's equations.

$h = $ Planck's constant $= 6.62377 \pm 0.00018 \times 10^{-27}$ (erg)(sec)
$c = $ velocity of light in vacuum $= 2.997902 \pm 0.0000009 \times 10^{10}$ (cm)(sec)
$k = $ Boltzmann's constant $= 1.38026 \times 10^{-16}$, (erg)(°k⁻¹)

The c_1 and c_2 listed in Table 2-1 refer to combinations of π, c, h, and k such that the following expression holds.

$$q_{b,\,\lambda} = \frac{c_1}{\lambda^5}\,\frac{1}{c_2/e^{c_2/\lambda T} - 1} \tag{2-44}$$

The following integration of (2-44) will give the numerical value of σ, the Stefan-Boltzmann constant.

$$q_b(T) = \int_0^\infty q_{b,\,\lambda}(T)\, d\lambda = \sigma T^4 \tag{2-45}$$

The shape of the plot of $I_{b,\lambda}$ or $q_{b,\lambda}$ (note that $q_{b,\lambda} = \pi I_{b,\lambda}$) versus λ is of special interest for the engineer concerned with heat transfer. Figure 2-6 gives this graph for various temperatures. While the integral in (2-45) is taken over all wavelengths, it can be noted that the bulk of radiative thermal energy falls within a relatively small spectral range. It is also important to note the shift of the maximum value of $I_{b,\lambda}$ to shorter wavelengths with the higher temperatures. Wien (in 1893) discovered the following important relationship concerning the wavelength at which this maximun occurs. The relationship states that the maximum value of intensity occurs at a wavelength inversely proportional to the absolute temperature characterizing the radiation. Stated as an equation, Wien's displacement rule is

$$(\lambda T)_{q_{\lambda,\,\max}} = \text{constant} \tag{2-46}$$

TABLE 2-1.

Constants To Be Used For Evaluating Planck's and Stefan-Boltzmann's Equations in cgs and U.S. Engineering Units

Quantity	cgs_1	cgs_2	U.S. Engineering
q_λ	$\dfrac{erg}{sec\ cm^2(cm)}$	$\dfrac{watts}{cm^2\mu}$	$\dfrac{Btu}{hr\ ft^2(\mu)}$
q	$\dfrac{erg}{sec\ cm^2}$	$\dfrac{watts}{cm^2}$	$\dfrac{Btu}{hr\ ft^2}$
λ	cm	μ(microns)	μ
c_1	$3.74041 \times 10^{-5}\dfrac{erg\ cm^2}{sec}$	$37{,}404.1\ \dfrac{watt \times \mu^4}{cm^2}$	$1.1870 \times 10^8\ \dfrac{Btu}{hr\ ft^2}\mu^4$
c_2	1.43868 cm °K (± 0.00006)	$14{,}386.8\ \mu$ °K (± 0.6)	$25896\ \mu$ °R
σ	$5.6699 \times 10^{-5}\ \dfrac{erg}{sec\ cm^2\ °K^4}$ (± 0.0009)	$5.6699 \times 10^{-12}\ \dfrac{watts}{cm^2\ °K^4}$ (± 0.00009)	$1714.0 \times 10^{-12}\ \dfrac{Btu}{hr\ ft^2\ °R^4}$
$(\lambda T)_{q_{max},\ \lambda}$	0.289757 cm °K (± 0.000012)	$2897.57\ \mu$ °K (± 0.12)	$5215.6\ \mu$ °R

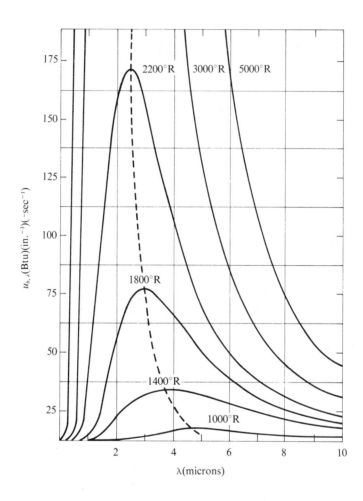

Figure 2-6.

The computed value of this constant is given in Table 2-1. Although Wien deduced this relationship from thermodynamic reasoning prior to Planck's development, the reader may readily verify this relationship by the differentiation of Equation (2-44).

Wien's law has many important applications; for example, the surface temperature of the sun may be estimated by a spectroscopic observation of the maximum intensity versus wavelength. It will be shown in later chapters that this may be used as a criteria for determining methods to be utilized in computing heat exchange between surfaces.

2-6.   Implications From Electromagnetic Wave Theory

Radiative heat transfer is concerned with the interaction of electromagnetic radiation and matter. In order to better understand the details of this, a review of the application of Maxwell's theory is desirable. Maxwell's studies of the interaction of electric and magnetic fields were responsible for the development of a set of equations that predict the propagation of electromagnetic energy through space. The equations describe a disturbance that has the spacial and temporal characteristics of a transverse wave propagating through an elastic medium.

An electromagnetic field may be described in terms of four vectors at any regular point. These vectors are

$$\bar{E} = \text{electrostatic intensity vector}$$
$$\bar{D} = \text{electric displacement vector}$$
$$\bar{H} = \text{magnetic intensity vector}$$
$$\bar{B} = \text{magnetic induction vector}$$

In an isotropic medium the electric displacement vector $\bar{D}$ is parallel to the electrostatic intensity vector $\bar{E}$, and the magnetic induction vector $\bar{B}$ is parallel to the magnetic intensity vector $\bar{H}$. It will serve the purpose of this review to restrict the analysis to isotropic, linear media. In such cases, the following linear relationships exist.

$$\bar{D} = \epsilon \bar{E} \qquad \bar{B} = \mu \bar{H} \qquad (2\text{-}47)$$

ϵ and μ are called *inductive capacities of the medium*, while ϵ_0 and μ_0 are designated as the *inductive capacity of free space*. The ratio ϵ/ϵ_0 is called the *dielectric constant of the medium* and μ/μ_0 is the *permeability*.

The following basic laws of electricity and magnetism form the basis of Maxwell's equations for the propagation of electromagnetic radiation.

The first law states that *the electrostatic flux integrated over a closed surface is proportional to the total electric charge contained within the volume enclosed by the surface.*

$$\oiint \bar{E} \cdot \bar{n} \, ds = \frac{1}{\epsilon} \oiiint q_v \, dv \qquad (2\text{-}48)$$

where $\bar{n}$ represents a unit vector normal to the surface, and q_v represents the charge per unit volume.

The second relationship is a statement of the fact that magnetic lines of force must be closed. Thus, the flux of the magnetic induction vector must be zero when taken over a closed surface.

$$\oiint \bar{B} \cdot \bar{n} \, ds = 0 \qquad (2\text{-}49)$$

Faraday's law of magnetic induction states that *the induced electrical field around a closed path is related to the time rate of change of the magnetic flux density over a surface bounded by the contour.*

$$\oint \bar{E} \cdot d\bar{l} = -\frac{d}{dt} \iint \bar{B} \cdot \bar{n} \, ds \qquad (2\text{-}50)$$

The fourth relationship is sometimes referred to as *Ampere's circuital theorem.* This is a statement that *the magnetic field induced around a closed path is proportional to the electric current flowing through a surface bounded by the contour and the time rate of change of the flux and the electric displacement vector taken over the surface.*

$$\oint \bar{H} \cdot d\bar{l} = \iint \left(\bar{i}_v + \frac{\partial \bar{D}}{\partial t} \right) \cdot \bar{n} \, ds \qquad (2\text{-}51)$$

In this equation $\bar{i}_v$ is the volume current vector.

If attention is now restricted to regions in which the field vectors and the properties of the medium are finite continuous functions of space and time and have finite continuous derivatives with respect to the independent variables, the integral relationships above may be restated in terms of a set of differential vector equations. The application of Gauss's divergence theorem to (2-48) and (2-49) results in the respective equations

$$\nabla \cdot \bar{D} = q_v \qquad (2\text{-}52)$$
$$\nabla \cdot \bar{B} = 0 \qquad (2\text{-}53)$$

The application of Stoke's theorem to (2-50) and (2-51) results in the following differential equations.

$$\nabla \times \bar{E} = -\frac{\partial \bar{B}}{\partial t} \qquad (2\text{-}54)$$

$$\nabla \times \bar{H} = \sigma \bar{E} + \frac{\partial \bar{D}}{\partial t} \qquad (2\text{-}55)$$

where the relationship between the current and field has been utilized for an isotropic linear medium. In this case, σ is the specific conductivity of the medium; in other words, Ohm's law must hold.

$$\bar{i}_v = \sigma \bar{E} \qquad (2\text{-}56)$$

The integral Expressions (2-48) through (2-51) may include discontinuities. The following boundary conditions may be developed by considering these relationships over a thin region including a boundary between a medium denoted by subscript 1 and a medium denoted by subscript 2.

$$\bar{n} \cdot (\bar{B}_2 - \bar{B}_1) = 0 \qquad (2\text{-}57)$$
$$\bar{n} \cdot (\bar{D}_2 - \bar{D}_1) = q_s \qquad (2\text{-}58)$$
$$\bar{n} \times (\bar{E}_2 - \bar{E}_1) = 0 \qquad (2\text{-}59)$$
$$\bar{n} \times (\bar{H}_2 - \bar{H}_1) = 0 \qquad (2\text{-}60)$$

The q_s refers to the surface charge density and the zero in (2-60) implies that the surface current is zero.

The development of Maxwell's wave equation follows readily by the process described below.

Take the curl of Equation (2-54)

$$\nabla \times (\nabla \times \bar{E}) = -\nabla \times \frac{\partial \bar{B}}{\partial t} \qquad (2\text{-}61)$$

Utilizing the vector indentity,

$$\nabla \times (\nabla \times \bar{E}) = \nabla(\nabla \cdot \bar{E}) - \nabla^2 \bar{E} \qquad (2\text{-}62)$$

and noting that for the case for which $q_v \equiv 0$ as is the case in most problems of interest, (2-52) implies that the first term on the right side of Equation (2-62) is zero. Therefore, the following must hold.

$$\nabla^2 \bar{E} = \nabla \times \frac{\partial \bar{B}}{\partial t} \qquad (2\text{-}63)$$

Noting that the order of differentiation of the term on the right may be interchanged, and substituting $\mu \bar{H}$ for $\bar{B}$ leads to the following expression:

$$\nabla^2 \bar{E} = \mu \frac{\partial}{\partial t} (\nabla \times \bar{H}) \qquad (2\text{-}64)$$

Substituting (2-55) into (2-64) gives

$$\nabla^2 \bar{E} = \mu\sigma \frac{\partial \bar{E}}{\partial t} + \mu\epsilon \frac{\partial^2 \bar{E}}{\partial t^2} \qquad (2\text{-}65)$$

In a similar fashion the following may be developed.

$$\nabla^2 \bar{H} = \mu\sigma \frac{\partial \bar{H}}{\partial t} + \mu\epsilon \frac{\partial^2 \bar{H}}{\partial t^2} \qquad (2\text{-}66)$$

From these relationships, it can be seen that the time-varying electric and magnetic fields satisfy identical differential equations.

For a closer insight into the behavior of these fields it is convenient to consider an infinite plane wave. The restriction to an infinite plane wave limits the problem to a single space dimension as an independent variable along with time. It should be noted, however, that the vectors $\bar{E}$ and $\bar{H}$ still may have components in three space directions that vary with the single, independent space variable.

For convenience, assume that $\bar{E}$ and $\bar{H}$ are functions of the coordinate direction z only. The resulting expression will be shown to describe an infinite plane wave with the z direction normal to the wavefront. The divergence of $\bar{E}$ and $\bar{H}$ are both equal to zero if the volume density of electric charge is zero from Expressions (2-52) and (2-53). If E_x, E_y, E_z and H_x, H_y, H_z represent the components of the vectors $\bar{E}$ and $\bar{H}$, the following expression can be written.

$$\frac{\partial E_x}{\partial x} + \frac{\partial E_y}{\partial y} + \frac{\partial E_z}{\partial z} = 0$$

$$\frac{\partial H_x}{\partial x} + \frac{\partial H_y}{\partial y} + \frac{\partial H_z}{\partial z} = 0$$

Since $\bar{E}$ and $\bar{H}$ are functions of z alone, $\partial E_x/\partial x = 0$, $\partial E_y/\partial y = 0$, $\partial H_x/\partial x = 0$, $\partial H_y/\partial y = 0$, and, therefore, $\partial E_z/\partial z = 0$, $\partial H_z/\partial z = 0$.

The resulting differential equation may be written as a set of equations by equating the individual components.

$$\frac{\partial^2 E_x}{\partial z^2} = \mu\sigma\frac{\partial E_x}{\partial t} + \mu\epsilon\frac{\partial^2 E_x}{\partial t^2}$$

$$\frac{\partial^2 E_y}{\partial z^2} = \mu\sigma\frac{\partial E_y}{\partial t} + \mu\epsilon\frac{\partial^2 E_y}{\partial t^2}$$

$$\frac{\partial^2 H_x}{\partial z^2} = \mu\sigma\frac{\partial H_x}{\partial t} + \mu\epsilon\frac{\partial^2 H_x}{\partial t^2}$$

$$\frac{\partial^2 H_y}{\partial z^2} = \mu\sigma\frac{\partial H_y}{\partial t} + \mu\epsilon\frac{\partial^2 H_y}{\partial t^2}$$

$$(2\text{-}67)$$

Before studying the solutions to the equations above, consider the the case of electromagnetic field propagation in a perfect dielectric. For this case $\sigma = 0$. The Equations (2-67) thus become the well-known form of the simple wave equation

$$\frac{\partial^2 E_x}{\partial z^2} = \frac{1}{v^2}\frac{\partial^2 E_x}{\partial t^2} \qquad (2\text{-}68)$$

where $v = (\mu\epsilon)^{-1/2}$ is the velocity of propagation of the wave. A solution of Equation (2-68) may be written as

$$E_x = A_1 \sin(z - vt) \qquad (2\text{-}69)$$

where A_1 is an amplitude depending on boundary conditions.

A definite relationship must exist between $\bar{E}$ and $\bar{H}$ in accordance with (2-54) or (2-55).

$$-i\frac{\partial E_y}{\partial z} + j\frac{\partial E_x}{\partial z} = -i\mu\frac{\partial H_x}{\partial t} - j\mu\frac{\partial H_y}{\partial t} \qquad (2\text{-}70)$$

Thus,

$$\frac{\partial E_y}{\partial z} = +\mu\frac{\partial H_x}{\partial t} \quad \text{and} \quad \frac{\partial E_x}{\partial z} = -\mu\frac{\partial H_y}{\partial t} \qquad (2\text{-}71)$$

It can be seen that the y component of the electric field must be associated with an x component of the magnetic field.

For purposes of simplicity, consider a field in which $E_y = 0$. Equation (2-69) therefore expresses the electric field vector. The associated magnetic field may be seen to be

$$H_y = \frac{A_1}{v\mu} \sin(z - vt) \qquad (2\text{-}72)$$

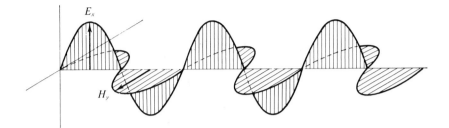

Figure 2-7.   Diagram showing the relation between the electric and magnetic vector in an undamped, infinite plane wave.

The wave might be displayed graphically as shown in Figure 2-7 for any fixed instant of time.

The phenomena of polarization may also be explained in terms of the infinite plane wave. Consider a wave in which the x and y components of the electric vector are not in phase. The resulting plot of the components are illustrated in Figure 2-8. Note that the resultant vector rotates as it propagates in space. If the maximum amplitude of the x and y components of the vectors are equal and the components are 90° out of phase, the magnitude of vector remains constant and the vector rotates with the tip projecting a circle on the x-y plane. Such a wave is called a *circularly-polarized wave*. (see Figure 2-9)

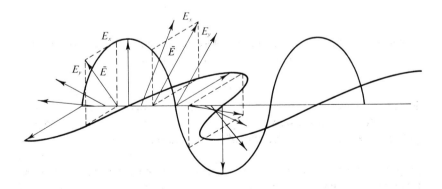

Figure 2-8.   Plot of a circularly-polarized wave.

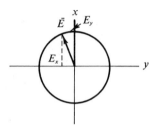

Figure 2-9.   Projection of a circularly-polarized electric vector on x-y plane.

Should the x and y components of the field vector not be 90° out of phase, or should they be of unequal magnitude, the field is said to be *elliptically polarized.* (see Figure 2-10)

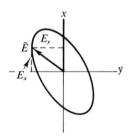

Figure 2-10.   Projection on x-y plane of an elliptically-polarized field vector propagating in z direction.

If the x and y components of the vector are exactly in phase the wave is said to be *plane polarized.* (see Figure 2-11) The wave described by Equation (2-71) and illustrated in Figure 2-7 is a special case of the plane-polarized wave in which the axis of polarization coincides with the x axis.

The polaroid filter serves to filter the electromagnetic component perpendicular to its axis and thus transmit a plane-polarized wave. Electromagnetic radiation often undergoes a polarization when it is reflected from a surface or scattered from clouds of particles.

The energy transport by the electromagnetic wave may be expressed in terms of the *Poynting vector* (which is named after J. H. Poynting,

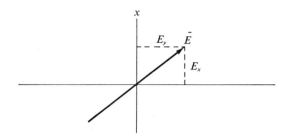

Figure 2-11. Projection on x-y plane of a plane-polarized field vector propagating in the z direction.

who first derived the result in 1884). This expression is demonstrated by scalar multiplication of Equations (2-54) and (2-55) as follows:

$$\bar{H} \cdot \nabla \times \bar{E} = -\bar{H} \cdot \frac{\partial \bar{B}}{\partial t} \qquad (2\text{-}73)$$

$$\bar{E} \cdot \nabla \times \bar{H} = (\bar{E} \cdot \sigma \bar{E}) + \left(\bar{E} \cdot \frac{\partial \bar{D}}{\partial t}\right) \qquad (2\text{-}74)$$

Subtracting Equations (2-73) and (2-74) gives

$$(\bar{H} \cdot \nabla \times \bar{E}) - (\bar{E} \cdot \nabla \times \bar{H}) = -\sigma E^2 - \left[\frac{\epsilon}{2} \frac{\partial (E^2)}{\partial t}\right] - \left[\frac{\mu}{2} \frac{\partial (H^2)}{\partial t}\right] \qquad (2\text{-}75)$$

The vector identity $\nabla \cdot (\bar{E} \times \bar{H}) = (\bar{H} \cdot \nabla \times \bar{E}) - (\bar{E} \cdot \nabla \times \bar{H})$ applied to the left side of Equation (2-75) gives

$$\nabla \cdot (\bar{E} \times \bar{H}) = -\sigma E^2 - \frac{\partial}{\partial t}\left(\frac{\epsilon}{2} E^2 + \frac{\mu}{2} H^2\right) \qquad (2\text{-}76)$$

The right-hand side of this equation is interpreted as a rate of change of energy within a differential element, while the left side is interpreted as the divergence of an energy flux vector. This vector is $(\bar{E} \times \bar{H})$ and is the one known as the Poynting vector. Note that it is in the direction of the wave propagation.

In a conducting medium, the wave equation is represented by Equations (2-67). Considering $E_y = 0$, a solution for E_x may be written as

$$E_x = A \exp\left[i\omega\left(t - \frac{z}{y}\right)\right] \qquad (2\text{-}77)$$

This can be seen to represent a satisfactory solution to (2-67) if the relationship in (2-78) holds.

$$\frac{1}{v^2} = \mu\epsilon\left(1 - \frac{i\sigma}{\omega\epsilon}\right) \qquad (2\text{-}78)$$

The refractive index of a medium, n, is defined as the ratio of the speed of light in a vacuum, c, to the wave velocity, v.

$$n = \frac{c}{v} \qquad (2\text{-}79)$$

Thus, for a conducting medium the refractive index is complex.

$$n^2 = \frac{\mu\epsilon}{\mu_0\epsilon_0}\left(1 - \frac{i\sigma}{\omega\epsilon}\right) \qquad (2\text{-}80)$$

It can be readily seen that for a perfect dielectric, n is real and is reduced to the following expression.

$$n = \sqrt{\frac{\mu\epsilon}{\mu_0\epsilon_0}} = \sqrt{\kappa_e\kappa_m} \qquad (2\text{-}81)$$

where κ_e and κ_m represent the dielectric constant and the magnetic permeability, respectively. Since $\kappa_m \approx 1$ for most dielectric materials, the refractive index for these materials is usually taken as the square root of the dielectric constant, $\sqrt{\kappa_e}$.

From Expression (2-78) it can be seen that the phase velocity v is a function of the characteristic frequency in a conducting medium. This effect is called *dispersion*. Thus, a flux consisting of a range of frequencies and propagating through such a medium not only will be attenuated but also will undergo a fundamental change of character because of the selective absorption.

For a metal with high electrical conductivity and in frequency intervals such that

$$\mu\sigma \gg \omega \qquad (2\text{-}82)$$

the complex phase velocity may be represented in the following form:

$$\frac{1}{v} \approx \sqrt{-i\frac{\mu\sigma}{\omega}} \qquad (2\text{-}83)$$

If (2-83) is then substituted into (2-77), the expression becomes

$$E_x = A\exp\left(-\alpha z\right)\exp\left[i\omega\left(t - \frac{\alpha z}{\omega}\right)\right] \qquad (2\text{-}84)$$

where

$$\alpha = \sqrt{\frac{\omega\mu\sigma}{2}} \qquad (2\text{-}85)$$

It is obvious that the wave is damped exponentially in a highly conducting media. Sometimes α is called the *absorption coefficient* but should not be confused with the same symbol that is used for the absorptivity of a surface.

2-7.   Reflection and Refraction of Electromagnetic Waves

Consider now a plane wave propagating in a perfect isotropic dielectric medium and incident on a perfectly smooth plane interface bounding a second semi-infinite, perfect isotropicdielectric medium. In such a system, one must consider three waves: the *incident wave*, the *reflected wave*, and the wave which is transmitted through the interface into the second medium. The third wave is called a *refracted wave*. It is helpful to think in terms of the normal ray to the propagating wave front. Figure 2-12 illustrates diagrammatically the incident, reflected, and refracted rays. Recall that the infinite plane wave will have no variable field component along the direction of propagation. The electric field vector components are divided into a component in the plane perpendicular to the interface that contains the ray and the component perpendicular to the plane.

There are various methods of proving that all three rays illustrated

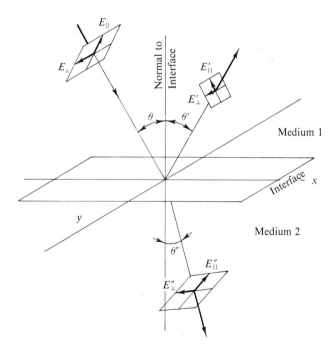

Figure 2-12.   Schematic diagram of electric field vector of the incident, reflected, and refracted waves at an infinite plane interface between two semi-infinite dielectrics.

in Figure 2-12 are contained in the plane perpendicular to the interface that contains the incident ray. In addition, it can be shown that the reflection angle θ' is equal to the incident angle θ and that Snell's law relates the incident and refracted angle as

$$n_1 \sin \theta = n_2 \sin \theta'' \qquad (2\text{-}86)$$

These laws may be proven from geometric optics by experiment or by electromagnetic wave theory utilizing the boundary conditions of Equations (2-57) and (2-58). The laws may also be proven by application of *Fermat's principle of least time.* According to this principle, a wave disturbance always proceeds from one point in a medium, whether homogeneous or not, or whether or not discontinuous boundaries are encountered, in such a way that the time of transit is a minimum compared with all possible alternative methods of transmission. The reader may refer to almost any text on optics or electromagnetic theory for the demonstration of these proofs.

In the study of radiative heat transfer the reflected and transmitted energies are of particular interest. Solution of the wave equation with the boundary conditions (2-59) and (2-60) may be utilized to obtain these. Noting the coordinate system on the interface in Figure 2-12, these boundary conditions may be rewritten as

$$\begin{aligned}
E_x + E'_x &= E''_x \\
E_y + E'_y &= E''_y \\
H_x + H'_x &= H''_x \\
H_y + H'_y &= H''_y
\end{aligned} \qquad (2\text{-}87)$$

In terms of the components of the incident, reflected, and refracted waves, the first equation of (2-87) becomes

$$E_{||} \cos \theta - E'_{||} \cos \theta = E''_{||} \cos \theta'' \qquad (2\text{-}88)$$

The second equation becomes

$$E_{\perp} + E'_{\perp} = E''_{\perp} \qquad (2\text{-}89)$$

It is necessary to utilize the relationship between the magnetic vector and the electric vector. Since μ is approximately unity for a dielectric media, the application of Equations (2-69) and (2-72) give the following for the infinite plane wave.

$$H_x = \frac{1}{v} E_y, \qquad H_y = \frac{1}{v} E_x \qquad (2\text{-}90)$$

Therefore, the last two equations of (2-87) may be written as

$$n_1(E_{\perp} - E'_{\perp}) \cos \theta = n_2 E''_{\perp} \cos \theta'' \qquad (2\text{-}91)$$
$$n_1(E_{||} + E'_{||}) = n_2 E''_{||} \qquad (2\text{-}92)$$

Equations (2-88), (2-89), (2-91), (2-92) may now be solved for the four unknown, electric-field components. The refractive indices may be eliminated by use of Snell's law. The resulting set of equations are known as *Fresnel's equations*.

$$E'_{\parallel} = E_{\parallel} \frac{\tan(\theta - \theta'')}{\tan(\theta + \theta'')} \qquad (2\text{-}93)$$

$$E'_{\perp} = -E_{\perp} \frac{\sin(\theta - \theta'')}{\sin(\theta + \theta'')} \qquad (2\text{-}94)$$

$$E''_{\parallel} = E_{\parallel} \frac{2\sin\theta''\cos\theta}{\sin(\theta + \theta'')\cos(\theta - \theta'')} \qquad (2\text{-}95)$$

$$E''_{\perp} = E_{\perp} \frac{2\sin\theta''\cos\theta}{\sin(\theta + \theta'')} \qquad (2\text{-}96)$$

The reflectivity of a surface is proportional to the ratio of the square of the amplitude of the incident and reflected waves.

$$\rho_{\perp} = \left(\frac{E'_{\perp}}{E_{\perp}}\right)^{2}, \qquad \rho_{\parallel} = \left(\frac{E'_{\parallel}}{E_{\parallel}}\right)^{2} \qquad (2\text{-}97)$$

For the case of normal incidence, the Equations (2-93) and (2-94) become indeterminate. However, by taking the limit the resultant reflectivity for a normal incident ray may be obtained. Note that as $\theta \rightarrow 0$ and $\theta'' \rightarrow 0$, the tangent of the sum and difference of the angles will approach the sine of the corresponding angles.

$$-\frac{E'_{\perp}}{E_{\perp}} = \frac{E'_{\parallel}}{E_{\parallel}} = \frac{\sin(\theta - \theta'')}{\sin(\theta + \theta'')} = \frac{\sin\theta\cos\theta'' - \cos\theta\sin\theta''}{\sin\theta\cos\theta'' + \cos\theta\sin\theta''} \qquad (2\text{-}98)$$

Dividing by $\sin\theta''$ and replacing $\sin\theta/\sin\theta''$ with n_2/n_1 in accordance with Snell's law and letting $n_2/n_1 = n$, which is called the *relative refractive index*, results in the following expression.

$$\frac{E'}{E} = \frac{n\cos\theta - \cos\theta}{n\cos\theta + \cos\theta} \approx \frac{n - 1}{n + 1} \qquad (2\text{-}99)$$

The reflectivity for a normal incident plane wave may therefore be expressed as

$$\rho = \left(\frac{n - 1}{n + 1}\right)^{2} \qquad (2\text{-}100)$$

For the case of an electromagnetic wave traversing a dielectric and incident upon an absorbing medium where the relative refractive index may by written as $n(1 - ik)$, Snell's law and Fresnel's equations still may be assumed to hold. However, the resulting angles may be complex. The values of the sine and cosine of the angle of refraction may be stated as

$$\sin\theta'' = \frac{\sin\theta}{n(1 - ik)} \qquad (2\text{-}101)$$

$$\cos\theta'' = \frac{1}{n(1 - ik)}[n^{2}(1 - ik)^{2} - \sin^{2}\theta]^{1/2} \qquad (2\text{-}102)$$

For the case of a normal incident ray on the absorbing medium, (2-100) may be restated with the complex refractive index substitution for n,

$$\rho = \frac{(n-1)^2 + n^2 k^2}{(n+1)^2 + n^2 k^2} \qquad (2\text{-}103)$$

Here the magnitude of ρ was determined by multiplying the complex amplitude ratio by its conjugate.

The reflectivity for various angles may be obtained by substituting the complex angle of refraction into (2-93) and (2-94). Let θ'' be designated as

$$\theta'' = \alpha + i\beta \qquad (2\text{-}104)$$

The reflectivities may then be expressed in the manner developed below.

$$\rho_\perp = \left[\frac{\sin(\theta - \alpha - i\beta)}{\sin(\theta + \alpha + i\beta)}\right]^2$$
$$= \left[\frac{\sin(\theta - \alpha)\cosh\beta - i\cos(\theta - \alpha)\sinh\beta}{\sin(\theta + \alpha)\cosh\beta + i\cos(\theta + \alpha)\sinh\beta}\right]^2$$

Using the identity $\cosh^2\beta - \sinh^2\beta = 1$ this expression becomes

$$\rho_\perp = \left[\frac{\sin^2(\theta - \alpha) + \sinh^2\beta}{\sin^2(\theta + \alpha) + \sinh^2\beta}\right] \qquad (2\text{-}105)$$

For the case of the parallel component

$$\rho_{\|} = \left[\frac{\tan(\theta - \theta'')}{\tan(\theta + \theta'')}\right]^2 = \left[\frac{\sin(\theta - \theta'')}{\sin(\theta + \theta'')}\right]^2 \left[\frac{\cos(\theta + \theta'')}{\cos(\theta - \theta'')}\right]^2$$

For the first term on the right $\rho_\perp$ may be substituted.

$$\rho_{\|} = \rho_\perp \left[\frac{\cos(\theta + \theta'')}{\cos(\theta - \theta'')}\right]^2$$

Now $\theta'' = \alpha + i\beta$ may be substituted into this expression resulting in

$$\rho_{\|} = \rho_\perp \left[\frac{\cos^2(\theta + \alpha) + \sinh^2\beta}{\cos^2(\theta - \alpha) + \sinh^2\beta}\right] \qquad (2\text{-}106)$$

For strongly absorbing materials some authors have utilized a somewhat simpler formula that may be shown to be a limiting case of (2-105) and (2-106).

$$\rho_\perp = \frac{n^2(1 + k^2) - 2n\cos\theta + \cos^2\theta}{n^2(1 + k^2) + 2n\cos\theta + \cos^2\theta}$$
$$\rho_{\|} = \frac{n^2(1 + k^2)\cos^2\theta - 2n\cos\theta + 1}{n^2(1 + k^2)\cos^2\theta + 2n\cos\theta + 1} \qquad (2\text{-}107)$$

Additional interesting phenomena must be omitted from the present discussion. The principles listed here are only a minimum background for the study of radiative heat transfer. One can select further materials from the references listed on the next page.

Later chapters dealing with radiative heat transfer in absorbing and scattering media will present additional applications of electromagnetic theory.

References

1. Planck, M., *Theory of Heat Radiation*, Dover Publications Inc., New York, 1959.

2. French, A. P., *Principles of Modern Physics*, John Wiley & Sons, New York, 1958.

3. Stratton, J. A., *Electromagnetic Theory*, McGraw-Hill Book Co., New York, 1941.

4. Harnwell, G.P., *Principles of Electricity and Electro-magnetism*, McGraw-Hill Book Co., New York, 1949.

5. Jenkins, F. A., and White, H. E., *Fundamentals of Optics*, McGraw-Hill Book Co., New York, 1957.

6. Condon, E. V., and Odishaw, H., *Hand Book of Physics*, McGraw-Hill Book Co., New York, 1958.

7. Drude, P., *The Theory of Optics*, Dover Publications, New York, 1959.

8. Lorentz, H. A., *The Theory of Electrons*, Dover Publications, New York, 1952.

9. Landau, L. D., and Lifshitz, E. M., *The Classical Theory of Fields*, Addison-Wesley Publishing Co., Reading, Massachusetts, 1962.

10. Snyder, N. W., "A Review of Thermal Radiation Constants," *Transactions of The A.S.M.E.*, Vol. 76, No. 4, (May 1954).

3   Radiative Characteristics
of Surfaces

3-1.   Definition of the Radiative Properties of Surfaces

In the previous chapter the study of electromagnetic wave theory included the effect of reflection and refraction at the interface between two media. In that discussion, the interface was assumed to be perfectly smooth and the reflected ray always left the surface at an angle equal to the angle of incidence. The reflection was mirrorlike, which is called a *specular reflection*. (The word *specular* should not be confused with the word *spectral*.) Many surfaces encountered in engineering practice are not perfectly smooth. That is, the surface irregularities may be on the order of a few microns, which is the order of magnitude of the wavelength of thermal radiation. As a result of these surface irregularities, the reflection will be "broken up" and a monodirectional flux will contribute to the reflected intensities in many directions. Figure 3-1 illustrates this in a schematic fashion, by picturing graphically the reflection of a narrow pencil of rays from a rough surface.

    The amount and character of the reflected energy is very important

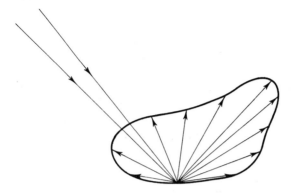

Figure 3-1.   Schematic graph showing the reflection of a pencil of rays from a rough surface. The arrows leaving the surface indicate the magnitude and direction of the intensity of reflected radiation.

in the determination of radiative heat transfer. The manner in which a surface reflects radiation is also related to the manner in which the surface emits energy. In general, the reflection from a surface may be described in terms of a function of two directions and the characteristic frequency of the radiation. McNicholas (1) and Dunkle (5) have discussed this function and have given it the name of *biangular reflectance*. In this book, the function is defined in a slightly different fashion and will be given the name *reflection function*.

In visualizing the reflection function it will perhaps be helpful to look again at Figure 3-1. If an incident flux is composed of radiation with more than one characteristic direction, the intensity of radiation from each of these directions will contribute to the reflected intensity in all other directions. The reflection function relates the energy incident from one direction to the reflected energy in another direction in such a manner that if the intensity distribution of an incident flux is known, the intensity distribution in the reflected flux may be determined.

The reflection function is denoted by the symbol $\rho_\nu(\mu, \phi, \mu', \phi')$. When it is multiplied by the incident intensity $I_\nu(\mu', \phi')$ and the cosine of the polar angle μ', which the incident intensity makes with the normal to the surface and the solid angle $d\mu' d\phi'$, and then integrated over the hemispherical solid angle bounded by the surface and divided by π, the results are the reflected intensity in the direction (μ, ϕ), where μ is the cosine of the polar angle from the surface normal and ϕ is an azimuthal angle.

The definition is more readily apparent when expressed in terms of the relationship

$$I_\nu(\mu, \phi)_{\text{Reflected}} = \frac{1}{\pi} \int_0^{2\pi} \int_0^1 I_\nu(\mu', \phi')\rho_\nu(\mu, \phi, \mu', \phi')\mu' \, d\mu' \, d\phi' \qquad \textbf{(3-1)}$$

Here, μ' and ϕ' describe the incident direction, and μ and ϕ the leaving direction. The symbol μ denotes the cosine of the polar angle from the surface normal and ϕ is an azimuthal angle. The factor $1/\pi$ is included for convenience as will be seen later in the discussion.

In addition to the reflection from a surface, it is necessary to know the manner in which a surface emits and absorbs energy. However, it will be shown below that if the reflection function is known, the emission and absorption of a surface may be determined by direct integration. In this discussion, the term *surface* will have a somewhat special meaning. It will denote the interface between a transparent medium and an opaque body. The radiant energy emerging from a surface originates within the body and does not result from transmission of energy incident on some other part of the body. The emission is thus a characteristic of the interface composition and configuration. In many elementary heat transfer texts, the transmittance of a surface is included with the discussion of absorptance and emittance. The transmittance must necessarily be dependent upon the over-all geometry of a body. This results in added complications that do not apply to many engineering situations. The problem of the semitransparent medium will be developed in detail in Chapter 5.

In order to relate reflection to emission and absorption, consider a surface located within an isolated isothermal enclosure in thermodynamic equilibrium. Recall that it was demonstrated in Chapter 2 that the monochromatic intensity of radiation within such an enclosure is everywhere isotropic and homogeneous, and that it corresponds to the emission from an ideal black body at the temperature of the enclosure. The radiation leaving the surface will be made up of energy emitted by the surface and energy reflected from the surface.

$$I_\nu(\mu, \phi)_{\text{Leaving}} = I_\nu(\mu, \phi)_{\text{Emitted}} + I_\nu(\mu, \phi)_{\text{Reflected}} \qquad \textbf{(3-2)}$$

The intensity of the radiation incident on the surface and the intensity leaving the surface must correspond to black-body radiation. Rewriting (3-2) by utilizing the expression (3-1) for the reflected energy and the intensity of black-body radiation for the incident and leaving radiation results in

$$I_{b,\nu}(T) = I_\nu(\mu, \phi)_{\text{Emitted}} + \frac{1}{\pi} \int_0^{2\pi} \int_0^1 I_{b,\nu}(T)\rho_\nu(\mu, \phi, \mu', \phi')\mu' \, d\mu' \, d\phi'$$

$$\textbf{(3-3)}$$

Noting that $I_{b,v}(T)$ is not a function of direction, and rearranging (3-3) results in the relationship in (3-4).

$$I_v(\mu, \phi)_{\text{Emitted}} = \left(1 - \frac{1}{\pi} \int_0^{2\pi} \int_0^1 \rho_v(\mu, \phi, \mu', \phi')\mu' \, d\mu' d\phi'\right) I_{b,v}(T)$$

(3-4)

The *monochromatic directional emittance* of a surface is defined as the ratio of the monochromatic intensity of radiation emitted by a surface in the direction characterized by μ and ϕ to the intensity of radiation emitted by a black surface at the same temperature. The symbol $\epsilon_v(\mu, \phi)$ will denote the monochromatic directional emittance.

$$I_v(\mu, \phi)_{\text{Emitted}} = \epsilon_v(\mu, \phi)I_{b,v}(T)$$

(3-5)

Comparison of (3-4) and (3-5) reveals the relationship in (3-6).

$$\epsilon_v(\mu, \phi) = 1 - \frac{1}{\pi} \int_0^{2\pi} \int_0^1 \rho_v(\mu, \phi, \mu', \phi')\mu' \, d\mu' d\phi'$$

(3-6)

The relationship above was derived for conditions of thermodynamic equilibrium. However, it is logical to assume that the emittance and reflectance of a surface is a function of the physical and chemical configuration of the surface and that Relationship (3-6) must hold in general. It should be noted, however, that for the definition of emittance to have meaning, the radiation emitted from a surface must originate within an isothermal region. For nonmetallic surfaces, or very rough surfaces, this may be a severe restriction. Since electromagnetic radiation is strongly attenuated in metals, any radiation emitted by the metal must originate in a thin region near the surface. The high thermal conductivity thus assures the approximate isothermal condition within this thin region. In nonmetals, the thermal conductivity is likely to be low and the material semitransparent so that the radiant flux emitted is likely to originate from regions of different temperature. For rough surfaces, it may be possible for a temperature gradient to exist between the roughness peaks and valleys and again it is impossible to characterize the surface by a single temperature.

The *monochromatic directional absorptance* is designated by the symbol $\alpha_v(\mu, \phi)$ and is defined as the fraction of the incident intensity of radiation characterized by the direction (μ, ϕ) that is absorbed by a surface.

Again considering a surface in the evacuated, isolated, isothermal enclosure, the absorbed energy plus the reflected energy must equal the total incident on the surface. Let the primes denote the incident directions and the unprimed terms designate the leaving directions.

$$\int_0^{2\pi} \int_0^1 I_{b,v}(T)\mu' \, d\mu' d\phi' = \int_0^{2\pi} \int_0^1 I_{b,v}(T)\alpha_v(\mu', \phi')\mu' \, d\mu' d\phi'$$

$$+ \frac{1}{\pi} \int_0^{2\pi} \int_0^1 \int_0^{2\pi} \int_0^1 I_{b,v}(T)\rho_v(\mu, \phi, \mu', \phi')\mu' \, d\mu' d\phi' \, \mu \, d\mu d\phi$$

(3-7)

Von Fragstein (2) has applied the principle of reciprocity in optics and has demonstrated by careful development that the following relationship holds.

$$\rho_v(\mu, \phi, \mu', \phi') = \rho_v(\mu', \phi', \mu, \phi) \tag{3-8}$$

This reciprocity permits the change of order of integration in the last term of Expression (3-7). Dividing out $I_{b,v}(T)$, results in the relationship

$$\alpha_v(\mu', \phi') = 1 - \frac{1}{\pi} \int_0^{2\pi} \int_0^1 \rho_v(\mu, \phi, \mu', \phi')\mu' \, d\mu' d\phi' \tag{3-9}$$

It follows immediately that

$$\epsilon_v(\mu, \phi) = \alpha_v(\mu', \phi') \tag{3-10}$$

Thus, the reflection function describes the radiative properties of surface.

For a perfectly smooth surface as described in the development of Fresnel's equation, the reflection is "mirrorlike" and as indicated in Chapter 2 is called *specular*. Figure 3-2 illustrates the reflection at a specular surface.

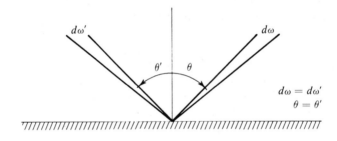

Figure 3-2.   Schematic diagram of reflection at a specular surface.

For a specular surface, the reflection function may be written as

$$\rho_v(\mu, \phi, \mu', \phi')_{\text{Specular}} = \frac{\pi}{\mu} \rho_v(\mu, \phi)\delta(\mu' - \mu)\delta[\phi' - (\phi + \pi)] \tag{3-11}$$

where $\delta(\mu' - \mu)$, $\delta[\phi' - (\phi + \pi)]$ are Dirac delta functions defined as

$$\delta(\mu' - \mu) = 0 \qquad \mu' \neq \mu$$
$$\delta(\mu' - \mu) = \infty \qquad \mu' = \mu$$
$$\int_0^1 \delta(\mu' - \mu)d\mu' = 1 \qquad 0 \leqslant \mu \leqslant 1$$
$$\delta[\phi' - (\phi + \pi)] = 0 \qquad \phi' \neq \phi + \pi$$
$$\delta[\phi' - (\phi + \pi)] = \infty \qquad \phi' = \phi + \pi$$
$$\int_0^{2\pi} \delta[\phi' - (\phi + \pi)] \, d\phi' = 1 \qquad 0 \geqslant \phi + \pi \geqslant 2\pi$$

By substitution into Expression (3-6) for a specular surface the emittance is related to the reflectance as

$$\epsilon_v(\mu, \phi) = 1 - \rho_v(\mu, \phi) \qquad (3\text{-}12)$$

For an isotropic material the reflection is not dependent on ϕ, and (3-12) becomes

$$\epsilon_v(\mu) = 1 - \rho_v(\mu) \qquad (3\text{-}13)$$

The $\rho_v(\mu)$ in Equation (3-13) corresponds to the reflectivity developed by utilizing Fresnel's equations in Chapter 2. Since in most heat transfer work the polarization of the radiation is unknown, the development above has neglected polarization. It is possible, however, to utilize similar reasoning in the development of expressions that take polarization into account. When the polarization of the radiation is unknown, it is common practice to assume $\rho_v(\mu)$ equal to the average of Fresnel's reflectivities for the parallel and perpendicularly polarized components.

The reader will note that the words *reflectivity* and *reflectance* have been utilized above in what may seem to be an arbitrary manner. Indeed one finds the words rather indiscriminately used in the literature. However, there has been a movement to standardize the definitions so that the words *reflectivity, emissivity,* and *absorptivity* refer to a perfectly smooth surface of a pure homogeneous material and are considered properties of the material. Most surfaces of engineering interest may be roughened and may be covered by an oxide layer or some other adherent. The words *reflectance, emittance,* and *absorptance* refer to the radiative properties of a surface configuration.

Accounting for the directional properties of surfaces in actual heat transfer computations is very involved and has been done for only a few simple cases. For most computations in the past, the assumption has been made that the surfaces involved in the heat exchange are diffuse. The definition for a *diffuse surface* is a surface for which the reflection-function is not dependent on direction.

$$\rho_v(\mu, \phi, \mu', \phi')_{\text{Diffuse}} = \rho_v \qquad (3\text{-}14)$$

Figure 3-3 illustrates the reflection at a diffuse surface. The relationship between the emittance and the reflectance for a diffuse surface may be shown by substituting (3-14) into (3-6).

$$\epsilon_v(\mu, \phi) = 1 - \rho_v = \epsilon_v$$

In other words a diffuse surface emits and absorbs radiation equally in all directions. Note that the factor $1/\pi$ included with the definition of the reflection function permits the reduction to the usual relationship between the reflectance and emittance.

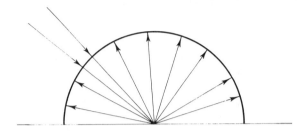

Figure 3-3. Schematic diagram of reflection at a diffuse surface.

R. A. Seban in a discussion of a paper by Sparrow, Eckert and Jonsson (6) suggested that real-surface reflectance might be approximated by assuming the reflection to be composed of a specular component and a diffuse component. This is illustrated in Figure 3-4.

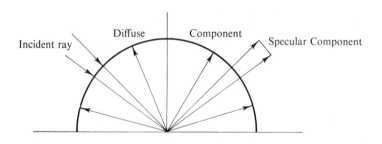

Figure 3-4. Illustration showing the approximation of the reflection function by diffuse and specular components.

The analytical expression for such an approximation takes the form

$$\rho_v(\mu, \phi, \mu' \phi') = \rho_D(\mu', \phi') + \frac{\pi}{\mu'} \rho_S(\mu, \phi)\delta(\mu' - \mu)\delta[\phi' - (\phi + \pi)]$$

$$(3\text{-}15)$$

where ρ_D, (μ', ϕ') is the diffuse reflection for a flux incident from the μ', ϕ' direction and $\pi/\mu', \rho_s(\mu, \phi)\delta(\mu' - \mu)\delta[\phi' - (\phi + \pi)]$ is the specular reflection for the same angle of incidence. It can be readily shown that the directional emittance may be expressed as

$$\epsilon_v(\mu, \phi) = 1 - \rho_S(\mu, \phi) - \frac{1}{\pi} \int_0^{2\pi} \int_0^1 \rho_D(\mu', \phi')\mu' \, d\mu' d\phi' \quad (3\text{-}16)$$

For a surface on which the specular and diffuse components of reflection may be assumed to be invariant with direction, the Relationship (3-17) must hold:

$$\epsilon_\nu = 1 - \rho_S - \rho_D \qquad (3\text{-}17)$$

So far the discussion has centered around monochromatic reflectance, emittance, and absorptance. In order to simplify computations the total emittance values are utilized. The relationship for a diffuse surface between the monochromatic emittance and total emittance may be described by

$$\epsilon = \frac{\pi \int_0^\infty \epsilon_\nu I_{b,\nu}(T)\,d\nu}{\sigma T^4} \qquad (3\text{-}18)$$

Notice that this is not just an integration over frequency as was the case with monochromatic flux and total flux. It is a ratio of the emitted flux divided by the flux that would be emitted by a black body at the same temperature. For the more general surface a similar relationship may be written relating the directional emittance $\epsilon_\nu(\mu,\phi)$ to the *total hemispherical emittance* ϵ.

$$\epsilon = \frac{\int_0^\infty \int_0^{2\pi} \int_0^1 \epsilon_\nu(\mu,\phi)I_{b,\nu}(T)\mu\,d\mu d\phi d\nu}{\sigma T^4} \qquad (3\text{-}19)$$

This is the value usually given in most tables. Experimentally this value is the simplest radiative property to obtain and is accomplished by a calorimetric technique. This procedure will be described in the chapter on experimental methods.

When the monochromatic or spectral value of emittance is given, it is usually the value obtained by viewing the emission of a surface in a direction normal to the surface. These values are usually presented in graphical form. Several plots of the normal spectral emittance of typical engineering materials have been taken from the literature and are presented in the appendices. The total normal emittance may be obtained from these graphs by numerical integration of Equation (3-18). Since the integral is taken over an infinite interval, it is necessary to utilize a quadrature formula. The usual caution must be taken when utilizing a numerical integration procedure. The more irregular the spectral emittance curve the more questionable will be the accuracy of the integration. Hickok (8) has demonstrated, however, that the method may be quite accurate in comparison with other more lengthy methods of numerical integration over wavelength. This will be seen to be of particular value in the computation of total flux in Chapter 4.

The quadrature formula to be utilized is based on the Laguerre polynomial. This formula is stated

$$\int_0^\infty e^{-x} f(x)\, dx = \sum_{p=1}^{M} a_p f(x_p) \tag{3-20}$$

where a_p and x_p, respectively, are the weight factors and ordinates specified by the quadrature formula. Values of a_p and x_p are tabulated in the appendix for various orders of magnitude of approximation. If $f(x)$ is a polynomial of order $2M - 1$ or less, Relationship (3-20) becomes exact. For other cases, the accuracy of the expression depends upon the accuracy with which $f(x)$ may be approximated by such a polynomial.

The utilization of this quadrature is made possible because of the form of Planck's expression of the monochromatic intensity of radiation from a black body. Equation (2-39) is written as follows in a slightly modified form.

$$I_{b,\nu}(T) = e^{-h\nu/kT} \left[\frac{2h\nu^3}{c^2(1 - e^{-h\nu/kT})} \right] \tag{3-21}$$

Thus, a relatively simple transformation is required to change Equation (3-18) into the form of Equation (3-20).

$$\int_0^\infty e^{-h\nu/kT} \left[\epsilon(\nu) \frac{2h\nu^3}{c^2(1 - e^{-h\nu/kT})} \right] d\nu = \int_0^\infty e^{-x} f(x)\, dx \tag{3-22}$$

This is accomplished by the following substitution.

$$\nu = \frac{xkT}{h} \quad \text{and} \quad d\nu = \frac{kT}{h} dx \tag{3-23}$$

Thus, the expression in (3-22) corresponding to $f(x)$ may be stated as

$$f(x) = \frac{2\epsilon(x)k^4 T^4 x^3}{h^3 c^2 (1 - e^{-x})} \tag{3-24}$$

In terms of the quadrature, the integration of the monochromatic emission over all frequencies becomes

$$\int_0^\infty e_\nu I_{b,\nu}(T)\, d\nu = T^4 \sum_{p=1}^{M} A_p \epsilon(x_p) \tag{3-25}$$

Where $\epsilon(x_p)$ corresponds to ϵ_ν as determined from the graph for the particular surface in question at the frequencies corresponding to the ordinates specified by the quadrature and Relationship (3-22). A_p is expressed as follows:

$$A_p = \frac{2k^4 x_p^3 a_p}{h^3 c^2 (1 - e^{x_p})} \tag{3-26}$$

The values of A_p and the values of the frequencies and wavelengths for which the emittance values are to be obtained from the graphical data are listed below as a function of temperature.

The following example illustrates the use of the quadrature formula.

TABLE 3-1.

Values of A_p, v_p, and λ_p for Fifth-order Approximation; Temperature (T) Is in Rankine Degrees, λ_p Is in Mierons.

P	A_p	v_p	λ_p
	$(BTU)(hr^{-1})(ft^{-2})(R^{-4})$		
1	0.347×10^{-11}	$(0.305 \times 10^{10})(T)$	$(9.8360 \times 10^4)(1/T)$
2	12.46×10^{-11}	$(1.637 \times 10^{10})(T)$	$(1.8326 \times 10^4)(1/T)$
3	30.42×10^{-11}	$(4.164 \times 10^{10})(T)$	$(0.72046 \times 10^4)(1/T)$
4	10.78×10^{-11}	$(8.206 \times 10^{10})(T)$	$(0.36558 \times 10^4)(1/T)$
5	0.396×10^{-11}	$(14.638 \times 10^{10})(T)$	$(0.20494 \times 10^4)(1/T)$

Values for various higher orders of approximation are presented in the Appendix.

Example. Compute the total normal emittance of chromium from the spectral-emittance curve, if the temperature is 600°F. Compare with experimental observation.

Utilize room temperature data of the spectral-emittance curve.

Solution. First, compute wavelengths corresponding to quadrature points for $T = 1060$

1. 92.6 μ 4. 3.45 μ
2. 17.3 μ 5. 1.935 μ
3. 6.82 μ

The corresponding values of spectral emittance from curve are

1. 0.07 (Estimated)   4. 0.27
2. 0.07 (Estimated)   5. 0.36
3. 0.12

Multiplication with corresponding values of A_p gives

1. 0.0243×10^{-11} 4. 2.910×10^{-11}
2. 0.872×10^{-11} 5. 0.14×10^{-11}
3. 3.640×10^{-11}

$$\text{Total} = 7.576 \times 10^{-11}$$

$$\epsilon = \frac{(7.576 \times 10^{-11})(3.14)}{1714 \times 10^{-12}} = 0.139$$

In the design of thermal control systems for spacecraft, a parameter α/ϵ is frequently utilized. In view of Kirchhoff's law, the first impulse is that this value should always be identically one. However, the α in this case refers to the absorption of solar energy while the ϵ refers to the emittance at the temperature of the spacecraft surface. Thus both α and ϵ may be computed from a spectral-emittance curve by utilizing the numerical integration technique demonstrated above. In computation of the α, the apparent temperature of the sun would be used in selecting the wavelengths at which the spectral-emittance graph is to be read. The temperature of the surface will be utilized in computing the emittance ϵ.

3-2. Selection of Radiative Properties for Computation of Radiative Heat Transfer

Although the monochromatic reflection function is required for a complete description of the radiative properties of a surface, such functions are not currently known for most surfaces. The reason this information is not available is twofold. First, the measurement and presentation of the reflection function is exceedingly complicated, since for each surface data would be required over a range of frequencies, incidence directions, and leaving directions. The second reason will be apparent in the next chapter when methods for computing heat transfer are formulated. The computation involving such complicated functions when inter-reflections are involved becomes virtually impossible. The preceeding discussion has been included, however, because it gives some insight into the problem involved and it is entirely possible that in the future such reflection functions may be automatically measured and stored on a memory device suitable for direct computer input.

In general, the only radiative properties available in the literature are total hemispherical emittance, normal spectral emittance, and spectral or total reflectance. Information on directional properties or the diffuse or specular character of surfaces is almost totally lacking. For precise predictions, values from published tables ordinarily cannot be used. The reason for this is that the surface condition may have a large effect on the value of emittance. Surface roughness, oxides, dust, and other contaminants may greatly influence the radiative properties. Organic surfaces such as paints may undergo chemical changes and decomposition, which may cause significant effects. In particular, care must be taken in the selection of paints for space vehicles. Significant problems of thermal control may arise from decomposition of painted surfaces resulting from the low pressures and intense ultraviolet and cosmic radiation encountered outside the Earth's atmosphere.

Figure 3-5, which has been reproduced from the work of Wood, Deem, and Lucks (9) at Battelle, gives a comparison of several reported measurements on a single type of stainless steel. Note that values range from approximately 0.1 up to 0.85 at a single wavelength.

Figure 3-6 illustrates the effects of ultraviolet radiation on a type of titanium dioxide paint. This graph is a result of simulation tests conducted by Olson, McKellar, and Stewart (10). The ultraviolet flux corresponds to 10 times the flux that would be incident at one astronomical unit (one

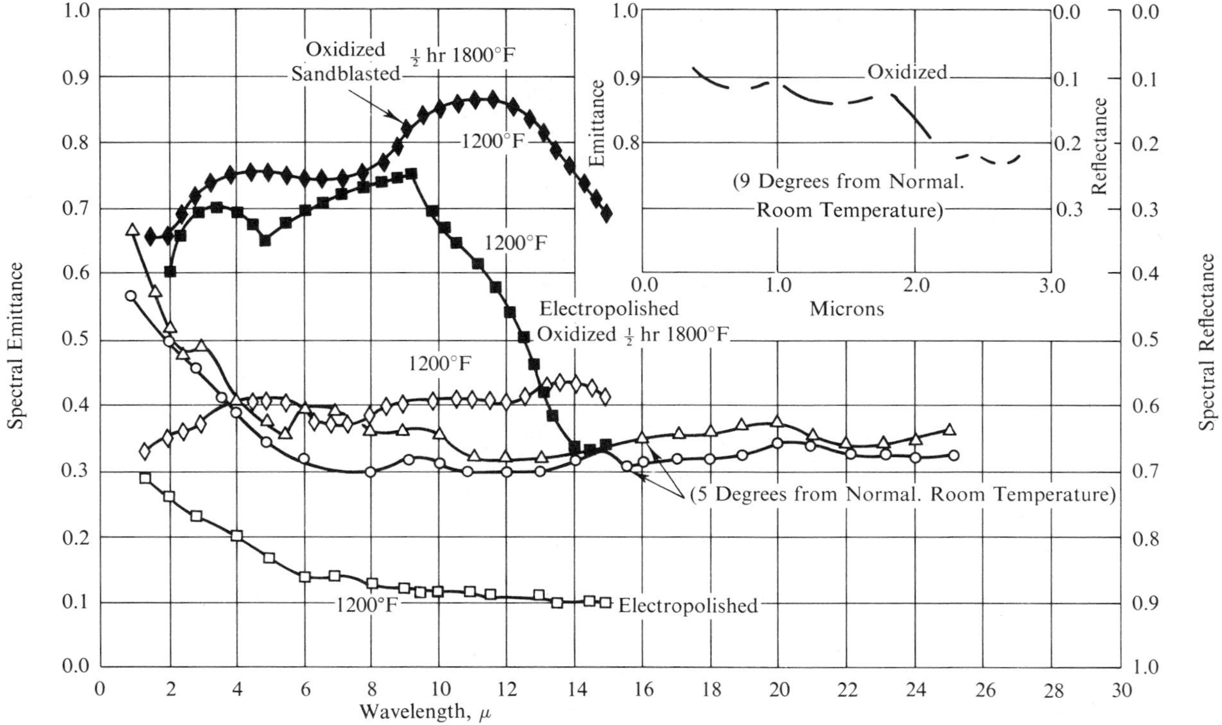

Figure 3-5. Spectral Emittance of Stainless Steel Type 321
(Reproduced from D.M.I.C. Memorandum III, Battelle
Memorial Institute 6-12-61.)

49

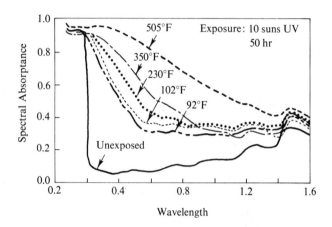

Figure 3-6.   Spectral absorptance—TiO$_2$/epoxy from Reference (10).

Earth orbit radius) and the exposure time on the specimen was 50 hours as indicated.

Directional emittance or reflectance values are seldom found in the literature. Directional emissivities for substances of known refractive index may be computed, however, from Fresnel's equations.

Figure 3-7 illustrates the directional emission that might be expected from a dielectric material and a conducting material.

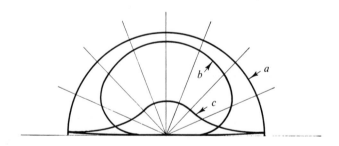

Figure 3-7.   Polar graph of directional emission for (1) diffuse surface, (2) dielectric surface, (3) metallic surface.

Oxide or paint coatings on metal surfaces will cause the surface to emit with a characteristic typical of a dielectric. In Chapter 5, additional methods of analysis will be presented to enable some prediction to be made for the effects of dielectric coatings on metals.

A smooth surface is defined as *a surface on which the irregularities are an order of magnitude smaller than the wavelength of the incident radiation.* Such a surface will always reflect in a specular fashion even though the emission may approximate a diffuse flux. As the surface roughness increases, the reflection becomes more diffuse although experiments show that some specular components persist. In as much as visible radiation is at the short wavelength end of the thermal spectrum, visual inspection will usually indicate the specular reflection characteristics of a surface. If a surface reflects visible light in a specular fashion, then one is assured that the reflection at the longer infrared wavelengths will also be specular.

At the present time there has not been a large amount of work published giving the properties of rough surfaces. Some insight into the character of the interaction of electromagnetic waves and rough surfaces may be found in literature dealing with the transmission of radio and radar signals. A review of work in this area prior to 1963 is given in the book *The Scattering of Electromagnetic Waves by Rough Surfaces* by Beckman and Spizzichino (11). Of more direct interest to the engineer involved with radiative heat transfer, however, is the experimental work that was done at the Heat Transfer Laboratories at the University of Minnesota.

Birkebak, Sparrow, Eckert, and Ramsey (12) made measurements of both total hemispherical and specular reflectance of metallic surfaces of controlled roughness. Nickel samples were irradiated with thermal radiation from the aperture of a black cavity. Figure 3-8 presents some of the results of this study. In this figure, ψ is the angle that the incident ray makes with the surface normal, ρ_S is the specular reflectance of the specimen, ρ_h is the hemispherical reflectance, ρ_{pn} is the reflectance of the reference specimen of polished nickel, and σ_m is the root mean square of the surface roughness. The temperatures refer to the temperature of the irradiating black body. Notice that the hemispherical reflectance includes the specular component and the diffusely-reflected radiation.

Several trends may be noted from Figure 3-8. The specular reflectance decreases markedly with the increase of surface roughness and with an increase in temperature. Both of these changes are, in effect, an increase in the relative roughness.

Torrance and Sparrow (13) made spectral measurements of the reflectance of fused polycrystalline magnesium oxide. Some of the results of their experiment are shown in Figure 3-9. Results are shown for two angles of incidence $\psi = 10°$ and $\psi = 45°$. Reflectance values are also given for values of the azimuthal angles of 0°, 45°, 90°, 180° measured from the direction of incidence. Although the authors made measurements for other surface roughnesses, only results for a root-mean-square roughness of

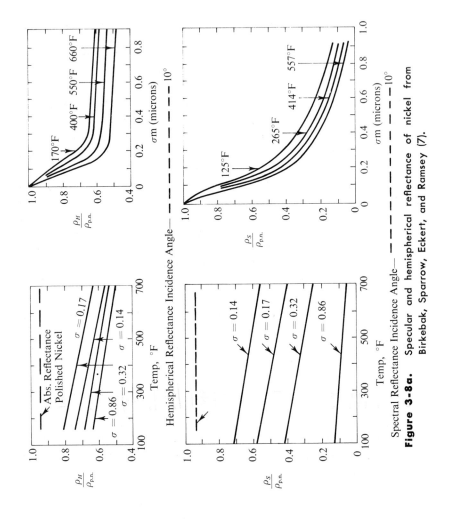

Figure 3-8a. Specular and hemispherical reflectance of nickel from Birkebak, Sparrow, Eckert, and Ramsey (7).

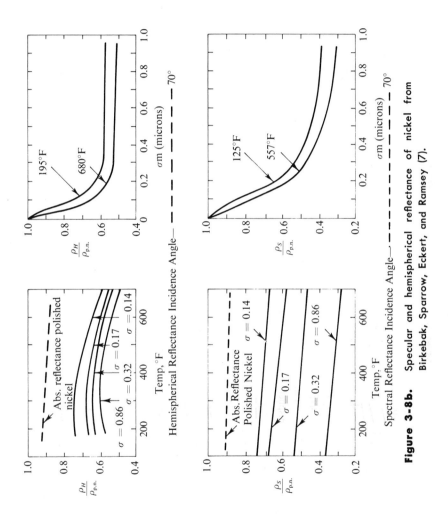

Figure 3-8b. Specular and hemispherical reflectance of nickel from Birkebak, Sparrow, Eckert, and Ramsey (7).

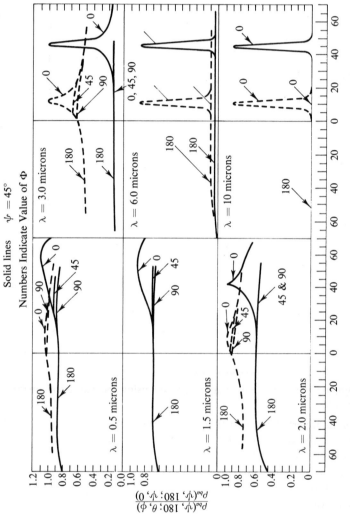

Figure 3-9. Spectral direction and specular reflectance of roughened magnesium oxide root-mean-square of roughness equal to 1.0 μ. From Torrance and Sparrow (13).

54

1.0μ is given here. The reflectance is given as a ratio to the reflectance in the specular direction.

For wavelengths as large as one-half the root-mean-square roughness, the surface appears to be essentially diffuse. Wavelengths an order of magnitude larger than the roughness give an almost purely specular reflection.

In the next chapter, methods of computing the radiative heat exchange between surfaces will be studied. The type of reflection should usually determine the method of analysis.

It will be seen, however, that at the present time the accuracy of such computations are greatly affected by the lack of knowledge concerning the radiative properties of surfaces and the limitations of the computational methods that have been developed in the past.

PROBLEMS

1. Show that a surface may emit diffusely and yet reflect in a specular fashion.

2. Explain how the reflection function can be determined experimentally.

3. Write the expression for the intensity of reflected radiation from a monodirectional flux, $I_\nu(\mu_0, \phi_0)\mu_0\Delta\mu_0\Delta\phi_0$, incident on a diffuse surface.

4. If a cooled specimen is mounted on a goniometer in an isothermal enclosure and then viewed through a small aperture, describe how the directional emittance may be derived from the resultant measurement. (The experiment should be conducted at two different surrounding temperatures with a fixed specimen temperature.)

5. Write the expression for the reflected intensity if an isotropic flux is incident on a specularly-reflecting surface.

6. Compute α/ϵ for copper at 70°F.

7. Compute the Stefan-Boltzmann constant using the numerical quadrature formula.

8. A diffuse, perfectly-conducting sphere orbits the sun. Develop an expression for the equilibrium temperature of the sphere in terms of α/ϵ and its distance from the sun.

9. If the reflection function in Figure 3-9 may be represented by an expression of the form $\rho = \rho_S + \rho_D$, approximate the value of ρ in terms of ρ_S for each wavelength.

References

1. McNicholas, H. J., *Absolute Methods in Reflectometry*, National Bureau of Standards Journal of Research, Vol. 1 (1928), p. 29.

2. Von Fragstein, C., *Uber die Formulierung des Kirchoffschen Gesetzes und ihre Bedeutung fur eine zweckmassige Definition von Remissionzahlen*, Optik, Vol. 12 (1955), p. 660.

3. Polyak, G. L., *Radiative Transfer Between Surfaces of Arbitrary Spatial Distribution of Reflection*, Purdue University, School of Aeronautical and Engineering Sciences Radiative Transfer Project Translation TT-9, October 1961.

4. Dunkle, R. V., Edwards, D. K., Gier, J. T., Nelson, K. E., and Roddick, R. D., "*Heated Cavity Reflectometer for Angular Reflectance Measurements*," Progress in International Research on Thermodynamic and Transport Properties, A.S.M.E., Academic Press, New York, 1962.

5. Dunkle, R. V., *Thermal Radiation Characteristics of Surfaces*, Theory and Fundamental Research in Heat Transfer, Edited by J. A. Clark, Pergamon Press, New York, 1963.

6. Seban, R. A., Discussion of Paper by Sparrow, E. M., Eckert, E. R. G., and Jonsson, V. K., *An Enclosure Theory for Radiative Exchange Between Specularly and Diffusely Reflecting Surfaces*, Journal of Heat Transfer, Vol. 84, Series C, No. 4 (November 1962) p. 294.

7. Birkebak, R. C., Sparrow, E. M., Eckert, E. R. G., and Ramsey, J. W., "Effect of Surface Roughness on the Total Hemispherical and Specular Reflectance of Metallic Surfaces," *Journal of Heat Transfer*, Vol. 86, Series C, No. 2 (May 1964) p. 193.

8. Hickok, R. L., *Radiative Heat Transfer From Non-Grey Surfaces*, M. S. Thesis, University of Oklahoma, 1963.

9. Wood, W. D., Deem, H. W., and Lucks, C. F., *The Emittance of Stainless Steels*, Defense Metals Information Center, Memorandum III, Batelle Memorial Institute, Columbus, Ohio, June 12, 1961.

10. Olson, R. L., McKellar, L. A., and Stewart, J. V., *The Effects of Ultraviolet Radiation on Low α/ϵ Surfaces*, Symposium on Thermal Radiation of Solids, A. S. D., N. B. S., NASA, San Francisco, California, March 1964.

11. Beckmann, P., and Spizzichino, A., *The Scattering of Electromagnetic Waves From Rough Surfaces*, The Macmillan Co., New York, 1963.

12. Birkebak, R. C., Sparrow, E. M., Eckert, E. R. G., and Ramsey, J. W., *Effect of Surface Roughness on the Total Hemispherical and Specular Reflectance of Metallic Surfaces*, Journal of Heat Transfer, Vol. 86, Series C, No. 2 (May 1964) p. 193.

13. Torrance, K. E., and Sparrow, E. M., "Bi-Angular Reflectance of an Electric Non-conductor as a Function of Wavelength and Surface Roughness," *Journal of Heat Transfer*, Vol. 87, Series C, No. 2 (May 1965) p. 283.

14. Gubareff, G. G., Jansen, J. E., and Torborg, R. H., *Thermal Radiation Properties Survey*, Honeywell Research Center, Minneapolis-Honeywell Regulator Co., Minneapolis, Minnesota, 1960.

4   Evacuated Enclosures

4-1.   Formulation of the General Problem

Many problems in radiative heat transfer may be categorized as problems of exchange within evacuated enclosures. The term *enclosure* is used here as a hypothetical region somewhat similar to a control volume in thermodynamics. An enclosure is a region completely bounded by real surfaces of known reflection function, and temperatures, and/or imaginary surfaces over which the entering radiation is completely specified. The term *evacuated* implies that the enclosure does not contain any partially transparent medium such as an absorbing gas, liquid, glass, dust, smoke, or other media that might alter the character of the radiant energy propagating between the boundaries of the enclosure. Theoretically, the radiative flux may be analytically determined in such an enclosure if the reflection function of the surfaces and the temperature are known. The purpose of this chapter is to present methods that may be used to predict radiative transfer in such an enclosure.

The defined enclosure satisfies the conditions of a rather large class of problems of engineering interest for practical purposes; enclosures containing air may be treated by this theory in most instances. The theory is particularly adaptable to radiative transfer analyses in spacecraft. Figure

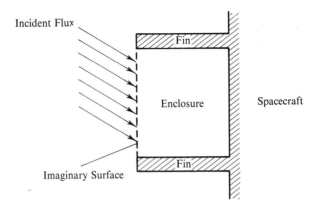

Figure 4-1.   Cross section of a typical enclosure.

4-1 illustrates an example of a radiant space fin. The surface of the fin forms three sides of the enclosure while an imaginary surface completes it. Through the imaginary surface, radiant energy may enter or leave. The entering radiation must be completely specified.

The expression for the intensity of radiation within such an enclosure may be stated in terms of an integral equation. Recall that the intensity of radiation leaving a surface is composed of both emitted and reflected energy. This may be expressed in terms of emittance and reflectance in an expression such as (4-1).

$$I_\nu(\mu, \phi)_{\text{Leaving}} = \epsilon_\nu(\mu, \phi)I_{b,\nu}(T)$$
$$+ \frac{1}{\pi} \int_0^{2\pi} \int_0^1 I_\nu(\mu', \phi')\rho_\nu(\mu, \phi, \mu'\phi')\mu' \, d\mu'd\phi' \tag{4-1}$$

The interior surface of an enclosure may be mapped by two independent variables x,y so that for the enclosure, (4-1) should be written as

$$I_\nu(x, y, \mu, \phi) = \epsilon_\nu(x, y, \mu, \phi)I_{b,\nu}(T)$$
$$+ \frac{1}{\pi} \int_0^{2\pi} \int_0^1 I_\nu(x, y, \mu'\phi')\rho_\nu(x, y, \mu, \phi, \mu', \phi')\mu' \, d\mu'd\phi'$$
$$\tag{4-2}$$

where $I_\nu(x,y,\mu'\phi')$ represents the intensity of the radiant energy incident on the element of area dx,dy from the direction μ', ϕ'. By tracing along the reverse path of this incident ray, this incident intensity may be related to the radiation leaving another element of the enclosure located at $x = \xi$ and $y = \eta$ with leaving directions designated by the cosine of the polar angle and the azimuthal angle ζ and ψ, respectively. The solid angle of the incident intensity which originates from the differential element of area $d\xi$ and $d\eta$ may be expressed as follows:

$$d\mu'd\phi' = \frac{\zeta d\xi d\eta}{[r(x, y, \xi, \eta)]^2} \qquad (4\text{-}3)$$

where $r(x,y,\xi,\eta)$ represents the distance from x, y to ξ, η. Equation (4-2) may be written as Equation (4-4).

$$I_\nu(x, y, \mu, \phi) = \epsilon_\nu(x, y, \mu, \phi)I_{b,\nu}[T(x, y)]$$
$$+ \frac{1}{\pi} \oiint \frac{I_\nu(\xi, \eta, \zeta, \psi)\rho_\nu(\mu, \phi, \mu', \phi')}{[r(x, y, \xi, \eta)]^2} \mu'\zeta d\xi\, d\eta \qquad (4\text{-}4)$$

In Equation (4-4), μ' and ϕ' must be functionally related to ξ, η, ζ, ψ, x, y. The integral in the equation is to be taken over the surface of the enclosure that can be "seen" directly from the point x, y. Figure 4-2 illustrates the geometry involved.

In Equation (4-4) there are two unknown functions $I_\nu(x, y, \mu, \phi)$ and $I_\nu(\xi, \eta, \zeta, \psi)$. The rest of the quantities in the equation are known from the geometry of the enclosure, the radiative properties of the enclosure, and the temperature distribution. The functions $I_\nu(x, y, \mu, \phi)$ and $I_\nu(\xi, \eta, \zeta, \psi)$ describe the intensity of radiation leaving the surface of the enclosure and are the same function. Thus, Equation (4-4) is a linear integral equation of the second kind. It is, however, an equation involving two variables and the kernel is usually very complicated even for simple geometries. For this reason and because information concerning the reflection function of surfaces is scarce, an exact solution of Equation (4-4) is not feasible. This chapter then is devoted to approximate solutions of the equation.

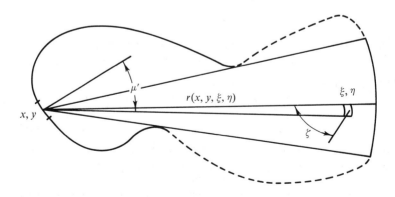

Figure 4-2.   Schematic illustration of geometry for intensity within enclosure.

4-2.   Diffuse Surfaces

The simplest form of Equation (4-4) results when the surface is diffuse. In other words $\rho_v(\mu, \phi, \mu', \phi') = \rho_v$, that is, the reflectance is not a function of the incident or leaving direction. For such a surface the radiation leaving the surface will not be a function of direction and the leaving flux will just be π times the intensity. The flux leaving a diffuse surface is given the special name of *radiosity*. In this book the monochromatic radiosity will be designated by the symbol R_v.

For a diffuse surface, Equation (4-4) may be rewritten as an integral equation for radiosity.

$$R_v(x, y) = \pi \epsilon_v(x, y) I_{b,v}[T(x, y)] + \frac{\rho_v(x, y)}{\pi} \int\!\!\int R_v(\xi, \eta) \frac{\mu' \zeta \, d\xi d\eta}{[r(x, y, \xi, \eta)]^2}$$

(4-5)

The integral in (4-5) is again taken over the interior surface of the enclosure which can be "seen" directly from the point x, y.

4-3.   Lumped-system Approximation

Before considering solutions of (4-5) that result in a continuous analytical expression for $R_v(x, y)$ over the interior of the enclosure, the lumped-system approximation will be utilized. This method has been the most widely used method of radiant heat-transfer computation. For this approximation, the interior of the enclosure is divided into a finite number of areas. The surface temperature, reflectance, and radiosity are assumed to be constant over each area. Equation (4-5) may be rewritten in terms of a summation over the finite areas. Each area is indexed such that $i = 1, 2, 3, \ldots, j, \ldots, n$.

$$R_{v,i} = \pi \epsilon_{v,i} I_{b,v}(T_i) + \frac{\rho_{v,i}}{\pi} \sum_{j=1}^{n} R_{v,j} \int\!\!\int_{A_j} \frac{\mu_i \mu_j}{(r_{ij})^2} dA_j$$

(4-6)

In order to utilize a more nearly average value of the radiosity, Equation (4-6) is integrated over A_i and then divided by A_i. The resulting expression may be written in the form

$$R_{v,i} = \pi \epsilon_{v,i} I_{b,v}(T_i) + \rho_{v,i} \sum_{j=1}^{n} R_{v,j} F_{ij}$$

(4-7)

where F_{ij} is called the *configuration factor* or *view factor* and is defined by the expression

$$F_{ij} = \frac{1}{A_i} \int\!\!\int_{A_i} \int\!\!\int_{A_j} \frac{\mu_i \mu_j}{\pi (r_{ij})^2} dA_j \, dA_i$$

(4-8)

This configuration factor F_{ij} may also be defined as the *fraction of diffuse energy leaving area A_i that is directly incident on area A_j.* Derivations for F_{ij} are normally developed in most elementary heat transfer books. Later in this chapter, various methods utilized in the determination of these configuration factors will be discussed. In general, this determination is the most tedious part of diffuse radiant-exchange problems.

A further simplification of Equation (4-7) can be made if it is assumed that the diffuse reflectance is not a function of the radiation frequency. Such a surface is called a *gray surface*. For this surface, (4-7) may be integrated over all frequencies, resulting in Expression (4-9).

$$R_i = \epsilon_i \sigma T_i^4 + \rho_i \sum_{j=1}^{n} R_j F_{ij} \qquad (4\text{-}9)$$

Equation (4-9) represents n simultaneous, linear algebraic equations. When n is small, the set of equations may be solved readily by hand. For values of n greater than 3, a digital computer will normally be utilized. In the latter case, Equation (4-9) should be written in matrix form.

$$(\delta_{ij} - \rho_i F_{ij})(R_i) = (\epsilon_i \sigma T_i^4) \qquad (4\text{-}10)$$

The first matrix is a square matrix with n^2 terms, while the other two are column matrices. The δ_{ij} is the Kronecker delta and is defined as

$$\delta_{ij} = 0 \qquad i \neq j$$
$$\delta_{ij} = 1 \qquad i = j$$

The solution of (4-10) thus involves a matrix inversion, and is written as

$$(R_i) = (\delta_{ij} - \rho_i F_{ij})^{-1}(\epsilon_i \sigma T_i^4) \qquad (4\text{-}11)$$

Notice that once the inversion has been made, the computation of the radiosity for various temperature combinations may be made by a simple matrix multiplication.

The expression for the net flux at any surface of the enclosure may be written in terms of the radiosities and configuration factors within the enclosure

$$Q_i = R_i - \sum_{j=1}^{n} R_j F_{ij} \qquad (4\text{-}12)$$

In this expression the second term on the right is the irradiation term. Combining Expressions (4-9) and (4-12) gives

$$Q_i = \frac{\epsilon_i}{\rho_i}(\sigma T_i^4 - R_i) \qquad (4\text{-}13)$$

In this method of computation, there are two special types of surfaces that require modified handling. One of them is a black surface. For such a surface the reflectance is zero and the radiosity is σT^4. It can be readily seen that the rows of the square matrix in Equation (4-10) that correspond to black surfaces will be identically zero except for the diagonal element, which will be one. The terms corresponding to black surfaces in the column matrix on the right side of Equation (4-10) become just σT_i^4. Equation (4-12) must be used to compute the net flux at a black surface.

The other type of surface that receives special consideration is the *refractory* surface. This is a surface that is in radiative equilibrium, that is, the flux leaving the surface is exactly equal to the flux incident. Thus, Q for such a surface is zero, and the surface may be treated as one having a perfect reflectance, that is, $\rho = 1$ and $\epsilon = 0$.

4-4. Electric Circuit Analogy

Although Equation (4-9) is normally solved by utilizing a digital computer, the equation may be solved by utilizing an electrical network analog. Examination of Equation (4-13) reveals a similarity with electric circuit theory.

$$I = \frac{1}{R}(E_1 - E_2) \qquad (4\text{-}14)$$

$$A_i Q_i = \frac{A_i \epsilon_i}{\rho_i}(\sigma T_i^4 - R_i) \qquad (4\text{-}15)$$

In this analogy current is analogus to net heat transfer, resistance is analogus to $\rho/A\epsilon$ and voltage is analogus to radiosity. Now, utilizing the following relationship for the configuration factor,

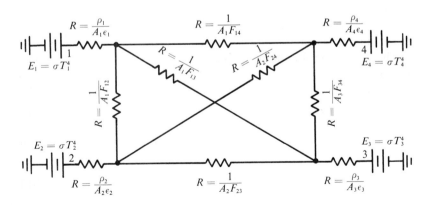

Figure 4-3.   Analogus electric circuit for a four-zone enclosure.

$$\sum_{j=1}^{n} F_{ij} = 1 \tag{4-16}$$

Equation (4-12) may be written as

$$A_i Q_i = \sum_{j=1}^{n} A_i F_{ij}(R_i - R_j) \tag{4-17}$$

Thus, the analogus electric circuit for a four-zone enclosure may be drawn as in Figure 4-3.

Prior to the widespread availability of digital computers the network analog was very useful in the solution of many zoned enclosures. However, the accuracy and ease with which digital computers may be programmed have outmoded the network analog for most computations.

4-5.   Determination of Configuration Factors

The solution of the lumped, diffuse-enclosure problem by either digital or analog method involves the determination of the configuration factor F_{ij}. This factor depends only on the geometry of the enclosure. It may be defined as representing the fraction of diffuse energy leaving a uniform surface A_i that is directly incident on surface A_j. Equation (4-8) may be developed directly from this definition. Such a development will be found in most elementary heat transfer texts.

The value of F_{ij} for any particular geometry may be found by direct integration, which is usually rather complicated and often must be accomplished by a numerical scheme. For many problems, however, the engineer may resort to published formulae, tables, or graphical and photometric schemes for the determination of the needed configuration factors. Values for these factors may be obtained by the following methods that are listed in the usual order of preference.

1.   Published formulae, tables, and charts
2.   Configuration-factor algebra and geometry
3.   Graphical methods
4.   Mechanical and photometric integrators
5.   Integration of line integrals (use of Stoke's theorem to reduce surface integrals to line integrals)
6.   Direct Integration

4-6.   Published Values of Configuration Factors

Many cases of geometries encountered in engineering have been determined and published in the literature. In searching for such factors, publications dealing with illumination and nuclear reactor shielding should be searched as well as the heat transfer literature. The following is a list of sources in which most of the published values may be found. The first two references serve as the source for many of the values reported in the remaining references; however, the latter are generally more available.

1. *Scientific Basis of Illumination Engineering*, P. Moon (1).
2. *Radiant-Interchange Configuration Factors*, D. C. Hamilton and W. R. Morgan (2).
3. *Heat Transmission*, W. H. McAdams (3).
4. *Radiation Heat Transfer for Spacecraft and Solar Power Plant Design*. F. Kreith (4).
4. *Heat and Mass Transfer*, E. R. G. Eckert and R. M. Drake (5).
6. *Heat Transfer*, Vol. II, M. Jakob (6).

In Appendix II some of these values are tabulated.

4-7.   Configuration-factor Algebra

There are certain relationships that may be developed between the configuration factors that will reduce the number of independent determinations required for a given problem. These relationships will also often provide a method for combining values reported in tables and graphs into values for configurations that are not reported.

(1) Basic Reciprocal Relation. This relationship immediately allows a reduction from n^2 separate factors to $(n^2 + n)/2$ factors required to solve the enclosure problem. The reciprocal relation is

$$A_i F_{ij} = A_j F_{ji} \qquad (4\text{-}18)$$

This can be readily seen to hold because of the symmetry of the integral defining the configuration factor.

$$\iint_{A_i} \iint_{A_j} \frac{\mu_i \mu_j}{(r_{ij})^2} \, dA_j \, dA_i = \iint_{A_j} \iint_{A_i} \frac{\mu_j \mu_i}{(r_{ji})^2} \, dA_i \, dA_j \qquad (4\text{-}19)$$

(2) Summation Relationship. This may be readily developed from the definition of F_{ij} that states that F_{ij} *is the fraction of the diffuse energy leaving surface i that is directly incident on surface j.*

$$\sum_{j=1}^{n} F_{ij} = 1 \qquad (4\text{-}20)$$

(3) Decomposition Rule. This may be developed by recognizing that the energy leaving an area and incident on an area that may be considered to be composed of two or more subdivisions, is equal to the sum of the energy

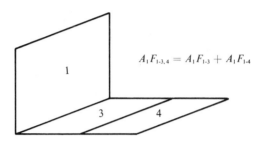

$$A_1 F_{1\text{-}3,4} = A_1 F_{1\text{-}3} + A_1 F_{1\text{-}4}$$

Figure 4-4.   Example of decomposition rule.

incident on the individual subdivisions. For example, consider Figure 4-4.

It can be seen that the geometry configuration factor $F_{1\text{-}3,4}$ is similar to $F_{1\text{-}3}$. Both geometries are for adjacent plane surfaces and would be specified, in all probability, by a single formula or graph. The configuration factor $F_{1\text{-}4}$, not given directly by the formula for adjacent areas, could be determined by subtracting two of the values given.

$$F_{1\text{-}4} = F_{1\text{-}3,4} - F_{1\text{-}3}$$

(4) Rule of Corresponding Corners.   This is frequently helpful in determining the relationships between plane rectangular areas. If two finite rectangular planes have a common edge and are segmented into areas by lines running parallel and perpendicular to their sides (the lines perpendicular to the intersection extend over both planes), then the product of the area of an exterior corner segment of plane A and the configuration factor from that area to the opposite exterior corner of the adjacent plane B is equal to the product of the other exterior corner of A and its configuration factor to the corresponding exterior corner of B. This is illustrated by Figure 4-5.

From Figure 4-5 the integral of the configuration factor may be represented as

$$A_1 F_{12} = \int_{y_A=e}^{d} \int_{x_A=0}^{a} \int_{y_s=f}^{g} \int_{x_s=b}^{c} \frac{\cos \theta_A \cos \theta_B \, dx_B dy_B dx_A dy_A}{\pi(r_{AB})^2} \qquad (4\text{-}21)$$

In this expression the following relationships hold.

$$(r_{AB})^2 = (x_A - x_B)^2 + (y_B + y_A \cos \psi)^2 + (y_A \sin \psi)^2$$

$$\cos \theta_A = \frac{y_B \sin \psi}{r_{AB}}$$

$$\cos \theta_B = \frac{y_A \sin \psi}{r_{AB}}$$

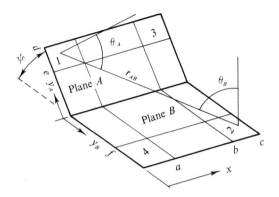

Figure 4-5. Illustration of the rule of corresponding corners for adjacent rectangles.

Examination of Figure 4-5 and the integral in Expression (4-21) will reveal that the expression for the integral representing $A_3 F_{3,4}$ is identical to Expression (4-21) except for the interchange of the limits on X_A and X_B. However, the integral is symmetrical with respect to X_A and X_B. Therefore, its value is unchanged, and the following expression must hold

$$A_1 F_{1\text{-}2} = A_3 F_{3\text{-}4} \qquad (4\text{-}22)$$

In a similar fashion it may be demonstrated that if two congruent rectangles are parallel and directly opposed and are subdivided by identical sets of lines that are parallel and perpendicular to the sides of the rectangles, then the product of the area of each corner segment and its configura-

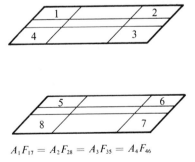

$$A_1 F_{17} = A_2 F_{28} = A_3 F_{35} = A_4 F_{46}$$

Figure 4-6. Illustrating rule of corresponding corners for parallel, opposed, congruent rectangles.

tion factor, with respect to the diagonally opposite segment on the other rectangle, is equal to the corresponding product of the area of each corner and its configuration factor to the opposite diagonal corner area. This is illustrated in Figure 4-6.

(5) Special Consideration for Parallel Strips of Infinite Length.
The configuration factors that relate to the diffuse energy exchange between parallel strips of infinite length are of considerable interest in the computation of heat transfer in long passages and long fin surfaces or grooves. In such geometries, the configuration factor reduces to a two-dimensional determination. Further, it will be shown below that for this case, the configuration factors may be determined without resorting to complicated integration.

In the context considered here, a strip is a surface generated by the translation of an infinite straight line. The reciprocity relationship for two parallel infinite strips involves the widths of the respective strips.

$$W_i F_{ij} = W_j F_{ji} \tag{4-23}$$

where W is the distance measured along the surface perpendicular to the sides of the strip. Hottel (3) developed a method using configuration-factor algebra to determine the factors for infinite parallel strips. This method is called the *method of crossed and uncrossed strings.*

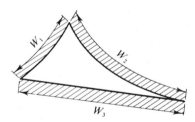

Figure 4-7. Cross section or enclosure formed by three parallel infinite strips.

Consider an enclosure composed of three parallel strips that are convex in the sense that $F_{ii} = 0$. Three equations may be written by applying the summation rule to the configuration factors for each side

$$W_1 F_{12} + W_1 F_{13} = W_1$$
$$W_2 F_{21} + W_2 F_{23} = W_2 \tag{4-24}$$
$$W_3 F_{31} + W_3 F_{32} = W_3$$

The number of unknown F's in Equation (4-24) may be reduced by the application of the reciprocity rule resulting in Equations (4-25).

$$\begin{aligned} W_1 F_{12} + W_1 F_{13} &= W_1 \\ W_1 F_{12} + W_2 F_{23} &= W_2 \\ W_1 F_{13} + W_2 F_{23} &= W_3 \end{aligned} \qquad \text{(4-25)}$$

Solving these equations for $W_1 F_{12}$ gives Equation (4-26).

$$W_1 F_{12} = \frac{W_1 + W_2 - W_3}{2} \qquad \text{(4-26)}$$

The relationship may now be applied to assist in the determination of the configuration factor between any two parallel strips in an infinite cylindrical enclosure.

Consider the two strips within an enclosure such as the one illustrated in Figure 4-8. Here, note that the concave enclosure is first modified by sketching in the dashed lines connecting the end points of the surfaces of interest. The configuration factor from the convex area AG to the convex area DE may be determined by applying the summation rule and by repeated application of Equation (4-26) to give the following two equations.

$$\begin{aligned} \overline{AG} F_{AG-AD} &= \frac{\overline{AG} + \overline{AD} - \overline{DG}}{2} \\ \overline{AG} F_{AG-GE} &= \frac{\overline{AG} + \overline{GE} - \overline{AE}}{2} \end{aligned} \qquad \text{(4-27)}$$

Application of the summation rule gives Equation (4-28).

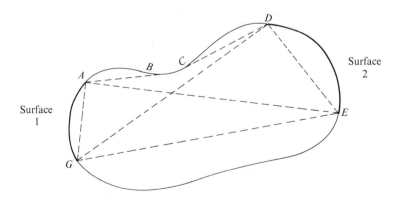

Figure 4-8.   Illustration of the geometry for the configuration-factor determination by the method of the crossed and uncrossed strings.

$$\overline{AG}F_{AG-DE} = \overline{AG} - \frac{\overline{AG} + \overline{AD} - \overline{DG}}{2} - \frac{\overline{AG} + \overline{GE} - \overline{AE}}{2} \qquad (4\text{-}28)$$

Collecting terms results in

$$\overline{AG}F_{AG-DE} = \frac{(\overline{DG} + \overline{AE}) - (\overline{AD} + \overline{GE})}{2} \qquad (4\text{-}29)$$

It can be readily seen that all of the radiant energy that is leaving AG and is directly incident on DE is equal to the energy leaving AG and incident on area 2. Further, it may be shown with little additional difficulty that the net radiation streaming away from a diffuse concave surface of uniform radiosity is the same as the radiation streaming away from a convex surface formed by replacing all of the concave areas by a plane surface. Thus, Equation (4-29) may be rewritten as Equation (4-30).

$$W_1 F_{12} = \frac{(\overline{DG} + \overline{AE}) - (\overline{AD} + \overline{GE})}{2} \qquad (4\text{-}30)$$

This rule may be easily remembered by thinking of the dashed lines as strings that are stretched between the ends of the areas 1 and 2. The distance $\overline{DG} + \overline{AG}$ represents the length of the crossed strings and $\overline{AD} + \overline{GE}$ represents the length of the uncrossed strings.

Often, one is interested in the configuration factor between a strip of finite length and an infinite strip. Let F_{dA-B} represent the configuration factor from an element of strip A having a differential length dX. Now, because of the constant relationship between A and B over their infinite lengths, F_{dA-B} must be the same for all dX_i and the fraction of energy leaving the total strip A that is incident on strip B may be expressed as

$$(\sum_i W_A \, dX_i) F_{AB} = \sum_i W_A \, dX_i F_{dA-B} \qquad (4\text{-}31)$$

However, since F_{dA-B} is the same for each element, it may be removed from the summation with the result that

$$F_{AB} = F_{dA-B} \qquad (4\text{-}32)$$

Stated in words, the configuration factor from a strip of constant width and of any length to a parallel strip of infinite length is the same for all lengths of the finite strip, including an infinite length.

4-8.   Graphical Method

The basis of the graphical method, as well as the mechanical and photometric methods of the next section, is the geometry of the unit sphere. Consider Figure 4-9 that illustrates an imaginary spherical surface intersecting the solid angle subtended at dA in the center of the sphere and in the plane of the base of the hemisphere.

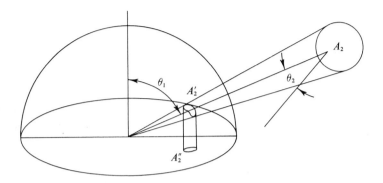

Figure 4-9. Illustration of the geometry of the unit sphere.

In Figure 4-9, A_2' represents the area enclosed by the solid angle subtended by A_2, and A_2'' represents the projection of that area onto the base of the hemisphere. From the definition of the configuration factor and examination of the geometry, the following analysis can be made.

$$F_{dA_1-A_2} = \iint_{A_2} \frac{\cos \theta_1 \cos \theta_2 \, dA_2}{\pi (r_{12})^2} \tag{4-33}$$

From the geometry, the following relationship may be substituted in the expression above.

$$dA_2' = \frac{\cos \theta_2 \, dA_2}{(r_{12})^2} \tag{4-34}$$

It can also be readily seen that (4-35) must also hold.

$$A_2'' = \iint_{A_2'} \cos \theta_1 \, dA_2' \tag{4-35}$$

Thus, the result of integration of (4-33) may be stated as Equation (4-36).

$$F_{dA_1-A_2} = \frac{A_2''}{\pi} \tag{4-36}$$

In words, the configuration factor from a differential area to a finite area may be expressed as a ratio of the area of the projection A_2'' to the area of the base of the hemisphere.

A graphical procedure was developed by Juhasz and Hooper (7) for utilizing the unit sphere for computation of configuration factors of the type F_{d1-2}. The procedure is essentially an application of fundamental principles of descriptive geometry. Figure 4-10 illustrates the procedure for making a projection of a single point. The outline of the area A_2 would

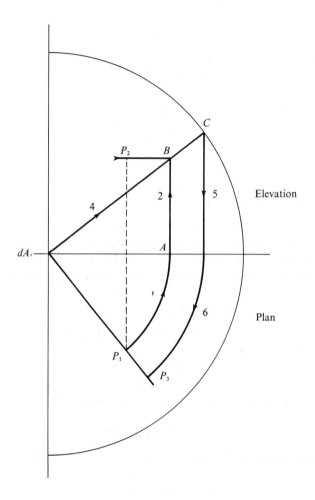

Figure 4-10.   Illustration of graphical projection method.

thus be projected by repeating the procedure for the single point as many times as necessary so that the total projected outline would appear on the sketch.

The initial step in the method is to draw an outline of an elevation and plan view of the area A_2. These views are to be so located that the elevation of A_2 is in the upper right-hand quadrant of the drawing with dA_1 located at the same origin. In Figure 4-10, the point P_2 represents a point on the edge of area A_2 in the elevation. Point P_1 represents the plane view of the same point. A base circle is then drawn with its center at dA_1. The steps in the projection are

1. From P_1 swing an arc to the horizontal axis locating point A.
2. From A erect a vertical line.
3. Through point P_2 draw a horizontal line locating B, which is the intersection of this line and the line drawn in Step 2.
4. Draw a radial line from the origin through B to the base circle locating C.
5. Drop a vertical line from point C to the horizontal axis locating D.
6. From D swing an arc in the lower quadrant.
7. Draw a radial line from the origin through P_1 to intersect the arc drawn in Step 6 locating the point P_3.

Thus, P_3 is the resulting projection of the point P onto the base circle of the unit sphere. After sufficient points have been drawn to locate the outline of the projection, the area may be measured by counting squares, random dots, or by using a planimeter. The ratio of this area to the area of the base circle is the configuration factor F_{d1-2}.

There is an additional graphical method devised by H. Zijl (8). This method requires the use of specially prepared charts. It may be useful in obtaining factors of the type F_{d1-2} for plane areas either perpendicular or parallel to the plane of dA_1. These charts will not be reproduced in this book since they are of limited value. Copies and instructions may be found either in the original paper or in Kreith (4).

4-9. Mechanical and Photographic Methods

D. C. Hamilton (2) developed a mechanism that may be utilized to obtain configuration factors of the type F_{d1-2} for relatively large areas. This method requires the placement of a sighting device fastened to a pivoted parallel linkage and plotting table on the position of dA_1. The operator sights through the device and moves the sight around the outline of A_2. Next, the stylus traces the projection of A_2 corresponding to A_2'' in the unit sphere discussion. The area A_2'' plotted on the board is then measured and divided by the area of the base circle of the machine. Figure 4-11 is a schematic illustration of the device.

Eckert (4) presents a photographic technique by using a cardboard model of area A_2 in a milk-glass hemisphere that has a point light source corresponding to the position of dA_1 relative to A_2. The shadow cast on the

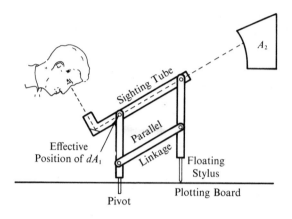

Figure 4-11.   Schematic of Hamilton's mechanical integrator.

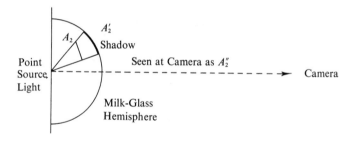

Figure 4-12.   Schematic illustration of Eckert's photographic method
of configuration-factor determination.

milk-glass hemisphere is then photographed from a large distance. The
area of the shadow on the photograph thus corresponds to the projected
area A_2'' on the base circle. Figure 4-12 illustrates this method schematically.

Hickman (9), working with radiative exchange between sections of a
spacecraft, developed a small parabolic convex mirror that may be
placed at the position of dA_1 and photographed. The mirror has a grid
embossed in its surface. The reflection of A_2 is photographed. The configuration factor is then computed from the area of the reflection in the
surface by utilizing a calibration curve for the mirror shape.

4-10. Determination of Configuration Factors Using Line Integrals

Parry Moon (1) presents a method of reducing the double integral required for the evaluation of configuration factors of the type F_{d1-2} to the evaluation of a single line integral. Sparrow (10) has more recently modified the method so that the quadruple integral required for configuration factors of the type F_{1-2} may be reduced to the evaluation of two line integrals. The first method is presented as follows.

Consider the expression for the configuration factor F_{d1-2}.

$$F_{d1-2} = \iint_{A_2} \frac{\cos \theta_1 \cos \theta_2}{\pi (r_{12})^2} \, dA_2 \tag{4-37}$$

The equation is rewritten utilizing vector notation. Let $\bar{r}$ be a unit vector in the r_{12} direction and $\bar{n}_1$ and $\bar{n}_2$ be unit normals to Surface 1 and Surface 2, respectively.

$$F_{d1-2} = -\iint_{A_2} \frac{(\bar{n}_1 \cdot \bar{r})(\bar{n}_2 \cdot \bar{r})}{\pi (r_{12})^2} \, dA_2 \tag{4-38}$$

Using the associative rule of vector multiplication (4-38) may be rewritten as (4-39).

$$F_{d1-2} = -\frac{1}{\pi} \iint_{A_2} \bar{n}_2 \cdot \left[\frac{\bar{r}(\bar{n}_1 \cdot \bar{r})}{(r_{12})^2} \right] dA_2 \tag{4-39}$$

The following identity may be used to further simplify Equation (4-39).

$$-\frac{\bar{r}(\bar{n}_1 \cdot \bar{r})}{(r_{12})^2} = \frac{1}{2} \left(\nabla \times \frac{\bar{r} \times \bar{n}_1}{r_{12}} \right) \tag{4-40}$$

Equation (4-39) is then rewritten with this substitution.

$$F_{d1-2} = +\frac{1}{2\pi} \iint_{A_2} \left(\nabla \times \frac{\bar{r} \times \bar{n}_1}{r_{12}} \right) \cdot \bar{n}_2 \, dA_2 \tag{4-41}$$

The area integral in Equation (4-41) reduces to the line integral expressed by Equation (4-42) through the application of Stoke's theorem.

$$F_{d1-2} = +\frac{1}{2\pi} \oint_{A_2} \left(\frac{\bar{r} \times \bar{n}_1}{r_{12}} \right) \cdot \bar{l} \, dl \tag{4-42}$$

In this equation $\bar{l}$ is a unit vector directed along the boundary of A_2, and dl is a differential length along the boundary of A_2. The scalar triple-product rule of vector analysis allows the interchange of the dot and cross products in Equation (4-42). The equation is rewritten as Equation (4-43).

$$F_{d1-2} = -\frac{1}{2\pi} \oint_{A_2} n_1 \cdot \left(\frac{\bar{r} \times \bar{l}}{r_{12}} \right) dl \tag{4-43}$$

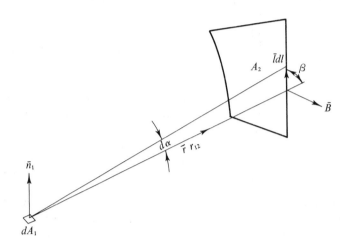

Figure 4-13. Illustration of geometry for line integration.

The crossproduct $\bar{r} \times \bar{l}$ may be written as $\bar{B} \sin \beta$, where $\bar{B}$ is a unit vector mutually perpendicular to $\bar{r}$ and $\bar{l}$, and β is the angle between $\bar{r}$ and $\bar{l}$.

Figure 4-13 illustrates the geometry of the integration. From this illustration it can be seen that the following relationship must hold.

$$d\alpha = \frac{dl \sin \beta}{r_{12}} \tag{4-44}$$

Thus, Equation (4-43) may be written as Equation (4-45).

$$F_{d1-2} = -\frac{1}{2\pi} \oint_{A_2} \bar{n}_1 \cdot \bar{B} \, d\alpha \tag{4-45}$$

In order to illustrate this method, consider the following.

Example. Compute F_{d1-2} if dA_1 is positioned at the rectangular coordinate location $(0, 0, 3)$ and is oriented so that the unit vector normal to it is expressed by the vector $(1/\sqrt{3})i + (1/\sqrt{3})j - (1/\sqrt{3})k$. Also, A_2 is a square located in the xy plane such that the coordinates of its corners are $(1, 1, 0)$, $(-1, 1, 0)$, $(-1, -1, 0)$, $(1, -1, 0)$. Figure 4-14 is a sketch of the geometry.

Solution. Notice that as the integration is made along each side of the rectangle, the vector $\bar{B}$ remains constant. Figure 4-15 illustrates the geometry determining $\bar{B}$ along the line cd.

From Figure 4-15 it can be seen that the unit vector along cd is
$\bar{B} = (3\sqrt{10})i + 0j + (1/\sqrt{10})k;$

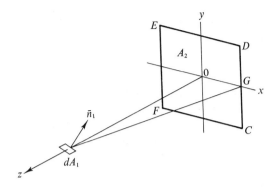

Figure 4-14. Illustration of geometry for example.

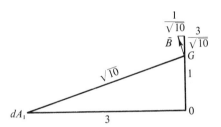

Figure 4-15. Illustration of geometry for $\bar{B}$ in example.

along de, $\bar{B} = 0i + (3\sqrt{10})j + (1/\sqrt{10})k$;
along ef, $\bar{B} = -(3\sqrt{10})i + 0j + (1/\sqrt{10})k$;
and along fc, $B = 0i - (3\sqrt{10})j + (1/\sqrt{10})k$.

Along each side $\int d\alpha = 2 \operatorname{Tan}^{-1} (1/\sqrt{10})$. Thus, the expression of the evaluation of Equation (4-45) may be written as

$$F_{d1-2} = -\frac{1}{\pi} \operatorname{Tan}^{-1} \left(\frac{1}{\sqrt{10}}\right) \left(\frac{1}{\sqrt{3}} i + \frac{1}{\sqrt{3}} j - \frac{1}{\sqrt{3}} k\right)$$

$$\cdot \left(\frac{3}{\sqrt{10}} i + \frac{1}{\sqrt{10}} k + \frac{3}{\sqrt{10}} j + \frac{1}{\sqrt{10}} k - \frac{3}{\sqrt{10}} i + \frac{1}{\sqrt{10}} k - \frac{3}{\sqrt{10}} j + \frac{1}{\sqrt{10}} k\right)$$

$$F_{d1-2} = \frac{4}{\pi\sqrt{30}} \operatorname{Tan}^{-1} \left(\frac{1}{\sqrt{10}}\right) \qquad \text{Answer}$$

Sparrow (10) has presented a similar formulation to Equation (4-45).

He has, however, taken the integration one step further and developed an expression for configuration factors between finite areas of the type F_{12}. Equation (4-46) is the expression that he derived.

$$F_{12} = \frac{1}{2\pi A_1} \oint_{c_1} \oint_{c_2} [\ln (r_{12}) \, dx_1 dx_2 + \ln (r_{12}) \, dy_1 dy_2 + \ln (r_{12}) \, dz_1 dz_2]$$

(4-46)

In this equation, c_1 and c_2 are the curves bounding A_1 and A_2, r_{12} is the distance from a point on the boundary of A_1 to a point on the boundary of A_2. The subscripts on the differential distances represent distances along the boundaries of the corresponding areas. Sparrow (10) gives two examples for the application of this equation. For certain geometries the determination is relatively simple and much easier than evaluating the corresponding area integrals. However, for complicated geometries, Equation (4-46) may become very difficult as does the corresponding, quadruple-area integral.

The direct integration method will not be discussed here since it involves the straightforward integration of the configuration factor.

4-11.   Some Applications of Lumped-System Approximation

The solution of Equation (4-9) may be readily developed in a general form for enclosures with only two zones. The solution to this equation substituted into Equation (4-12) results in an expression that may be written as Equation (4-47).

$$Q_{12} = \mathscr{F}_{12} \sigma (T_1^4 - T_2^4) \qquad (4\text{-}47)$$

The $\mathscr{F}_{12}$ symbol has been used in many elementary books on heat transfer and is called the *gray-body configuration factor*. This factor may be readily derived in its general form from Equations (4-9) and (4-12). For the two-zone problem, the first equation may be stated as

$$(1 - \rho_1 F_{11})R_1 - \rho_1 F_{12} R_2 = \epsilon_1 \sigma T_1^4$$
$$-\rho_2 F_{21} R_1 + (1 - \rho_2 F_{22})R_2 = \epsilon_2 \sigma T_2^4 \qquad (4\text{-}48)$$

Solving for R_1 results in Equation (4-49).

$$R_1 = \frac{\epsilon_1 (1 - \rho_2 F_{22}) \sigma T_1^4 + \rho_1 F_{12} \epsilon_2 \sigma T_2^4}{(1 - \rho_1 F_{11})(1 - \rho_2 F_{22}) - \rho_1 \rho_2 F_{12} F_{21}} \qquad (4\text{-}49)$$

A similar expression may be found for R_2. Substitution of Equation (4-49) into Equation (4–12) provides an expression for $\mathscr{F}_{12}$.

$$\mathscr{F}_{12} = \frac{1}{(1/F_{12}) + (\rho_1/\epsilon_1) + (A_1 \rho_2/A_2 \epsilon_2)} \qquad (4\text{-}50)$$

It should be restated that Equation (4-47) gives the net flux at Surface 1 only if Surface 1 and Surface 2 are connected such that one surface completely encloses the other surface.

Example. Utilizing the two-zone approximation, compute the effective emittance (ϵ_{eff}) of a groove having a total surface area of A_1 and an opening area of A_2. Figure 4-16 illustrates the example. The surface of the groove has a diffuse emittance of ϵ_1.

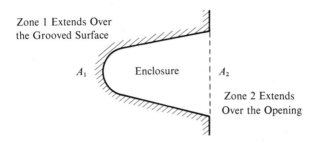

Zone 1 Extends Over the Grooved Surface

A_1 Enclosure A_2

Zone 2 Extends Over the Opening

Figure 4-16.   Illustration of groove for example.

Solution. The effective emittance of the groove is the ratio of radiant energy issuing from the groove divided by the energy that would radiate from a black surface having the same area as the opening.

$$\epsilon_{\text{eff}} = \frac{A_1 R_1 F_{12}}{A_2 \sigma T_1^4}$$

From Equation (4-9), and based on the fact that area 2 acts like a black surface at zero temperature, an expression for radiosity may be derived.

$$R_1 = \frac{\epsilon_1 \sigma T_1^4}{1 - \rho_1 F_{11}}$$

Substituting R_1 into the expression for ϵ_{eff} gives

$$\epsilon_{\text{eff}} = \frac{A_1 F_{12} \epsilon_1}{A_2 (1 - \rho_1 F_{11})}$$

However, $F_{12} = (A_2/A_1)$ and $F_{11} = 1 - (A_2/A_1)$. Therefore, the expression for ϵ_{eff} may be simplified as follows:

$$\epsilon_{\text{eff}} = \frac{1}{1 + (\rho_1 A_2/\epsilon_1 A_1)} \qquad \text{Answer}$$

The answer could also have been obtained by substitution of Equation (4-50)

$$\epsilon_{\text{eff}} = \frac{A_1 \mathscr{F}_{12} \sigma T_1^4}{A_2 \sigma T_1^4} = \frac{1}{1 + (\rho_1 A_2/\epsilon_1 A_1)}$$

Note that ϵ_{eff} approaches 1 for $A_2 \ll A_1$ and approaches ϵ_1 as A_2 approaches A_1.

It is also interesting to note some of the special and limiting cases of Equation (4-50). Consider Surface 1 to be convex so that $F_{11} = 0$ and, further, that Surface 2 completely surrounds Surface 1. Equation (4-50) thus becomes Equation (4-51).

$$\mathscr{F}_{12} = \frac{1}{1 + (\rho_1/\epsilon_1) + (A_1 \rho_2/A_2 \epsilon_2)} \qquad \textbf{(4-51)}$$

If $A_1 \ll A_2$, that is, if Surface 1 is small compared to its surrounding enclosure, then Equation (4-52) must hold.

$$\mathscr{F}_{12} \approx \epsilon_1 \tag{4-52}$$

This is to be expected for a gray surface since the small Surface 1 would not effectively disturb the radiation within the large isothermal enclosure. Thus, the net flux is the difference between the emitted radiation and the absorbed, incident black radiation.

The reader should recognize that the two-zone enclosure represents only the first approximation to radiative transfer. However, the results may be surprisingly close to more rigorous analyses and for many purposes where the radiative flux represents only a fraction of the total heat transfer it gives satisfactory results. When a computer is available and time allows, enclosures such as the groove in the example above should be divided into several zones and the radiosity determined numerically by Equation (4-11).

4-12.   Radiosity Distribution in Enclosures

In the previous paragraphs, the analysis has "lumped" the enclosure into zones, and the radiosity, surface properties, and temperature are considered constant over each area. It was noted that radiosity usually varies continuously over the interior of an enclosure with discontinuities occuring with surface discontinuity or discontinuities in directional radiation that may enter through openings.

For a gray enclosure, Equation (4-5) may be written as

$$R(x, y) = \epsilon(x, y)\sigma T^4(x, y) + \rho(x, y) \int\int R(\xi, \eta)K(x, y, \xi, \eta)\, d\xi d\eta \tag{4-53}$$

The $K(x, y, \xi, \eta)$ is called the *kernel of the integral equation* and for this problem is a function of the geometry of the enclosure. Equation (4-54) gives this relationship.

$$K(x, y, \xi, \eta) = \frac{\mu'\zeta}{\pi[r(x, y, \xi, \eta)]^2} \tag{4-54}$$

In the following paragraphs, solutions for this equation will be discussed. Because the type of solution that may be considered practical for various problems will depend on the mathematical form of the kernel and other parameters involved, it will be necessary to consider some specific geometries.

4-13.   One-dimensional Problems

Many problems of interest have geometries involving an element of symmetry that will allow Equation (4-53) to be expressed in terms of a single variable.

$$R(x) = \epsilon\sigma T^4(x) + \rho \int_a^b R(\xi)K(x, \xi)\, d\xi \qquad \text{(4-55)}$$

This equation is a linear integral equation of the second kind and is called the *Fredholm equation*. Before discussing its solution, some examples of enclosures, for which (4-54) may be utilized, will be given.

Figures 4-17 and 4-18 illustrate some of the types of geometry for which Equation (4-53) may be reduced to the form of Equation (4-55). Normally, problems of the type given by the geometry in Figures 4-17b and 4-18a require the temperature distribution to be equal on each half of the enclo-

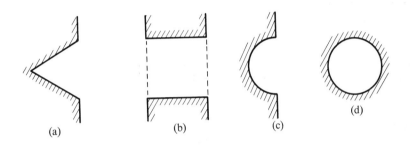

(a)   (b)   (c)   (d)

Figure 4-17. Some enclosures of infinite length to which Equation (4-55) may be applied. $T(x)$ and ρ should be the same on each portion of the straight-sided enclosures.

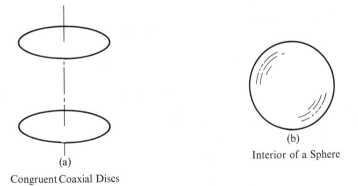

(a)
Congruent Coaxial Discs

(b)
Interior of a Sphere

Figure 4-18. Two examples of axially-symmetric geometries to which Equation (4-55) may be applied. $T(x)$ should be axially-symmetric.

sure. However, techniques will be discussed later for solving problems with different temperatures.

4-14. General Discussion of Integral Equations

Although it is beyond the scope of this book to present a lengthy discourse on integral equations, it is desirable to present a brief discussion of some of the fundamentals. A special list of references will be given at the end of the chapter for the interested reader.

Integral equations include the class of equations that contain terms with unknown functions as a portion of an integrand. The following are examples of integral equations that are listed by their classification.

(1) Linear integral equation of the first kind.

$$\int_a^b K(x, t)u(t)\, dt = f(x) \tag{4-56}$$

In this equation, the functions $K(x,t)$ and $f(x)$ are known, as are the limits a and b.

The function $K(x,t)$ is called the kernel of the equation. The unknown function $u(t)$ is to be determined for all values of x in the interval $a \le x \le b$.

(2) Linear integral equation of the second kind.

$$u(x) = f(x) + \int_a^b K(x, t)u(t)\, dt \tag{4-57}$$

In this equation, $u(x)$ and $u(t)$ are the same unknown function; $f(x)$, the kernel $K(x, t)$, and the limits a, b are known. If $f(x) = 0$, the equation is a homogeneous equation. If a known constant parameter λ is introduced, as in Equation (4-58), the equation is called a *linear integral equation of the second kind with a parameter.*

$$u(x) = f(x) + \lambda \int_a^b K(x, t)u(t)\, dt \tag{4-58}$$

Equation (4-58) is the Fredholm equation if a, b and λ are constants. It is this equation that is of interest in most radiative heat-transfer problems. If the upper limit in the integral of Equation (4-58) is x, then the equation is called *Volterra's equation.*

(3) Linear integral equation of the third kind.

$$\psi(x)u(x) = f(x) + \int_a^b K(x, t)u(t)\, dt \tag{4-59}$$

Again, in this equation $u(x)$ and $u(t)$ are the same unknown function, while $\psi(x)$ is an additional known function.

(4) Nonlinear integral equations.

$$u(x) = f(x) + \int_a^b K(x, t)[u(t)]^n \, dt \qquad \textbf{(4-60)}$$

$$u(x) = f(x) + \int_a^b \Phi[x, t, u(t)] \, dt \qquad \textbf{(4-61)}$$

In Equations (4-60) and (4-61), the unknown function appears in the equation in a nonlinear fashion.

(5) An integral equation is said to be a singular integral equation if either or both limits of integration are infinite or if the kernel becomes infinite at one or more points within the interval of integration.

Three methods for the solution of the Fredholm equation will be briefly discussed. These are (1) a method of successive approximations, (2) a method based on variational calculus, and (3) a method utilizing a numerical quadrature.

4-15.　Method of Successive Approximation

Consider the Fredholm equation (4-58). If a, b, λ are real constants and $K(x, t), f(x)$ are real continuous functions in the interval $a \leq x \leq b$, $a \leq t \leq b$ and are not identically zero, then a method of successive approximations may be used. Success of the method will, however, depend upon certain convergence criteria. This method is quite old and has been used independently by Neumann-Liouville and Volterra. It consists essentially of successively substituting the expression for $u(x)$ into the integral in place of $u(t)$. This forms an infinite integral series in λ. Equation (4-58) is rewritten as the starting point for the procedure.

$$u(x) = f(x) + \lambda \int_a^b K(x, t)u(t) \, dt$$

Substituting $u(x)$ for $u(t)$ and using the dummy variable, t_1 yields Equation (4-62).

$$u(x) = f(x) + \lambda \int_a^b K(x, t)\left[f(t) + \lambda \int_a^b K(t, t_1)u(t_1) \, dt_1 \right] dt \qquad \textbf{(4-62)}$$

This equation may be rewritten as

$$u(x) = f(x) + \lambda \int_a^b K(x, t)f(t) \, dt$$
$$+ \lambda^2 \int_a^b K(x, t) \int_a^b K(t, t_1)u(t_1) \, dt_1 dt \qquad \textbf{(4-62a)}$$

Now the expression for $u(x)$ in Equation (4-62) is substituted for $u(t)$ in (4-62a). This results in Equation (4-63).

$$u(x) = f(x) + \lambda \int_a^b K(x, t) f(t) dt + \lambda^2 \int_a^b K(x, t) \int_a^b K(t, t_1) f(t_1) \, dt_1 dt$$

$$+ \lambda^3 \int_a^b K(x, t) \int_a^b K(t, t_1) \int_a^b K(t_1, t_2) f(t_2) \, dt_2 dt_1 dt$$

$$+ \lambda^4 \int_a^b K(x, t) \int_a^b K(t, t_1) \int_a^b K(t_1, t_2) \int_a^b K(t_2, t_3) u(t_3) \, dt_3 dt_2 dt_1 dt$$

$$\text{(4-63)}$$

An infinite number of substitutions leads to an infinite series in λ. This series represents a continuous function in the interval $a \leq x \leq b$ if the series is uniformly convergent. A sufficient criteria for convergence may be developed as follows.

Since $K(x, t)$ and $f(x)$ are finite and continuous over the interval $a \leq x \leq b$, $a \leq t \leq b$, it is possible to find positive real constants M and N such that the following relations hold.

$$|K(x, t)| \leq M \quad \text{and} \quad |f(x)| \leq N \tag{4-64}$$

Consider a typical term $S_n(x)$ of the infinite series that would follow from (4-63).

$$S_n(x) = \lambda^n \int_a^b K(x, t) \int_a^b K(t, t_1) \int_a^b K(t_1, t_2) \dots$$

$$\int_a^b K(t_{n-2}, t_{n-1}) f(t_{n-1}) \, dt_{n-1} \dots dt_2 dt_1 dt \tag{4-65}$$

By substitution of M and N for $K(x, t)$ and $f(x)$, a limiting value may be found for $S_n(x)$.

$$|S_n(x)| \leq |\lambda^n| NM^n(b - a)^n \tag{4-66}$$

It can be readily seen that the series will converge uniformly if the following inequality holds.

$$|\lambda| < \frac{1}{M(b - a)} \tag{4-67}$$

The successive substitution process above is equivalent to assuming an infinite series solution of the form

$$u(x) = \sum_{n=0}^{\infty} \lambda^n u_n(x) \tag{4-68}$$

Substitution of (4-68) into Equation (4-58) yields

$$\sum_{n=0}^{\infty} \lambda^n u_n(x) = f(x) + \sum_{n=0}^{\infty} \lambda^{n+1} \int_a^b K(x, t) u_n(t) \, dt \tag{4-69}$$

Equating coefficients of like powers of λ gives the following relationships.

$$u_0(x) = f(x)$$

$$u_1(x) = \int_a^b K(x, t)u_0(t)\, dt$$

$$u_3(x) = \int_a^b K(x, t)u_2(t)\, dt \qquad \text{(4-70)}$$

$$\vdots$$

$$u_n(x) = \int_a^b K(x, t)u_{n-1}(t)\, dt$$

For some cases, the series (4-65) will converge to an algebraic expression. However, in most instances, the series may be terminated after a finite number of terms and answers are obtained, which will have an accuracy that is better than the accuracy with which the surface reflectance is known.

4-16.   A Variational Method

Courant and Hilbert (14) have demonstrated that the solution of a Fredholm equation having a symmetrical kernel is equivalent to finding the extremum of a corresponding variational expression. This relationship has been utilized by Sparrow (11), (13) and by Usiskin and Siegle (12) in radiative heat-transfer computations. The variational expression is given by Equation (4-71).

$$I = \lambda \int_a^b \int_a^b K(x, t)u(x)u(t)\, dxdt$$
$$- \int_a^b [u(x)]^2\, dx + 2 \int_a^b u(x)f(x)\, dx \qquad \text{(4-71)}$$

In the equation above, $u(x)u(t)$ is the same unknown function; λ, a, b are constants; $K(x, t)$ is a known continuous function that is symmetrical with respect to x and t; $f(x)$ is a known function continuous over the interval of integration. Courant (14) has demonstrated that the function $u(x)$ that makes the value of I in Equation (4-71) to be an extremum (maximum or minimum) is also the solution to the Fredholm equation (4-58).

An exact solution for the variational problem is usually very difficult. The authors listed above, in applying this technique to the solution of problems in radiation, utilized the approximate method of Ritz. A discussion of this method is given in Hildebrand (15). The method consists of assuming a solution in the form of Expression (4-72).

$$u(x) = \sum_{p=1}^q c_p \Phi_p(x) \qquad \text{(4-72)}$$

Here the c_p are parameters and $\Phi_p(x)$ are selected functions of x.

The $\Phi_p(x)$ are usually selected from an insight into the physical behavior of $u(x)$. Both Sparrow (11), (13) and Usiskin (12) choose a polynomial in x for the function. Equation (4-72) is then substituted into Equation (4-71) and integrated. The resulting expression is differentiated with respect to the individual parameters c_p in order to find the extremum.

$$\frac{\partial I}{\partial c_p} = 0 \qquad p = 1, 2, 3, \ldots, q \qquad (4\text{-}73)$$

The resulting set of Equation (4-73) are linear algebraic equations and may be solved by conventional matrix methods.

4-17. The Method of Quadratures

A more direct method of approximate solution than the variational method stated above involves the substitution of a numerical quadrature for the integral in Equation (4-58), and then the solution of the resulting set of linear algebraic equations directly by matrix methods. Although Simpson's rule or the trapezoidal rule may be used for the quadrature, the Gaussian quadrature formula permits equal accuracy with fewer points.

The method of quadrature has a considerable advantage over the variational method above, since the integration of Equation (4-71) with the substituted series (4-72) usually is very difficult and time consuming. The Ritz approximation is still required in practical instances that involve a polynomial approximation. The method of quadrature, in effect, fits a polynomial directly to the function $u(x)$ without requiring the prior manipulation of Equation (4-71).

The Gaussian quadrature formula is given below in Equation (4-74).

$$\int_0^1 G(x)\, dx = \sum_{j=1}^n W_j G(x_j) \qquad (4\text{-}74)$$

Here, the W_j are weight functions and the x_j are ordinates specified by the approximation; n is the number of terms required for the approximation. A table of weight function and corresponding ordinates are given in the Appendix. The Expression (4-74) is an exact equality if $G(x)$ is a polynomial of order $(2n - 1)$ or less. Thus, substitution of the quadrature is, in effect, fitting a polynomial of order $2n - 1$ through the ordinates x_j.

In many problems the limits of the integration will be something other than those specified by Equation (4-74). In such case, a transformation may be made.

$$\int_a^b G(x)\, dx = (b - a) \sum_{j=1}^n W_j G(z_j) \qquad (4\text{-}75)$$

where $z_j = (b - a)x_j + a$, and W_j and x_j are the same weight factors and ordinates as specified in Equation (4-74). With this substitution, the integral Equation (4-58) becomes n simultaneous equations given by (4-76).

$$u(Z_i) = f(Z_i) + \lambda(b - a) \sum_{j=1}^{n} W_j K(Z_i, Z_j) u(Z_j) \qquad \text{(4-76)}$$

The solution of the set of equations represented by (4-76) is written in matrix notation in Expression (4-77).

$$[u(Z_i)] = \left[\frac{\delta_{ij}}{\lambda(b-a)} - W_j K(Z_i, Z_j) \right]^{-1} \left[\frac{f(Z_i)}{\lambda(b-a)} \right] \qquad \text{(4-77)}$$

The δ_{ij} is the Kronecker delta ($\delta_{ij} = 0$, $i \neq j$; $\delta_{ij} = 1$, $i = j$). Each bracket indicates a matrix, and the -1 exponent on the first bracket on the right indicates that it is the inverse of the matrix in the bracket.

There is one minor disadvantage of the quadrature method when compared either with the approximate iterative method or the approximation in the variational method. The value of $u(x)$ is determined only at discrete points with the quadrature method, while the other methods result in a functional relation. This disadvantage is offset, however, in radiative heat-transfer problems, since an integration over the surface is usually required for a total heat-transfer computation. The computed values $u(Z_i)$ fall exactly on the quadrature points for a numerical integration over the surface.

4-18.   Radiosity in a Spherical Enclosure

Moon (1) has presented the solution for the radiosity within a sphere having a uniform surface reflectance and an axially-symmetric temperature distribution. It can readily be seen that the radiosity may be expressed as a function of a single variable, ψ, the angle between the surface normal and the axis of symmetry. Figure 4-19 illustrates the geometry of the problem.

The equation for the radiosity of the interior surface of the sphere is given by (4-78).

$$R(\psi) = \epsilon\sigma T^4(\psi) + \rho \int_0^{2\pi} \int_0^{\pi} R(\eta) \frac{\cos\theta_1 \cos\theta_2}{\pi(r_{12})^2} a^2 \sin\eta \, d\eta \, d\Phi \qquad \text{(4-78)}$$

In (4-78), Φ is the azimuthal angle and η is a dummy variable. Consider the simplification of the kernel on the basis of the geometry. Note that both differential elements of area at either end of r_{12} will lie on a great circle containing r_{12}. Also, r_{12} and the radii to the center of the sphere form an isosceles triangle. Therefore, the following relations must hold.

$$\cos\theta_1 = \cos\theta_2$$
$$r_{12} = 2a\cos\theta \qquad \text{(4-79)}$$

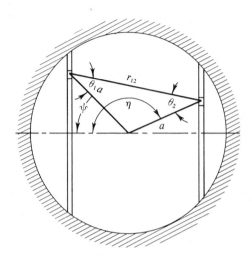

Figure 4-19. Illustration of geometry for axially-symmetric radiation within a sphere.

Substituting (4-79) into (4-78) and integrating over Φ (noting the integrand to be a constant function of Φ) results in Equation (4-80).

$$R(\psi) = \epsilon\sigma T^4(\psi) + \frac{\rho}{2}\int_0^\pi R(\eta)\sin\eta\,d\eta \tag{4-80}$$

This equation may be solved by the method of successive substitutions. Let $R(\psi)$ be represented by the following series.

$$R(\psi) = \sum_{n=0}^\infty \left(\frac{\rho}{2}\right)^n U_n(\psi) \tag{4-81}$$

Substituting Equation (4-81) into Equation (4-80) and equating coefficients of equal powers of $\rho/2$ yields the following sets of values for $U_n(\psi)$.

$$\begin{aligned}
U_0 &= \epsilon\sigma T^4(\psi)\\[4pt]
U_1 &= \int_0^\pi [\epsilon\sigma T^4(\eta)]\sin\eta\,d\eta\\[4pt]
U_2 &= \int_0^\pi U_1\sin\eta\,d\eta = 2U_1\\[4pt]
U_3 &= \int_0^\pi U_2\sin\eta\,d\eta = 2^2U_1\\[4pt]
U_n &= \int_0^\pi U_{n-1}\sin\eta\,d\eta = 2^{n-1}U_1
\end{aligned} \tag{4-82}$$

Substituting these values into Equation (4-81) results in Equation (4-83).

$$R(\psi) = \epsilon\sigma T^4(\psi) + \frac{\sigma\rho}{2}\int_0^\pi T^4(\eta)\sin\eta\,d\eta \tag{4-83}$$

Thus, for this geometry, an exact solution may be obtained provided the temperature function is such that the integral may be evaluated exactly.

4-19. Two Opposed Plates of Infinite Length

Sparrow (11) has presented a variational solution for the case of two opposed plates of infinite length. Figure 4-20 illustrates the geometry for this problem.

If the temperature is the same on both plates, the problem may be written in terms of a single integral equation.

$$R(x) = \epsilon \sigma T^4 + \rho \int_{-L/2}^{+L/2} R(y)K(x, y)dy \qquad \textbf{(4-84)}$$

In Equation (4-84), the kernel must be determined before the solution may proceed. Jakob (6) has given the form of the configuration factor between an infinite strip of differential width and a parallel strip.

$$F_{d1\text{-}2} = \frac{\sin \Phi_1 - \sin \Phi_2}{2} \qquad \textbf{(4-85)}$$

This may be rewritten for two parallel strips of differential width by taking the limit of (4-85). The result is (4-86).

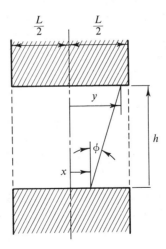

Figure 4-20.   Illustrating geometry for opposed parallel plates of infinite length.

$$F_{d1-d2} = \tfrac{1}{2} d\,(\sin \Phi) \tag{4-86}$$

In terms of the geometry of this problem, $\sin \Phi$ may be written as

$$\sin \Phi = \frac{y - x}{[(y - x)^2 + h^2]^{1/2}} \tag{4-87}$$

Differentiation of Equation (4-87), with respect to y holding x constant, gives Equation (4-88).

$$d(\sin \Phi) = \frac{h^2}{[(y - x)^2 + h^2]^{3/2}}\,dy \tag{4-88}$$

Equation (4-84) may now be rewritten as Equation (4-89).

$$R(x) = \epsilon\sigma T^4 + \frac{\rho h^2}{2} \int_{-L/2}^{+L/2} R(y)\,\frac{1}{[(y - x)^2 + h^2]^{3/2}}\,dy \tag{4-89}$$

The equation may be made nondimensional by dividing by the following transformations.

$$X = \frac{x}{L}, \qquad Y = \frac{y}{L}, \qquad H = \frac{h}{L}$$

$$B(X) = \frac{R(X)}{\epsilon\sigma T^4} \qquad\qquad B(Y) = \frac{R(Y)}{\epsilon\sigma T^4} \tag{4-90}$$

The resulting equation may be written as

$$B(X) = 1 + \frac{\rho H^2}{2} \int_{-1/2}^{+1/2} B(Y)\,\frac{1}{[(Y - X)^2 + H^2]^{3/2}}\,dY \tag{4-91}$$

The variational procedure now calls for writing the variational expression given in Equation (4-71) corresponding to Equation (4-91).

$$I = \frac{\rho H^2}{2} \int_{-1/2}^{+1/2} \int_{-1/2}^{+1/2} \frac{B(X)B(Y)dXdY}{[(X - Y)^2 + H^2]^{3/2}}$$
$$- \int_{-1/2}^{+1/2} [B(X)]^2\,dX + 2\int_{-1/2}^{+1/2} B(X)\,dX \tag{4-92}$$

A solution for $B(X)$ is now assumed using a polynomial with even powers of X since the function must be symmetrical with respect to $X = 0$. Sparrow (11) found good agreement between a quadratic and a quartic assumption. For simplification, a quadratic assumption will be followed here.

$$B(X) = C_1 + C_2 X^2, \qquad B(Y) = C_1 + C_2 Y^2 \tag{4-93}$$

These values are substituted into Equation (4-92). The equation is then integrated and the resulting expression may be written as

$$I = \rho(C_1^2 a_1 + C_1 C_2 a_2 + C_2^2 a_3) - C_1^2 - \tfrac{1}{6}C_1 C_2 - \tfrac{1}{80}C_2^2 + 2C_1 + \tfrac{1}{6}C_2 \tag{4-94}$$

Here, the constants a_1, a_2, and a_3 are the result of the integration and may be expressed in terms of the following function of H.

$$a_1 = (1 + H^2)^{1/2} - H$$

$$a_2 = \left(\frac{1}{6} - \frac{4H^2}{3}\right)(1 + H^2)^{1/2}$$

$$+ H^2\{\ln[1 + (1 + H^2)^{1/2}] - \ln H\} + \frac{4H^3}{3} - \frac{H}{2} \tag{4-95}$$

$$a_3 = \left(\frac{1}{80} - \frac{2H^2}{45} + \frac{4H^4}{45}\right)(1 + H^2)^{1/2}$$

$$+ \frac{H^2}{12}\{\ln[1 + (1 + H^2)^{1/2}] - \ln H\} - \frac{H}{16} - \frac{4H^5}{45}$$

Now Equation (4-95) is differentiated with respect to the parameter C_1 and C_2, respectively, and set equal to zero.

$$\frac{\partial I}{\partial C_1} = 0 \quad \text{results in} \quad 2C_1(\rho a_1 - 1) + C_2(\rho a_2 - \tfrac{1}{6}) = -2$$

$$\frac{\partial I}{\partial C_2} = 0 \quad \text{results in} \quad C_1(\rho a_2 - \tfrac{1}{6}) + 2C_2(\rho a_3 - \tfrac{1}{80}) = -\tfrac{1}{6} \tag{4-96}$$

Equations (4-96) may now be solved simultaneously for C_1 and C_2. Values for C_1 and C_2 computed by Sparrow (11) are given in Table 4-1 for several values of H and ϵ.

TABLE 4-1.

Value of C_1 and C_2 for Equation (4-93) According to Sparrow (11)

ϵ	$H = 1$		$H = 0.5$		$H = 0.1$	
	C_1	C_2	C_1	C_2	C_1	C_2
0.1	1.642	−0.5549	2.479	−2.367	7.388	−16.54
0.3	1.441	−0.3801	1.890	−1.403	3.192	−4.726
0.5	1.282	−0.2423	1.518	−0.8045	1.992	−1.832
0.7	1.153	−0.1315	1.262	−0.4013	1.433	−0.6996
0.9	1.047	−0.03998	1.075	−0.1139	1.113	−0.1624

The net heat flux over the surfaces may be computed by application of Equation (4-13).

$$Q = \frac{\epsilon\sigma T^4}{\rho}\left[1 - \epsilon C_1 - \epsilon C_2\left(\frac{x}{L}\right)^2\right] \tag{4-97}$$

The total heat transfer, Q_T is the integral of Equation (4-97) taken over the surface.

$$Q_T = \frac{\epsilon\sigma T^4 L}{\rho}\left(1 - \epsilon C_1 - \frac{\epsilon C_2}{12}\right) \tag{4-98}$$

For purposes of comparison, consider the application of the method of quadratures to the solution of the preceding problem. The quadrature of

Equation (4-75) is substituted for the integral in Equation (4-91). This results in the following expression.

$$B(Z_i) = 1 + \frac{\rho H^2}{2} \sum_{j=1}^{n} \frac{W_j B(Z_j)}{[(Z_i - Z_j)^2 + H^2]^{3/2}} \qquad (4\text{-}99)$$

As an example, use a three-point quadrature, and $\rho = 0.9$, and $H = 0.5$. Taking the values of the ordinates and weight factors from the Appendix results in the following three simultaneous equations (slide rule accuracy).

$$B_1 = (1 + 0.1125)\frac{0.278}{0.125} B_1 + \frac{0.444}{0.253} B_2 + \frac{0.278}{0.782} B_3$$

$$B_2 = (1 + 0.1125)\frac{0.278}{0.253} B_1 + \frac{0.444}{0.125} B_2 + \frac{0.278}{0.253} B_3 \qquad (4\text{-}100)$$

$$B_3 = (1 + 0.1125)\frac{0.278}{0.782} B_1 + \frac{0.444}{0.253} B_2 + \frac{0.278}{0.125} B_3$$

From an observation of the symmetry of Equations (4-100), it can be readily noted that $B_1 = B_3$. Thus, only two simultaneous equations need be solved. The results are

$$B_1 = B_3 = 2.11, \qquad B_2 = 2.53 \qquad (4\text{-}101)$$

Now, applying Equation (4-13) and utilizing the quadrature for the integration gives the following for the over-all heat flux, Q_T.

$$\frac{Q_T}{\epsilon \sigma T^4} = L \sum_{j=1}^{n} \frac{W_j}{\rho} (1 - \epsilon B_j) = \frac{L}{\rho}\left(1 - \epsilon \sum_{j=1}^{n} W_j B_j\right)$$

$$\frac{Q_T}{\epsilon \sigma T^4 L} = \frac{1 - 0.229}{0.9} = 0.857 \qquad (4\text{-}102)$$

The answer given in Expression (4-102) agrees with Sparrow's (11) answer for the same example, in which he utilized a quadratic expression. By the method of quadratures only two simultaneous equations need be solved and the tedious process of integration of the variational expression is avoided.

4-20.   The Problem of Coaxial Parallel Discs

The problem of coaxial parallel discs has been studied by Sparrow and Gregg (16). The problem is discussed here because of the manner in which an expression is developed for the kernel of the integral equation. The Sparrow and Gregg paper also includes a method for presentation of results for discs of different temperatures.

This method of finding the kernel involves taking an algebraic expression for F_{12} between two discs, and using configuration-factor algebra to modify the expression to the form $F_{d1\text{-}d2}$. Consider Figure 4-21.

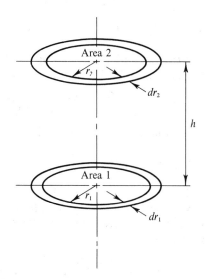

Figure 4-21. Geometry for coaxial parallel disc problems.

Jakob (6) gives the expression for the configuration factor between two parallel discs as

$$F_{21} = \frac{r_1^2 + r_2^2 + h^2 - \sqrt{(r_1^2 + r_2^2 + h^2)^2 - 4r_1^2 r_2^2}}{2r_2^2} \qquad \textbf{(4-103)}$$

By application of the decomposition rule, the following relationship may be written.

$$F_{d1-d2} = F_{d1-(2+d2)} - F_{d1-2} = \frac{\partial}{\partial r_2}(F_{d1-2})dr_2 \qquad \textbf{(4-104)}$$

Also, application of the same rule gives (4-105).

$$F_{2-d1} = F_{2-(1+d1)} - F_{21} = \frac{\partial}{\partial r_1}(F_{21})\,dr_1 \qquad \textbf{(4-105)}$$

However, F_{2-d1} is related to F_{d1-2} by the basic reciprocity relationship.

$$F_{d1-2} = \frac{A_2}{dA_1}F_{2-d1} = \frac{r_2^2}{2r_1\,dr_1}F_{2-d1} \qquad \textbf{(4-106)}$$

Thus, Equation (4-104) for F_{d1-d2} becomes

$$F_{d1-d2} = \frac{\partial}{\partial r_2}\left\{\frac{r_2^2}{2r_1}\left[\frac{\partial}{\partial r_1}(F_{21})\right]\right\}dr_2 \qquad \textbf{(4-107)}$$

Substituting Equation (4-103) into Equation (4-107) results in the following expression for F_{d1-d2}.

$$F_{d1\text{-}d2} = \left\{ \frac{2h^4 + 2h^2 r_1^2 + 2h^2 r_2^2}{[(h^2 + r_1^2 + r_2^2)^2 - 4r_1^2 r_2^2]^{3/2}} \right\} r_2 \, dr_2 \qquad (4\text{-}108)$$

The corresponding expression for $F_{d2\text{-}d1}$ may be found by the reciprocal relation.

If the two discs are the same diameter and of equal temperature, the corresponding nondimensional radiosity equation may be written as

$$B(X_1) = 1 + 2\rho H^2 \int_0^1 B(X_2) \frac{(H^2 + X_1^2 + X_2^2)(X_2)}{[(H^2 + X_1^2 + X_2^2)^2 - 4X_1^2 X_2^2]^{3/2}} \, dx_2 \quad (4\text{-}109)$$

In Equation (4-109) the following substitutions have been made.

$$B(X) = \frac{R(X)}{\epsilon \sigma T^4}, \qquad H = \frac{h}{r_0}, \qquad X = \frac{r}{r_0} \qquad (4\text{-}110)$$

Sparrow and Gregg utilized an iterative process to solve Equation (4-109). It would appear that the quadrature approximation is a much more direct approach. For this case, the equivalent set of simultaneous equations may be written as (4-111).

$$B_i = 1 + 2\rho H^2 \sum_{j=1}^{n} B_j \frac{W_j(X_j)(H^2 + X_i^2 + X_j^2)}{[(H^2 + X_i^2 + X_j^2)^2 - 4X_i^2 X_j^2]^{3/2}} \qquad (4\text{-}111)$$

In the event that the two discs are of different size, reflectance, or temperature, it is necessary to solve two integral equations simultaneously. It may or may not be advantageous to solve them in a nondimensional form. The two equations are written in terms of the variables as follows:

$$R_1(r_1) = \epsilon_1 \sigma T_1^4 + 2\rho_1 h^2 \int_0^{(r_0)_1} R_2(r_2) \frac{(r_2)(h^2 + r_1^2 + r_2^2)}{[(h^2 + r_1^2 + r_2^2)^2 - 4r_1^2 r_2^2]^{3/2}} \, dr_2$$

$$R_2(r_2) = \epsilon_2 \sigma T_2^4 + 2\rho_2 h^2 \int_0^{(r_0)_2} R_1(r_1) \frac{(r_1)(h^2 + r_1^2 + r_2^2)}{[(h^2 + r_1^2 + r_2^2)^2 - 4r_1^2 r_2^2]^{3/2}} \, dr_1$$

$$(4\text{-}112)$$

If the quadrature formula is substituted for the integrals, the result is $2n$ simultaneous equations. With the use of a digital computer, the kernels may be readily computed for each quadrature point and the subsequent matrix inversion accomplished. The result of these computations is the radiosity on each disc at the radii corresponding to the quadrature. The quadrature may then be used to compute the net radiant heat transfer at each surface.

4-21.   Some Two-dimensional Problems

Unfortunately, most geometries encountered in engineering practice can not be reduced to one-dimensional problems. It is beyond the scope of this book to discuss exact solutions for these equations; however, in some cases, the method of quadratures may be utilized to some advantage.

Sparrow and Haji-Sheikh (13) have proposed an extension of the variational method to two-dimensional problems. Because of the extent of effort required in most instances to integrate the variational expression and the questionable advantage that it has over the method of quadrature, the variational method will not be discussed further in this book.

The method of quadrature may be applied to the radiant heat-transfer computation involving two rectangular areas. Consider two congruent, parallel, and directly-opposed, plane rectangular areas. The geometry is illustrated in Figure 4-22.

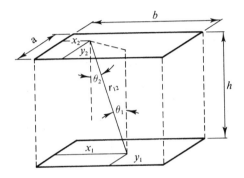

Figure 4-22. Geometry for two opposed, parallel, congruent, rectangular areas.

The integral equation for radiosity may be readily derived.

$$R(x_1, y_1) = \epsilon\sigma T_1^4 + \frac{\rho h^2}{\pi} \int_0^a \int_0^b \frac{R(x_2, y_2)}{[(x_2 - x_1)^2 + (y_2 - y_1) + h^2]^2} \, dx_2 dy_2$$

$$(4\text{-}113)$$

If the two plates have the same temperature and reflectance, a single equation may be solved by substitution of a Gaussian quadrature for each of the integrals. The resulting equation is given by (4-114).

$$B(X_p, Y_p) = 1 + \frac{\rho abh^2}{\pi} \sum_{j=1}^{n} \sum_{i=1}^{n} \frac{W_i \, W_j B(X_j, Y_i)}{[b^2(X_p - X_j)^2 + a^2(Y_q - Y_i)^2 + h^2]^2}$$

$$(4\text{-}114)$$

In Equation (4-114), the W_i, W_j are the Gaussian quadrature weight factors as given by the one-dimensional formula. The X, Y are given by the following expressions in accordance with Equation (4-74). The $B(X, Y)$ represents the nondimensional radiosity.

$$X_i = bx_i, \qquad Y_i = ay_i, \qquad B(X, Y) = \frac{R(X, Y)}{\epsilon \sigma T^4} \qquad \textbf{(4-115)}$$

Although the choice of a three-point quadrature in Equation (4-114) would lead to nine simultaneous equations, the effective number of equations may be reduced to four equations by symmetry considerations. A four-point quadrature results in greater accuracy, however, and reduces to the same number (four) of equations. In a similar fashion, it can be shown that for the geometry above, a quadrature formula having an even number of points will require the same number of simultaneous equations as the quadrature equation having one less point. For square plates it can be seen that the four-point quadrature will reduce to effectively three equations and three unknowns. Figure 4-23 illustrates the symmetry consideration.

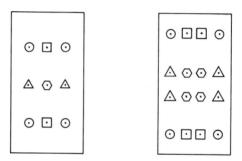

Figure 4-23.   Illustration of symmetry consideration for rectangular plates. The radiosity must be the same at each point with a similar geometric figure.

It should be pointed out that a very similar solution may be developed for the radiant exchange between any two rectangular areas. This would also include such geometries as the interior of a circular cylinder to its base.

4-22. *Enclosures Having One or More Specular Surfaces*

One can verify from observation of visible-light reflections that many surfaces of engineering interest reflect thermal radiation in a specular fashion. Radiation in such enclosures has been discussed in a paper by Sparrow and Eckert (17). The method is limited to plane surfaces that

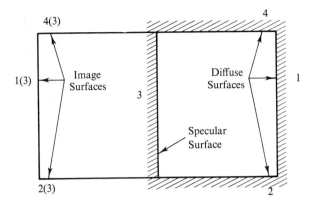

Figure 4-24.   A four-sided enclosure of infinite length with one specular surface. See McAdams (3).

are specularly reflecting in an enclosure that may include some diffuse surfaces. The method also assumes a surface that emits in a perfectly diffuse fashion.

In solving problems involving specular surfaces, these surfaces may be thought of as "dirty" mirrors. The effective enclosure includes all real surfaces plus the images in the specular surfaces. In the enclosure in Figure 4-24, the line marked 4(3) represents the mirror image of Surface 4 as seen in the reflection from the specular Surface 3. Similarly 1(3) represents the reflection of Surface 1 in 3, and 2(3) represents the reflection of 2 in 3. The effective diffuse enclosure now must treat these reflections as additional surfaces making up the enclosure. The apparent radiosity of an image surface is equal to the product of the specular surface reflectance and the radiosity of the object surface. Using the lumped-system method of analysis and treating each side as a zone, the raidosity equations may be written as

$$R_1 = \epsilon_1 \sigma T_1^4 + \rho_1 [R_2 F_{12} + R_4 F_{14}$$
$$+ \rho_3 (R_1 F_{1\text{-}1(3)} + R_2 F_{1\text{-}2(3)} + R_4 F_{1\text{-}4(3)}) + \epsilon_3 \sigma T_3^4 F_{1\text{-}3} \tag{4-118}$$

In a similar fashion, the radiosity equation for surfaces 2 and 4 could be written. The resulting three equations could then be solved for the three unknown radiosities.

For vee-shaped grooves that have specular surfaces, it is desirable to sketch the various mirror images of each surface in the enclosure. For example, consider the 60° groove illustrated in Figure 4-25.

In Figure 4-25, *ABC* represents a 60° vee groove with specularly-reflecting sides; *BC'* represents the reflection of *BC* in the surface *BA;*

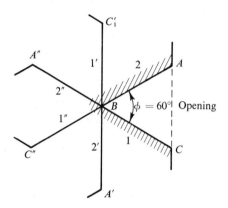

Figure 4-25.   Reflections for a 60° specular vee groove.

BA'' represents the reflection of BA seen in the reflection of BC' in BA. In order to compute the effective emittance of this fin it is necessary to account for the radiant energy that leaves each surface and each image surface and is incident on the opening AC. The surface is assumed to emit in a diffuse fashion and thus each image surface will in effect have a diffuse emission.

The total heat transfer (H) is thus represented by the following expression. Advantage is taken of the symmetry of the figure since Surface 1 is identical to Surface 2.

$$H = 2\epsilon(AB)\sigma T^4(F_{2-0} + \rho F_{1'-0} + \rho^2 F_{2''-0}) \qquad \text{(4-119)}$$

ϵ_{eff} may be determined by dividing Equation (4-119) by $(AC)\sigma T^4$, and noting that for the 60° wedge, AC equals AB.

$$\epsilon_{\text{eff}} = 2\epsilon(F_{2-0} + \rho F_{1'-0} + \rho^2 F_{2''-0}) \qquad \text{(4-120)}$$

The configuration factors may be readily obtained using the crossed strings method.

$$\epsilon_{\text{eff}} = \epsilon^2 + \epsilon^2\rho\sqrt{3} + 2\epsilon\rho^2 \qquad \text{(4-121)}$$

A similar analysis may be made for a vee groove of any angle. A simple aid for visualizing the reflections for various groove angles may be constructed with two inexpensive rectangular mirrors. The two mirrors may be taped together at one edge and then opened to the desired angle. A drafting triangle may be used to hold the desired angle. This device is illustrated in Figure 4-26.

A general expression may be derived for the effective emittance of a

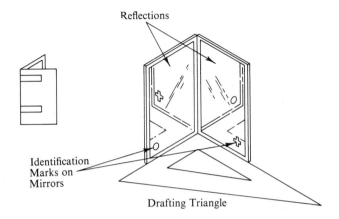

Figure 4-26.   Use of two mirrors for visualization of specular reflections in vee grooves.

vee groove with surfaces that emit diffusely and reflect in a specular fashion following the procedure explained above. The expression may be written as Equation (4-122).

$$\epsilon_{\text{eff}} = \frac{\epsilon^2}{\sin \Phi/2} \left[\frac{\rho^{m-1}}{\epsilon} \sin \left(\frac{m\Phi}{2} \right) + \sum_{n=1}^{n=m-1} \rho^{n-1} \sin \left(\frac{n\Phi}{2} \right) \right]$$ (4-122)

In this equation, Φ is the included angle of the vee groove and m is the maximum number of whole Φ angles contained in 180°. (For example, if $\Phi = 21°$, then $m = 8$.) Also, ϵ is the diffuse emittance of the walls of the groove and ρ is the specular reflectance of the walls.

4-23.   Combined Specular and Diffuse Reflection

In Chapter 3 it was noted that the reflection function may be approximated in some cases by assuming the function to be composed of a diffuse component and a specular component. Consider a vee groove with wall surfaces having a combined specular and diffuse reflectance. From Equation (3-17), the following relationship may be obtained.

$$\epsilon = 1 - \rho_S - \rho_D$$ (4-123)

The analysis of radiative heat transfer between such surfaces represents an extremely difficult problem since each reflection will have both a diffuse and specular component. Consider a vee-groove fin with a 60° included angle. Figure 4-25 illustrates this groove with its image surfaces.

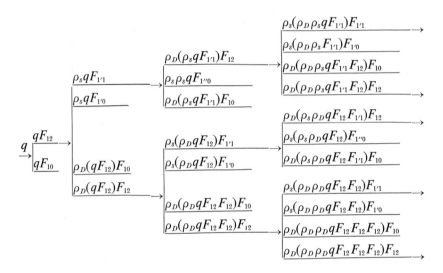

$$q = W \epsilon \sigma T^4 \text{ where } W = \text{width of fin}$$

Figure 4-27.   Accounting for a 60°, specular, diffuse groove.

The problem can perhaps be best visualized by an accounting system. The energy diffusely emitted from one side of the groove, say AB, is divided into two portions, that which leaves the groove and that which is incident on the opposite side BC. Of this latter energy, some is diffusely reflected out of the groove, some is reflected specularly from the groove, and some is diffusely and specularly reflected back to AB. The energy reflected back to AB is then subjected to the same division. The process is then repeated an infinite number of times. The chart in Figure 4-27 illustrates this accounting in a schematic way.

In Figure 4-27, the growth of the infinite series representing the inter-reflections may be seen. The diagram, of course, accounts for the energy leaving only one side. The additional energy leaving the other side will be equal. Summing the energy leaving the groove gives Expression (4-124).

$$
\begin{aligned}
H = 2We\sigma T^4(&F_{10} + \rho_s F_{1'0} + \rho_D F_{12}F_{10} + \rho_s^2 F_{1''0} \\
&+ \rho_s \rho_D F_{1'1}F_{10} + \rho_s \rho_D F_{12}F_{1'0} + \rho_D^2 F_{12}^2 F_{10} \\
&+ \rho_D \rho_s^2 F_{1'1}F_{1'0} + \rho_D^2 \rho_s F_{1'1}F_{12}F_{10} \\
&+ \rho_s^2 \rho_D F_{12}F_{1''0} + \rho_s \rho_D^2 F_{12}F_{1'1}F_{10} \\
&+ \rho_s \rho_D^2 F_{12}^2 F_{1'0} + \rho_D^3 F_{12}^3 F_{10} + \cdots)
\end{aligned}
\tag{4-124}
$$

Collecting similar terms leads to the equation

$$
\begin{aligned}
H = 2We\sigma T^4[&F_{10}(1 + \rho_D F_{12} + \rho_D^2 F_{12}^2 + \rho_D^3 F_{12}^3 + \cdots) \\
&+ \rho_s F_{1'0}(1 + \rho_D F_{12} + \rho_D^2 F_{12}^2 + \cdots) \\
&+ \rho_s^2 F_{1'0}(1 + \rho_D F_{12} + \cdots) \\
&+ \rho_s \rho_D F_{1'1}F_{10}(1 + \rho_D F_{12} + \cdots) \\
&+ \rho_D \rho_s^2 F_{1'1}F_{1'0}(1 + \cdots) + \cdots]
\end{aligned}
\tag{4-125}
$$

The infinite series in Equation (4-125) may be written as a quotient with the following result.

$$
H = \frac{2We\sigma T^4}{1 - \rho_D F_{12}}(F_{10} + \rho_s F_{1'0} + \rho_s^2 F_{1''0} + \rho_s \rho_1 F_{1'1}F_{10} + \rho_D \rho_s^2 F_{1'1}F_{1'0} + \cdots)
\tag{4-126}
$$

It should be noted that $\rho < 1$ and $F < 1$; therefore, the series should converge rapidly and only the first few terms need be considered for most applications.

Equation (4-126) will actually hold for any vee groove with only two reflections per side In other words for $60 \leq \Phi < 180$, the equation is somewhat simpler and may be readily worked out. For a vee groove with the included angle smaller than 60° and larger than or equal to 45° the calculation is considerably more complex, but may be developed to within a reasonable degree of accuracy without great difficulty.

4-24.   Effects of Directional Properties

Little work has appeared in the literature accounting for the directional dependence of the reflectance and emittance. Much work needs to be done in this area. Recently Holt, Grosh, and Geynet (18) computed the radiant heat transfer between parallel, infinite, metal plates using Fresnel's equations for the directional properties and assumed specularly-reflecting plates. The method suggested for such a computation in this book is slightly different than that used by Holt and co-workers. It is presented here as an introduction to a method that will be used in later chapters, as well as a method that should be equally effective in solving the problem above.

Consider the problem of infinite, parallel, smooth plates. The emittance and reflectance of such plates are assumed given by the Fresnel equations of Chapter 2, and are functions of the polar angle only. The equations for the monochromatic intensity of radiation leaving Surface 1 and Surface 2 may be expressed as

$$I_{v,1}(\mu) = \epsilon_{v,1}(\mu)I_{b,v}(T_1)$$
$$+ \frac{1}{\pi}\int_0^{2\pi}\int_0^1 I_{v,2}(\mu')\frac{\pi}{\mu}\rho_{v,1}(\mu)\delta(\mu'-\mu)\delta(\phi'-\phi+\pi)\mu'\,d\mu\,d\phi'$$
$$I_{v,2}(\mu) = \epsilon_{v,2}(\mu)I_{b,v}(T_2)$$
$$+ \frac{1}{\pi}\int_0^{2\pi}\int_0^1 I_{v,1}(\mu')\frac{\pi}{\mu}\rho_{v,2}(\mu)\delta(\mu'-\mu)\delta[\phi'-(\phi+\pi)]\mu'\,d\mu'\,d\phi'$$

$$(4\text{-}127)$$

The indicated integrations may be readily performed because of the Dirac delta functions resulting in a pair of simultaneous equations that may be readily solved.

$$I_{v,1}(\mu) = \epsilon_{v,1}(\mu)I_{b,v}(T_1) + \rho_{v,1}(\mu)I_{v,2}(\mu)$$
$$I_{v,2}(\mu) = \epsilon_{v,2}(\mu)I_{b,v}(T_2) + \rho_{v,2}(\mu)I_{v,1}(\mu)$$

$$(4\text{-}128)$$

The solution of Equation (4-128) is given as

$$I_{v,1}(\mu) = \frac{\epsilon_{v,1}(\mu)I_{b,v}(T_1) + \rho_{v,1}(\mu)\epsilon_{v,1}(\mu)I_{b,v}(T_2)}{1 - \rho_{v,1}(\mu)\rho_{v,2}(\mu)}$$

$$(4\text{-}129)$$

The net monochromatic flux may be determined in the following manner.

$$Q_v = \int_0^{2\pi}\int_0^1 [I_{v,1}(\mu) - I_{v,2}(\mu)]\mu\,d\mu\,d\Phi$$
$$= 2\pi[I_{b,v}(T_1) - I_{b,v}(T_2)]\int_0^1 \frac{\mu}{[1/\epsilon_{v,1}(\mu)] + [1/\epsilon_{v,2}(\mu)] - 1}\,d\mu$$

$$(4\text{-}130)$$

Normally, the integral in Expression (4-130) must be integrated by numerical integration; Q_v must subsequently be integrated numerically over wavelength in order to obtain the net heat flux.

Blanton and Picha (19) have considered the fraction of energy emitted from an element that has an area dA_1 and is directly incident on a second area. In that paper, an analysis was made for a metallic surface. The following analysis is somewhat similar; however, in this case, a dielectric is approximated.

Assume that $\epsilon(\mu)$ may be approximated by the product of a constant ϵ, and that μ is raised to a power α.

$$\epsilon(\mu) = \epsilon\mu^\alpha$$

$$(4\text{-}131)$$

One can readily verify by application of Equation (1-5) that (4-132) holds.

$$q_{\text{emitted}} = \frac{2\pi \epsilon I_b(T)}{2 + \alpha} \qquad (4\text{-}132)$$

The flux emitted from Surface 1 and incident on Surface 2 may be expressed by the following relation.

$$q_{12} = \int_{A_2} \int \frac{\epsilon(\mu_1) I_b(T) \mu_1 \mu_2}{(r_{12})^2} \, dA_2 \qquad (4\text{-}133)$$

Substitution of (4-131) in the expression above gives

$$q_{12} = \epsilon I_b(T) \int_{A_2} \int \frac{\mu_1^{1+\alpha} \mu_2}{(r_{12})^2} \, dA_2 \qquad (4\text{-}134)$$

If a directional configuration factor $\tilde{F}_{12}$ is defined as the ratio of q_{12} to q emitted and the geometry of Figure 4-28 is considered, then $\tilde{F}_{12}$ may be written as

$$\tilde{F}_{12} = \frac{(2 + \alpha)h}{2\pi} \int_0^{L_1} \int_0^{L_2} \frac{y^{1+\alpha}}{(x^2 + y^2 + h^2)^{2+(\alpha/2)}} \, dy\,dx \qquad (4\text{-}135)$$

One can readily integrate Equation (4-135) for the case where $[(x/h)^2 + (y/h)^2] \ll 1$. The resulting expression for $\tilde{F}_{12}$ is

$$\tilde{F}_{12} = \frac{1}{2\pi} \left(\frac{L_1}{h} \right) \left(\frac{L_2}{h} \right)^{2+\alpha} \qquad (4\text{-}136)$$

For the same case $\tilde{F}_{12}$ may be readily computed and Equation (4-136) may be written in terms of F_{12}

$$\tilde{F}_{12} = \left(\frac{L_2}{h} \right)^{\alpha} F_{12} \qquad (4\text{-}137)$$

Using similar techniques combined with the imaging techniques for spe-

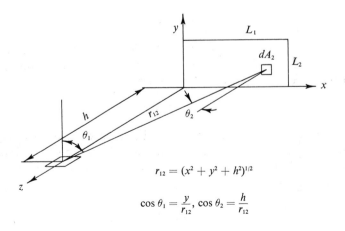

$$r_{12} = (x^2 + y^2 + h^2)^{1/2}$$

$$\cos \theta_1 = \frac{y}{r_{12}}, \quad \cos \theta_2 = \frac{h}{r_{12}}$$

Figure 4-28.   Illustration of geometry for Equation (4-135).

cular surfaces discussed earlier in the chapter, the effect of directional properties may be determined for vee-groove fins. Lam (20) has made such an analysis and demonstrated that such an effect is significant. However, because of computer limitations, he was required to use a rather coarse grid for his numerical computations and the accuracy of his results are open to question and, therefore, will not be presented here.

4-25.   Integration of Monochromatic Flux Over Wavelength

In many enclosure problems the monochromatic emittance variation with wavelength cannot be readily neglected. A numerical integration over wavelength may be accomplished following the technique developed in Chapter 3 using the Laguerre polynomial quadrature formula. Consider the solution of Equation (4-7) expressed in matrix notation.

$$(R_{v,j}) = \left(\frac{\delta_{ij}}{\rho_{v,i}} - F_{ij}\right)^{-1} \left[\frac{\pi(1 - \rho_{v,i})}{\rho_{v,i}} I_{b,v}(T_i)\right] \qquad \textbf{(4-138)}$$

In order to apply the quadrature given in Expression (3-25), it is convenient to express $R_{v,1}$ as the summation resulting from the matrix multiplication indicated in (4-138).

$$R_{v,i} = \sum_{j=1}^{n} M_{v,ij} I_{b,v}(T_j) \qquad \textbf{(4-139)}$$

In this expression $M_{v,ij}$ represents the product of the element in the ith row and the jth column of the inverted matrix in (4-138) and the factor $[\pi(1 - \rho_{v,j})]/\rho_{v,j}$ Application of Expression (3-25) gives the following result for the integration of R_v over wavelength.

$$R_i = \sum_{j=1}^{n} T_j^4 \sum_{q=1}^{m} A_q M_{q,ij} \qquad \textbf{(4-140)}$$

Here the matrix from which the factor $M_{q,ij}$ is derived must be computed and inverted for each frequency corresponding to each quadrature point and for temperature as prescribed by Equation (3-23).

$$v_q = \frac{k}{h}(x_q T_j)$$

Equation (4-140) may be readily applied to an enclosure consisting of two infinite, diffuse, parallel plates. For this case, Q is merely the difference between the radiosities of Plate 1 and Plate 2. The resulting integration over wavelength gives

$$
\begin{aligned}
Q = \pi T_1^4 \sum_{q=1}^{m} & \frac{A_q}{[1/\epsilon_{q,1}(T_1)] + [1/\epsilon_{q,2}(T_1)] - 1} \\
+ T_2^4 \sum_{q=1}^{m} & \frac{A_q}{[1/\epsilon_{q,1}(T_2)] + [1/\epsilon_{q,2}(T_2)] - 1}
\end{aligned}
\qquad \textbf{(4-141)}
$$

In Expression (4-141) notice that the emittances in the first summation are determined for both surfaces at the frequency prescribed by the quadrature points and the temperature of Plate 1, while in the second summation the emittances for both surfaces are determined by the temperatures of Plate 2.

In general, such a numerical integration will require the inversion of $n \times m$ matrices, where n is the number of zones in the enclosure and m is the number of terms in the quadrature.

Hickok (21) applied Equation (4-141) to the problem of radiant heat transfer between two tungsten plates over a range of temperature differences. He found that the seven-point approximation was in close agreement with the results of Branstetter (22) for the same problem even though the latter apparently utilized a much larger number of points.

Conclusion

The foregoing chapter suggests some approximate approaches to the solution of the radiative heat-transfer problem for surfaces in evacuated enclosures. It is obvious that much work is needed in order to develop better methods of analysis, particularly in order to more accurately predict the effects of directional properties.

PROBLEMS

1. Given a table of configuration factors for finite adjoining perpendicular planes of the type F_{ab}, find an expression using configuration-factor algebra for F_{12}. See Figure P. 4-1.

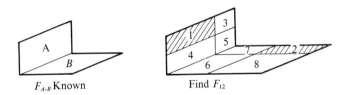

Figure P. 4-1.

2. If configuration factors of the type F_{ab} in Problem 1 are known, find an expression for the configuration factor F_{12} between two parallel congruent rectangles. See Figure P. 4-2 on the next page.

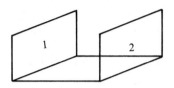

Figure P. 4-2.

3. If configuration factors are known for parallel coaxial discs, find the configuration factor for two parallel, coaxial-ring elements.

4. Use the graphical method to find F_{d1-2} if dA_1 is considered to be at the origin with the z axis normal to its surface and A_2 is the triangle with corners located at (1, 1, 1), (2, 1, 1), (1, 2, 1).

5. Compute the configuration factor between the infinite parallel strips that have the perpendicular cross section dimensioned in Figure P.4-5.

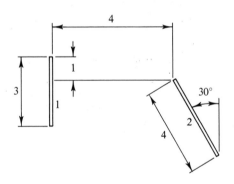

Figure P. 4-5.

6. Consider the triangular area A_2 with vertices at (0, 0, 0), (1, 1, 0), (−1, 1, 0); dA_1 is located at (0, 0, 3) and has its normal given by the vector $\bar{n}_1 = (1/\sqrt{2})j - (1/\sqrt{2})k$. Use the line integration method to find F_{d1-2}.

7. (a) Determine an expression for the dimensionless heat transfer $Q_T/e\sigma T^4$ for the two parallel infinite strips in Figure P.4-7. Assume each strip to have the same diffuse reflectance and temperature. There is no incident radiation on the enclosure. Use a two-zone approximation.
    (b) Compute $Q_T/e\sigma T^4$ for $h/L = 0.5$ and $\epsilon = 0.1$.

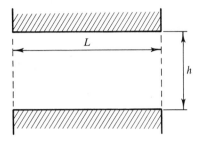

Figure P. 4-7.

8. Compute the radiant heat loss from a square opening in a furnace (Figure P.4-8). The wall is twice as thick as the opening dimension. Ambient temperature is 100°F and the furnace interior is 2000°F. (Assume the passage walls are diffuse.)
   (a) Treat the passage wall as a one-zone refractory.
   (b) Treat the passage as a two-zone refractory.

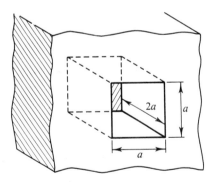

Figure P. 4-8.

9. Consider a fin of uniform cross section over its infinite length. The cross section is given in Figure P.4-9 on page 108.
   Assume that the surface of the fin is isothermal and diffuse.
   (a) Plot the effective emittance as a function of H/L for surface emittances of $\epsilon = 0.2, 0.6, 0.8$. Use all of the real surface as one zone.
   (b) Compare the results above with a two-zone system treating the base as one zone and the fin surfaces as one zone. Make the comparison for $H/L = 0.1, 1, 2$ and emittances of 0.2 and 0.8.

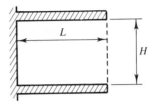

Figure P. 4-9.

10. A hemispherical dent is made in a surface. A cross section is shown in Figure P.4-10. Assume the temperature and diffuse surface emittance of the cavity are uniform.
    (a) Solve the integral equation for radiosity within the enclosure, assuming there is no incident radiation from sources exterior to the cavity.
    (b) Using the exact expression for radiosity compute the effective emittance of the total cavity for a surface emittance of 0.5.
    (c) Compare the exact answer in (b) with the value computed by treating the hemisphere as a single zone.
    (d) What would be the effective average emittance of a surface composed of such dents arranged in a simple-square arrangement with each circle tangent to four others.

Figure P. 4-10.

11. Solve the example worked on page 92 using a four-point quadrature formula and compare the results with that of the three-point.

12. Solve the Problem 10(b) using a three-point quadrature formula.

13. A satellite has two fins of square dimension and arranged at right angles with a common edge. The fins have the same uniform temperature and surface emittance (see Figure P.4-13).
    (a) Write the integral equation for radiosity, reducing the kernel to an explicit function of the surface coordinates. Use a dimensionless form for the equation.
    (b) Write out the terms of the series of algebraic equations that would result from the use of a three-point quadrature and reduce to the minimum number of equations required to solve the problem.

(c) If a computer is available, solve the problem for a surface emittance of 0.5. Computing the dimensionless, radiant heat transfer from the fins.

(d) How many simultaneous equations would result from a four-point formula?

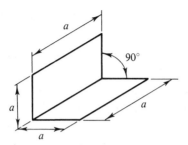

Figure P. 4-13.

14. Derive Equation (4-122).

15. Demonstrate by substitution into the equations for radiosity that the problem of radiant heat transfer between two congruent surfaces, such as shown in Figure 4-20 or 4-22, having two different temperatures, may be solved by the following dimensionless simultaneous equations.

$$B(x_1 y_1) = 1 + \rho_1 \iint_{A_2} B(x_2 y_2) K(x_1 y_1 x_2 y_2)\, dx_2\, dy_2$$

$$B(x_2 y_2) = \rho_2 \iint_{A_1} B(x_1 y_1) K(x_1 y_1 x_2 y_2)\, dx_1\, dy_1$$

In other words, the solution to the two equations above may be multiplied by $\epsilon_1 \sigma T_1^4$ and separately by $\epsilon_2 \sigma T_2^4$. The two resulting radiosities when properly superimposed represent the solution to the following set of equations.

$$R(x_1 y_1) = \epsilon_1 \sigma T_1^4 + \rho_1 \iint_{A_2} R(x_2 y_2) K(x_1 y_1 x_2 y_2)\, dx_2\, dy_2$$

$$R(x_2 y_2) = \epsilon_2 \sigma T_2^4 + \rho_2 \iint_{A_1} R(x_1 y_1) K(x_1 y_1 x_2 y_2)\, dx_1\, dy_1$$

16. Develop the set of integral equations for two parallel infinite plates of uniform, but different, temperatures that have reflection functions of the following form.

$$\rho_v(\mu, \phi, \mu', \phi') = \rho_D(\mu) + \frac{\pi}{\mu} \rho_s(\mu)\delta(\mu' - \mu)\delta(\phi' - \phi + \pi)$$

Reduce the integral equations by a quadrature formula into a set of linear algebraic equations.

References

1. Moon, P., *Scientific Basis of Illumination Engineering*, McGraw-Hill Book Co., Inc., New York, 1936. Republished by Dover Publications Inc., New York, 1961.

2. Hamilton, D. C. and Morgan, W. R., *Radiant Interchange Configuration Factors*, NACA TN 2836, 1952.

3. McAdams, W. H., *Heat Transmission*, McGraw-Hill Book Co., Inc., New York, 1954.

4. Kreith, F., *Radiation Heat Transfer for Spacecraft and Solar Power Plant Design*, International Textbook Co., Scranton, Pa., 1958.

5. Eckert, E. R. G. and Drake, R. M., *Heat and Mass Transfer*, McGraw-Hill Book Co., Inc., New York, 1959.

6. Jakob, M., *Heat Transfer*, Vol. II, John Wiley and Sons, Inc., New York, 1957.

7. Juhasz, E. S. and Hooper, F. C., *Graphical Evaluation of Radiation Interchange Factor*, ASME Paper 52-F-19. Presented at the fall meeting, September 1952.

8. Zijl, H., *Manual For the Illuminating Engineering on Large Size Perfect Diffusors*, Phillips Industries, Einkhaven, Netherlands, 1951.

9. Hickman, R. S., *Determination Of Radiation Configuration Factors*, Jet Propulsion Laboratory Technical Report No. 32-154, December 1961.

10. Sparrow, E. M., "A New and Simpler Formulation for Radiative Angle Factors," *Journal of Heat Transfer*, Vol. 85, Series C, No. 2 (May 1963).

11. Sparrow, E. M., "Application Of Variational Methods To Radiation Heat Transfer Calculations," *Journal of Heat Transfer*, Vol. 82, Series C., No. 4 (November 1960), p. 375.

12. Usiskin, C. M., and Siegel, R., "Thermal Radiation From A Cylindrical Enclosure with Specified Wall Heat Flux," *Journal of Heat Transfer*, Vol. 82, Series C, No. 4 (November 1960), p. 369.

13. Sparrow, E. M., and Haji-Sheikh, "A Generalized Variational Method For Calculating Radiant Interchange Between Surfaces," *Journal of Heat Transfer*, Vol. 87, Series C, No. 1 (February 1965).

14. Courant, R. and Hilbert, D., *Methods Of Mathematical Physics*, Vol. 1, Interscience Publishers, Inc., New York, 1953.

15. Hildebrand, F. B., *Methods Of Applied Mathematics*, Prentice-Hall, Inc., Englewood Cliffs, N. J., 1952.

16. Sparrow, E. M., and Gregg, J. L., "Radiant Interchange Between Circular Discs Having Arbitrarily Different Temperatures," *Journal of Heat Transfer*, Vol. 83, Series C, No. 4 (November 1961).

17. Sparrow, E. M., Eckert, E. R. G., and Jonsson, V. K., "An Enclosure Theory for Radiative Exchange Between Specularly and Diffusely Reflecting Surfaces," *Journal of Heat Transfer*, Vol. 84, Series C, No. 4 (November 1962).

18. Holt, V. E., Grosh, R. J., and Geynet, R., "Evaluation Of The Net Radiant Heat Transfer Between Specularly Reflecting Plates Including Computed Emissivities," *International Journal of Heat and Mass Transfer*, Vol. 6, pp. 755-758, Pergamon Press, New York, 1963.

19. Blanton, Roy W., and Picha, K. G., "Thermal Radiation Energy Exchange Factors For Non-Lambertonian Surfaces," *Journal of Heat Transfer*, Vol. 84, Series C, No. 3 (August 1962).

20. Lam, T. S., *The Effect Of Directional Properties In Some Problems Of Radiative Heat Transfer*, Master's Thesis, University of Oklahoma, 1964.

21. Hickok, R. L., *Radiation Heat Transfer in Evacuated Non-Gray Diffuse Enclosures*, Master's Thesis, University of Oklahoma, 1963.

22. Branstetter, J. R., *Radiation Heat Transfer Between Non-Gray Parallel Plates Of Tungsten*, NASA Technical Note D-1088, 1961.

5   Enclosures Containing an Absorbing and Emitting Medium

5-1.   The Equation of Transfer

Many problems of radiative heat transfer involve the exchange of radiant energy between surfaces separated by a medium that absorbs and emits radiant energy. Here, the concern is primarily with media that are "weakly" absorbing, such as glass, water, and air. Most media of this type have radiative properties that vary pronouncedly with the frequency characterizing the radiation. This chapter will first discuss the radiant transport equation or *equation of transfer* as it has sometimes been called. These analyses, in the first part of the chapter, will be for a monochromatic transfer. Later in the chapter, radiative property variations with radiation frequency will be discussed along with methods for integrating over frequency.

In Chapter 2, it was demonstrated that the intensity of radiation within an isolated evacuated enclosure in thermodynamic equilibrium is isotropic and is equal to the emitted intensity from a black surface at the temperature of the enclosure. A similar analysis assuming the enclosure to be filled with a partially transparent medium (such as water, glass, etc.) will yield a similar result. However, in this case, the intensity will correspond to the energy emitted from a black surface into the medium contained in the enclosure, which is not necessarily the same as the energy that a black surface will emit into a vacuum. Consider an isolated enclosure in thermodynamic equilibrium as schematically illustrated in Figure 5-1.

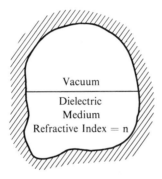

Figure 5-1. An isolated enclosure partially filled with a dielectric material.

The net flux of radiant energy across the interface between the dielectric and the vacuum in Figure 5-1 must be zero. The intensity of radiation incident on the interface from the vacuum is $I_{b,v}(T)$. Let the uniform isotropic intensity within the dielectric material be $I_v(T)$. This must then represent the intensity incident on the interface from the dielectric side. An energy balance is then made for the energy leaving the interface. Consider the geometry in Figure 5-2.

The intensity of radiation leaving the dielectric interface is composed of the reflected energy plus the energy transmitted across the interface. The reflected energy is $I_{b,v}(T)\rho \cos\theta \, d\omega dA d\nu$, while the energy transmitted across the interface is $I_v(T)(1 - \rho') \cos\theta' \, d\omega' \, dA d\nu$. Here the prime denotes the reflectivity from the dielectric side of the interface, as well as the direction and solid angle of the ray incident from the dielectric side. The energy

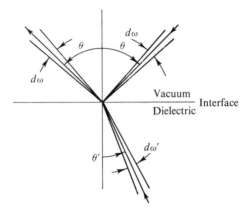

Figure 5-2.   Geometry for interface energy balance.

balance may be written as

$$I_{b,v}(T)\rho \cos\theta\, d\omega + I_v(T)(1-\rho')\cos\theta'\, d\omega' = I_{b,v}(T)\cos\theta\, d\omega \qquad (5\text{-}1)$$

The relationship between θ and θ' may be expressed as follows in terms of Snell's law, Equation (2-86).

$$n\sin\theta' = \sin\theta \quad \text{also} \quad n\cos\theta'\, d\theta' = \cos\theta\, d\theta \qquad (5\text{-}2)$$

Writing the solid angles $d\omega$ and $d\omega'$ in spherical coordinate form and noting that $d\Phi = d\Phi'$ results in the following relationship upon substitution of (5-2) into (5-1).

$$(1-\rho')I_v(T) = n^2(1-\rho)I_{b,v}(T) \qquad (5\text{-}3)$$

It can be seen from Fresnel's equations that $\rho = \rho'$; therefore, the intensity of radiation in a dielectric medium in thermal equilibrium is $n^2 I_{b,v}(T)$. Thus, in a medium having a refractive index greater than 1, the emission of a black surface into that medium is n^2 times as large as the emission of a black surface at the same temperature in a vacuum. It should be noted that the radiation "escaping" from the dielectric into the vacuum, however, can never exceed the emission of a black surface at the temperature of the dielectric. A ray of energy leaving a medium with a refractive index greater than 1 "expands" at the interface because of the refraction, and for values of θ' greater than arcsin $(1/n)$, the radiation is totally reflected back into the dielectric medium.

Beer's law was originally established as a result of experimental studies of the attenuation of light in colloidal suspensions. Early studies in this area were made by Bouguer in 1729 and later by Lambert. The law states that the intensity of radiant energy traversing a semitransparent medium is decreased by absorption in proportion to the intensity at that point. Equation (5-4) states this law in terms of a differential equation.

$$\frac{dI_v}{dx} = -\rho \kappa_v I_v \tag{5-4}$$

In the equation above, x is the distance along the direction of the intensity, ρ is the mass density of the medium being traversed, and κ_v is the monochromatic mass-absorption coefficient.

Equation (5-4) is, in a sense, an equation for the conservation of radiant energy along a ray in the x direction. However, Beer's law was developed for the attenuation of light and there is no provision made for local emission of thermal radiation as normally occurs in radiative heat-transfer problems. Thus, for such problems an additional term must be added to account for this emission. The symbol that will be used for this is J_v. The equation of transfer for an absorbing and emitting medium thus may be written as Equation (5-5).

$$\frac{dI_v}{dx} = -\rho \kappa_v I_v + J_v \tag{5-5}$$

For such a medium in thermodynamic equilibrium, the intensity of radiation does not change along the path, and thus the left-hand term of Equation (5-5) would be equal to zero. Noting the value of the radiant intensity in such a medium gives the following expression for J_v.

$$J_v = \rho \kappa_v n^2 I_{b,v}(T) \tag{5-6}$$

For thermal radiation transport through media in which rapid chemical reactions are not involved, a "local" thermal equilibrium is approximated and (5-6) may be substituted into Equation (5-5).

The equation of transfer may be written as

$$\frac{dI_v}{\rho \kappa_v \, dx} = -I_v + n^2 I_{b,v}(T) \tag{5-7}$$

Note that $\rho \kappa_v \, dx$ must be a dimensionless quantity and is usually called the *differential optical distance*. The Greek letter τ will be used here for this dimensionless distance.

$$\tau = \int_0^x \rho \kappa_v \, dx \tag{5-8}$$

Using this symbol, Equation (5-7) may be rewritten as Equation (5-9).

$$\frac{dI_v}{d\tau} = -I_v + n^2 I_{b,v}(T) \tag{5-9}$$

It should be noted that this nonhomogeneous, linear, first-order differential equation is valid for the intensity in a continuous homogeneous medium along a fixed direction only. In general, most problems require knowledge of the intensity in all directions and at the interface between the medium and other materials.

5-2.   The Plane Slab Problem

The problem of an infinite plane slab of absorbing and emitting medium is of interest in boundary layer problems and problems concerning the effects of ceramic and plastic coatings on metallic surfaces.

Consider first the solution of the problem for the case of radiative exchange between two parallel, infinite, diffuse surfaces bounding an isothermal, homogeneous, absorbing and emitting medium. The direction perpendicular to the surfaces is chosen as the reference direction. It can be seen that the problem is axially symmetric. That is, the intensity at any point within the medium is characterized by an angle θ from the system normal and will not vary with a change in the azimuthal direction. Thus, the monochromatic intensity within the enclosure will be a function of τ, the optical distance, and μ, which is the cosine of the polar angle.

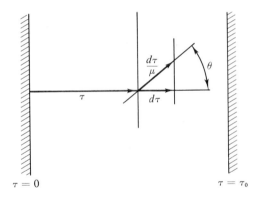

Figure 5-3.   Geometry of the plane slab problem.

In Figure 5-3 note that τ is taken along the normal to the surfaces. The differential optical path for a ray traveling at some angle θ with respect to this normal is thus equal to $d\tau/\mu$. For such a geometry, the differential equation for the intensity along any fixed direction may be written as

$$\mu \frac{dI_\nu(\tau, \mu)}{d\tau} = -I_\nu(\tau, \mu) + n^2 I_{b,\nu}(T) \qquad \textbf{(5-10)}$$

For such problems, it can be readily seen that the function $I_\nu(\tau, \mu)$ will be discontinuous at $\mu = 0$. It is, therefore, convenient to consider separately the intensities directed in the positive τ direction and those in the negative direction. Figure 5-4 illustrates this geometry.

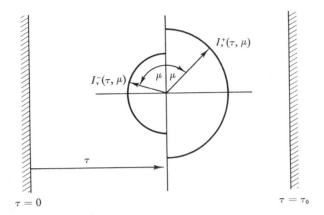

Figure 5-4.   Illustration of geometry for "positive" and "negative" intensities in the plane-parallel problem.

Equation (5-10) may now be written as two differential equations. The values of μ are considered to be positive for both equations and thus the term on the left of the second equation is negative. This also permits τ to be measured from the same reference for both equations.

$$\mu \frac{dI_v^+(\tau, \mu)}{d\tau} = -I_v^+(\tau, \mu) + n^2 I_{b,v}(T)$$

$$-\mu \frac{dI_v^-(\tau, \mu)}{d\tau} = -I_v^-(\tau, \mu) + n^2 I_{b,v}(T)$$

(5-11)

The boundary conditions for the two equations require a simultaneous solution of the equations. These conditions involve the intensity at both boundaries with the assumption that the boundaries are diffuse.

$$I_v^+(0, \mu) = n^2 \epsilon_1 I_{b,v}(T_1) + \frac{\rho_1}{\pi} \int_0^{2\pi} \int_0^1 I_v^-(0, \mu)\mu \, d\mu d\Phi$$

$$I_v^-(\tau_0, \mu) = n^2 \epsilon_2 I_{b,v}(T_2) + \frac{\rho_2}{\pi} \int_0^{2\pi} \int_0^1 I_v^+(\tau_0, \mu)\mu \, d\mu d\Phi$$

(5-12)

In Equations (5-12) ϵ_1 and ϵ_2 are the hemispherical emittances of Surface 1 and 2, respectively; and T_1 and T_2 are the temperatures of Surface 1 and 2.

For the problem of an isothermal medium, the solution of Equations (5-11) may be written as

$$I_v^+(\tau, \mu) = C_1 e^{-\tau/\mu} + n^2 I_{b,v}(T)$$
$$I_v^-(\tau, \mu) = C_2 e^{(\tau - \tau_0)/\mu} + n^2 I_{b,v}(T)$$

(5-13)

The C_1 and C_2 may be determined by substitution of (5-13) into Equation (5-12).

$$C_1 + n^2 I_{b,\nu}(T) = n^2 \epsilon_1 I_{b,\nu}(T_1) + 2\rho_1 C_2 \int_0^1 e^{-\tau_0/\mu} \mu \, d\mu + \rho_1 n^2 I_{b,\nu}(T)$$

$$C_2 + n^2 I_{b,\nu}(T) = n^2 \epsilon_2 I_{b,\nu}(T_2) + 2\rho_2 C_1 \int_0^1 e^{-\tau_0/\mu} \mu \, d\mu + \rho_2 n^2 I_{b,\nu}(T) \tag{5-14}$$

Rewriting Equation (5-14) and collecting terms leads to the expressions.

$$C_1 - 2\rho_1 E_3(\tau_0) C_2 = n^2 \epsilon_1 [I_{b\nu}(T_1) - I_{b\nu}(T)]$$

$$-2\rho_2 E_3(\tau_0) C_1 + C_2 = n^2 \epsilon_2 [I_{b\nu}(T_2) - I_{b\nu}(T)] \tag{5-15}$$

In the first equation in (5-15), a substitution has been made for the integral terms.

$$E_3(\tau_0) = \int_0^1 e^{-\tau_0/\mu} \mu \, d\mu \tag{5-16}$$

The left-hand term $E_3(\tau_0)$ is called an *exponential integral function of the third kind*. The general form of this function is given by Expression (5-17).

$$E_n(x) = \int_0^1 \mu^{n-2} e^{-x/\mu} \, d\mu \tag{5-17}$$

Tables of values for this function may be found in Kourganoff (2). However, it may also be readily computed by use of the quadrature approximation. Solving for C_1 and C_2 in Equation (5-15) results in (5-18).

$$C_1 = n^2 \left\{ \frac{\epsilon_1 I_{b\nu}(T_1) + [2\rho_1 \epsilon_2 E_3(\tau_0)] I_{b\nu}(T_2) - [\epsilon_1 + 2\rho_1 \epsilon_2 E_3(\tau_0)] I_{b\nu}(T)}{1 - \rho_1 \rho_2 [2E_3(\tau_0)]^2} \right\}$$

$$C_2 = n^2 \left\{ \frac{[2\rho_2 \epsilon_1 E_3(\tau_0)] I_{b\nu}(T_1) + \epsilon_2 I_{b\nu}(T_2) - [\epsilon_2 + 2\rho_2 \epsilon_1 E_3(\tau_0)] I_{b\nu}(T)}{1 - \rho_1 \rho_2 [2E_3(\tau_0)]^2} \right\} \tag{5-18}$$

The net monochromatic heat flux Q_ν at any optical distance τ may be expressed by Equation (5-19).

$$Q_\nu(\tau) = 2\pi \int_0^1 [I^+(\tau, \mu) - I^-(\tau, \mu)] \mu \, d\mu \tag{5-19}$$

Substitution of (5-13) into (5-19) yields

$$Q_\nu(\tau) = 2\pi C_1 E_3(\tau) - 2\pi C_2 E_3(\tau_0 - \tau) \tag{5-20}$$

It may be readily seen that the heat flux at $\tau = 0$ is given by the equation

$$Q_\nu(0) = \pi[C_1 - 2C_2 E_3(\tau_0)] \tag{5-21}$$

For specularly-reflecting walls the boundary conditions will cause the solution to vary some from the above. (It should be noted, however, that in the case treated in the previous chapter that where there is no intervening absorbing medium the diffuse and specular solutions will be identical.) For this problem, Equation (5-13) still holds. The boundary conditions, however, are written as

$$I_\nu^+(0, \mu) = n^2 \epsilon_1 I_{b,\nu}(T_1) + \rho_1 I_\nu^-(0, \mu)$$

$$I_\nu^-(\tau_0, \mu) = n^2 \epsilon_2 I_{b,\nu}(T_2) + \rho_2 I_\nu^+(\tau_0, \mu) \tag{5-22}$$

Equation (5-13) is substituted into (5-22) in order to determine C_1 and C_2. The resulting set of simultaneous equations are given by Equation (5-23).

$$C_1 - \rho_1 e^{-\tau_0/\mu} C_2 = n^2 \epsilon_1 [I_{b,\nu}(T_1) - I_{b,\nu}(T)]$$
$$-\rho_2 e^{-\tau_0/\mu} C_1 + C_2 = n^2 \epsilon_2 [I_{b,\nu}(T_2) - I_{b,\nu}(T)] \tag{5-23}$$

The similarity of Equations (5-23) and (5-15) may be readily noted. The problem of integration over all angles in order to determine the flux is somewhat more complicated in this problem since the C_1 and C_2 are now complicated functions of μ.

$$C_1(\mu) = n^2 \left[\frac{\epsilon_1 I_{b\nu}(T_1) + (\rho_1 \epsilon_2 e^{-\tau_0/\mu}) I_{b\nu}(T_2) - (\epsilon_1 + \rho_1 \epsilon_2 e^{-\tau_0/\mu}) I_{b\nu}(T)}{1 - \rho_1 \rho_2 (e^{-\tau_0/\mu})^2} \right]$$

$$C_2(\mu) = n^2 \left[\frac{(\rho_2 \epsilon_1 e^{-\tau_0/\mu}) I_{b\nu}(T_1) + \epsilon_2 I_{b\nu}(T_2) - (\epsilon_2 + \rho_2 \epsilon_1 e^{-\tau_0/\mu}) I_{b\nu}(T)}{1 - \rho_2 \rho_1 (e^{-\tau_0/\mu})^2} \right] \tag{5-24}$$

The net monochromatic flux may be stated in terms of the integral

$$Q_\nu(\tau) = 2\pi \int_0^1 [C_1(\mu) e^{-\tau/\mu} - C_2(\mu) e^{(\tau-\tau_0)/\mu}] \mu \, d\mu \tag{5-25}$$

It should be noted that in these equations ρ and ϵ may have a directional dependence. Normally, Fresnel's equation may be used to determine ρ and ϵ.

The analysis above has a special interest in the study of the effect of ceramic and plastic coatings on metallic surfaces. It may also be utilized in the study of radiative effects in planetary atmospheres that may be assumed to be approximated by a plane-parallel system. In the study of coatings on metal surfaces, note that the coating should have geometrical thickness much greater than the wavelength of the radiation for the analysis above to be valid.

Consider now a special case of the analysis above as an example.

Example. Determine the radiative flux leaving a plane-parallel, isothermal atmosphere having a refractive index of unity and bounded on one side by a diffuse surface (1) having the same temperature, and on the other side by a vacuum (2). Further, assume that there is no incident flux. This approximates an isothermal planetary atmosphere of interest in astrophysics.

Solution. For these conditions, Equations (5-18) for C_1 and C_2 may be written as

$$C_1 = -2\rho E_3(\tau_0) I_{b\nu}(T)$$
$$C_2 = -I_{b\nu}(T) \tag{5-26}$$

In (5-26), ρ is the diffuse reflectance of the planetary surface, τ_0 is the optical thickness of the atmosphere measured normal to the surface, and $I_{b\nu}(T)$ is the monochromatic intensity of black radiation at the temperature of the atmosphere. The intensity of the radiation at the outer edge of the atmosphere is determined by the substitution of (5-26) into (5-13).

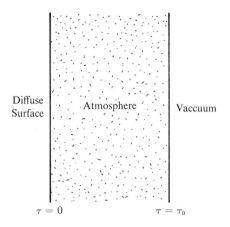

Figure 5-5.   Geometry for example.

$$I_v^+(\tau_0, \mu) = [1 - 2\rho E_3(\tau_0)e^{-\tau_0/\mu}]I_{bv}(T) \tag{5-27}$$

The net flux leaving the atmosphere may be determined from the basic relationship between intensity and flux.

$$Q_v(\tau_0) = \pi\{1 - 4\rho[E_3(\tau_0)]^2\}I_{bv}(T) \tag{5-28}$$

It is worthwhile at this point to compare the results of (5-28) with an analysis that may be referred to as the *attenuated-flux method*. This method has been widely used in analyses involving such topics as boundary layers and ceramics. The solution for this method may be written in terms of the flux q.

$$q_v^+(\tau) = C_1 e^{-\tau} + \pi I_{bv}(T)$$
$$q_v^-(\tau) = C_2 e^{\tau - \tau_0} + \pi I_{bv}(T) \tag{5-29}$$

The boundary conditions may be written as

$$q_v^+(0) = \epsilon\pi I_{bv}(T) + \rho q_v^-(0)$$
$$q_v^-(\tau_0) = 0 \tag{5-30}$$

Combining Equations (5-29) and (5-30)

$$Q_v(\tau_0) = \pi(1 - \rho e^{-2\tau_0})I_{bv}(T) \tag{5-31}$$

Both Equations (5-31) and (5-28) may be seen to be equal for $\tau_0 = 0$ and $\tau_0 = \infty$. The graph in Figure 5-6 shows the variation of the error in the attenuated-flux method as a function of τ_0 for $\rho = 0.5$.

As a second example, consider the case of a dielectric coating on a metal surface. For such a problem the metal-dielectric interface and the dielectric-vacuum interface may be considered to be specularly reflecting. The reflection at each interface may be determined from Fresnel's equations as given in Chapter 2. The reflections at the metal surface would be

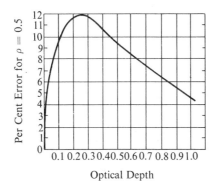

Figure 5-6. Error of Equation (5-31). The attenuated flux method in comparison with Equation (5-28).

determined by Equation (2-106). It should be noted that the complex relative-refractive index to be utilized must consider the refractive index of the dielectric. Francis and Love (6) have shown how the directional emittance of a metal into a dielectric varies with the refractive index of the coating.

At the dielectric-vacuum interface the reflectance will be given by Equa-

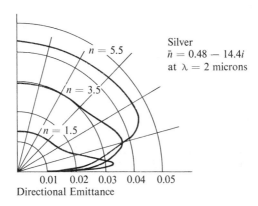

Figure 5-7. Polar plot of directional emission of silver into various dielectrics. As determined by Equation (2-106).

tion (2-97) for angles less than the critical angle. The reflectance at angles greater than the critical angle will be unity. The boundary conditions for Equation (5-13) for this case may be written as

$$
\begin{aligned}
I_v^+(0, \mu) &= n^2 \epsilon_{v1}(\mu) I_{bv}(T) + \rho_{v1}(\mu) I_v^-(0, \mu) \\
I_v^-(\tau_0, \mu) &= \rho_{v2}(\mu) I_v^+(\tau_0, \mu) \quad\quad \text{for } \mu > \mu_c \\
I_v^-(\tau_0, \mu) &= I_v^+(\tau_0, \mu) \quad\quad\quad \text{for } \mu \leq \mu_c
\end{aligned}
\tag{5-32}
$$

It is obvious from the last equation in (5-32) that for these specularly-reflecting boundaries there will be no contribution to the net flux for any direction such that $\mu \leq \mu_c$. Here, μ_c is the cosine of the critical angle. The value of μ_c may be determined by the application of Snell's law when $\sin \theta = 1$. For this case, where the dielectric is bounded by a vacuum, the following relationship must exist.

$$
\sin \theta_c = \frac{1}{n}, \quad\quad \therefore \mu_c = \left(\frac{n^2 - 1}{n^2} \right)^{1/2}
\tag{5-33}
$$

Thus, C_1 and C_2 are functions of μ and as described above are determined by substitution of (5-13) into the first two equations of (5-32). These functions, of course, are valid only for $\mu > \mu_c$.

$$
\begin{aligned}
C_1 + n^2 I_{bv}(T) &= n^2 \epsilon_{v1}(\mu) I_{bv}(T) + \rho_{v1}(\mu)[C_2 e^{-\tau_0/\mu} + n^2 I_{bv}(T)] \\
C_2 + n^2 I_{bv}(T) &= \rho_{v2}(\mu)[C_1 e^{-\tau_0/\mu} + n^2 I_{bv}(T)]
\end{aligned}
\tag{5-34}
$$

Solving (5-34) for C_1 and C_2 results in the expression

$$
\begin{aligned}
C_1 &= \frac{n^2 \rho_{v1}(\mu)[\rho_{v2}(\mu) - 1] e^{-\tau_0/\mu} I_{bv}(T)}{1 - \rho_{v2}(\mu) \rho_{v1}(\mu) e^{-2\tau_0/\mu}} \\
C_2 &= \frac{n^2 [\rho_{v2}(\mu) - 1] I_{bv}(T)}{1 - \rho_{v2}(\mu) \rho_{v1}(\mu) e^{-2\tau_0/\mu}}
\end{aligned}
\tag{5-35}
$$

The emitted intensity may be determined by computing the net intensity at τ_0 along a given direction and correcting for the refraction occurring at the interface. Writing the result in terms of the monochromatic directional emittance gives the relationship

$$
\epsilon(\mu') = \frac{[1 - \rho_{v2}(\mu)][1 - \rho_{v1} e^{-2\tau_0/\mu}]}{1 - \rho_{v2}(\mu) \rho_{v1}(\mu) e^{-2\tau_0/\mu}}
\tag{5-36}
$$

It should be noted that μ' represents the cosine of the polar angle θ OUTSIDE the coating and that it is related to the cosine of the polar angle inside the medium by the relationship

$$
\mu' = [1 - n^2(1 - \mu^2)]^{1/2}
\tag{5-37}
$$

Some results of this computation are presented as graphs of the directional emission of various dielectric coatings on metal surfaces in Figure 5-7.

5-3.   The Plane-Parallel Region with a Known Normal Temperature Distribution

For many problems, such as boundary layer flow with radiative contributions, a temperature profile is either known or assumed in a plane-parallel geometry. Equations 5-10 may be solved with the use of an integrating factor.

$$I_\nu^+(\tau, \mu) = C_1 e^{-\tau/\mu} + \frac{n^2}{\mu} \int_0^\tau e^{(t-\tau)/\mu} I_{b\nu}(t)\, dt$$

$$I_\nu^-(\tau, \mu) = C_2 e^{(\tau-\tau_0)/\mu} + \frac{n^2}{\mu} \int_\tau^{\tau_0} e^{-(t-\tau)/\mu} I_{b\nu}(t)\, dt \tag{5-38}$$

The C_1 and C_2 for Equation (5-38) may be determined either for specular or diffuse boundary conditions. For purpose of illustration, a flowing boundary layer will be assumed here with diffuse boundaries; n will be assumed to be unity. The surface at $\tau = 0$ will be assumed to be diffusely reflecting while the boundary at $\tau = \tau_0$ will be assumed to be black at some temperature corresponding to the environment.

$$I_\nu^+(0, \mu) = \epsilon I_{b\nu}(T_w) + 2\rho \int_0^1 I_\nu^-(0, \mu)\mu\, d\mu$$

$$I_\nu^-(\tau_0, \mu) = I_{b\nu}(T_\infty) \tag{5-39}$$

The combination of Equations (5-38) and (5-39) results in

$$C_1 = \epsilon I_{b\nu}(T_w) + 2\rho \int_0^1 \left[I_{b\nu}(T_\infty)e^{-\tau_0/\mu} + \frac{1}{\mu}\int_0^{\tau_0} e^{-t/\mu} I_{b\nu}(t)\, dt \right]\mu\, d\mu$$

$$C_2 = I_{b\nu}(T_\infty) \tag{5-40}$$

In terms of the exponential integral function, Equation (5-40) may be written as

$$C_1 = \epsilon I_{b\nu}(T_w) + 2\rho E_3(\tau_0)I_{b\nu}(T_\infty) + 2\rho \int_0^{\tau_0} E_2(t)I_{b\nu}(t)\, dt \tag{5-41}$$

Integration of Equations (5-38) at the wall where $\tau = 0$ and at the outer edge of the boundary layer where $\tau = \tau_0$ yields the following expressions for the monochromatic net flux.

$$Q_\nu(0) = \pi\epsilon\left[I_{b\nu}(T_w) - 2I_{b\nu}(T_\infty)E_3(\tau_0) - 2\int_0^{\tau_0} I_{b\nu}(t)E_2(t)\, dt \right]$$

$$Q_\nu(\tau_0) = \pi\left\{ 2\epsilon I_{b\nu}(T_w)E_3(\tau_0) + [4\rho E_3^2(\tau_0) - 1]I_{b\nu}(T_\infty) \right.$$

$$\left. + 4\rho E_3(\tau_0)\int_0^{\tau_0} I_{b\nu}(t)E_2(t)\, dt + 2\int_0^{\tau_0} I_{b\nu}(t)E_2(\tau_0 - t)\, dt \right\} \tag{5-42}$$

Equations (5-42) may be used in determination of the radiative contribution in approximate methods of boundary layer analysis.

5-4.   *Reflection of an Incident Flux*

So far, the discussion has been concerned with the emittance of a semidiathermanous coating on an opaque surface. The reflectance may be determined by a technique similar to that for emittance determination with slightly different boundary conditions. The net flux from such a coated surface may be determined by superposition of the emission as determined by the analysis above and the reflection as determined below.

Consider a monodirectional flux uniformly incident over a coated surface. The flux first undergoes a Fresnel reflection at the air or vacuum-coating interface. Once inside the coating, the flux will be attenuated in accord with a modification of Equation (5-13), undergoing an infinite number of reflections between the opaque surface and the coating-vacuum interface.

Since the concern is with reflection only, the solution of the equation of transfer for this problem may be written as

$$I_v^+(\tau, \mu) = C_1 e^{-\tau/\mu}$$
$$I_v^-(\tau, \mu) = C_2 e^{(\tau-\tau_0)/\mu} \tag{5-43}$$

Assume a specularly-reflecting boundary at the coating-vacuum interface and a diffuse boundary at the opaque surface with the incident radiation given by the expression

$$q_{\text{incident}} = I_0(\mu')\mu' \, \Delta\mu' \Delta\Phi \tag{5-44}$$

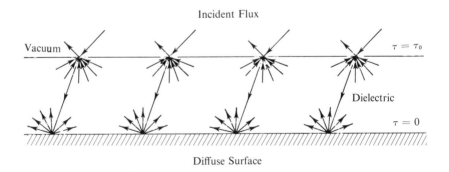

Figure 5-8.   Diagram of reflection from a surface with semidiathermous coating.

The boundary conditions for this problem may be represented as

$$I^+(0, \mu) = 2\rho_1 \int_0^1 I^-(0, \mu)\mu \, d\mu + \frac{\rho_1}{\pi} e^{-\tau_0/\mu_i}[1 - \rho(\mu')]I_0\mu' \, \Delta\mu'\Delta\Phi$$

$$I^-(\tau_0, \mu) = \rho(\mu)I^+(\tau_0, \mu) \qquad \mu > \mu_c$$
$$I^-(\tau_0, \mu) = I^+(\tau_0, \mu) \qquad \mu \leq \mu_c$$

(5-45)

In the first equation of (5-45), the second term is the diffusely-reflected, attenuated, incident radiation. It is treated separately because it does not fit into the axial symmetry required for the solution of the diffuse boundary. The term ρ_1 is the diffuse reflectance of the opaque surface into the coating; μ_i is the cosine of the polar angle of the attenuated incident radiation in the coating. It is related to μ', the incident cosine, by the following relation derived from Snell's law.

$$\mu_i = \left[1 - \frac{1}{n^2}(1 - \mu'^2)\right]^{1/2}$$

(5-46)

Here $\rho(\mu)$ and $\rho(\mu')$ are the reflectance of the coating-vacuum interface from the internal direction μ and the external direction μ', respectively—μ_c is the cosine of the critical internal angle of reflection. Substitution of (5-43) into Equations (5-45) provides the set of equations for the determination of C_1 and C_2. Note that C_2 is a function of μ.

$$C_1 = 2\rho_1 \int_0^1 C_2 e^{-\tau_0/\mu}\mu \, d\mu + q_0$$

$$C_2 = \rho(\mu)C_1 e^{-\tau_0/\mu} \qquad \mu > \mu_c$$
$$C_2 = C_1 e^{-\tau_0/\mu} \qquad \mu \leq \mu_c$$

(5-47)

Here q_0 represents the last term in the first equation of (5-45). The equations above may be readily solved for C_1 and C_2, although a numerical integration will normally be required.

$$C_1 = \frac{q_0}{1 - 2\rho_1 \int_0^{\mu_c} e^{-2\tau_0/\mu}\mu \, d\mu - 2\rho_1 \int_{\mu_c}^1 \rho(\mu)e^{-2\tau_0/\mu}\mu \, d\mu}$$

(5-48)

The resulting over-all reflection will include a specular component corresponding to the Fresnel reflection of the incident flux at the coating-vacuum interface plus the transmitted internally-reflected intensity.

$$I_v(\mu_0) = \frac{1}{n^2}[1 - \rho(\mu_0)]C_1 e^{-\tau_0/\mu} + \rho(\mu')I_0 \qquad \text{when } \mu_0 = \mu'$$

$$= \frac{1}{n^2}[1 - \rho(\mu_0)]C_1 e^{-\tau_0/\mu} \qquad \text{when } \mu_0 \neq \mu'$$

(5-49)

In Equation (5-49), μ is related to μ_0 by Equation (5-46), where μ_i is replaced with μ and μ' is replaced with μ_0.

5-5.   The Plane-Parallel Atmosphere in Radiative Equilibrium

In each of the discussions above, the temperature of the semidiather-manous medium was assumed to be either a known constant or a known function of τ. When a situation involves an unknown temperature distri-bution, which must be determined from an energy balance, the problem is much more complicated. It is particularly difficult if thermal energy is being simultaneously transported by the conductive and convective modes. These cases will be discussed in a later chapter. The problem of radiative equilibrium will be considered in this section.

Radiative equilibrium is defined as the *condition whereby a steady-state radiative transfer of thermal energy occurs in a semidiathermanous stationary medium having zero conductivity and in which there are no other forms of energy converted to or from thermal energy.* In other words, each volume element of the medium through which the radiation propagates must emit an amount of energy equal to the energy absorbed. The radiative equilibrium problem is completely analogous to the conductive equilib-rium problem in that the divergence of the flux must be equal to zero.

For the axially-symmetric problem of plane-parallel atmospheres, the flux may vary only with optical depth. It is, therefore, possible to express the divergence as the derivative of the radiative flux with respect to the optical distance τ.

$$\frac{d}{d\tau}[Q(\tau)] = 0 \tag{5-50}$$

The integral relationship between $Q(\tau)$ and $I(\tau)$ may now be substituted into (5-50).

$$\frac{d}{d\tau}\left[\int_0^{2\pi}\int_{-1}^{+1} I(\tau,\mu)\mu\, d\mu d\Phi\right] = 0 \tag{5-51}$$

Integrating Equation (5-51) over Φ and noting the integration over μ to be independent of τ, results in the expression

$$\int_{-1}^{+1}\left[\mu\frac{dI(\tau,\mu)}{d\tau}\right] d\mu = 0 \tag{5-52}$$

Substitution of the equality of Equation (5-10) for the integrand above gives Expression (5-53).

$$\int_0^1 I^+(\tau,\mu)\, d\mu + \int_0^1 I^-(\tau,\mu)\, d\mu = 2n^2 I_b(\tau) \tag{5-53}$$

Where $I_b(\tau)$ is the intensity of black radiation at the temperature of the matter located at τ.

Equation (5-53) relates the $I_b(\tau)$ to the integral of the local intensity. Since the temperature profile is unknown, $I_b(\tau)$ is an unknown function of

τ. Equation (5-53) may, however, be substituted for $n^2 I_b(\tau)$ in Equation (5-11), resulting in the following pair of homogeneous, linear, integro-differential equations.

$$\mu \frac{dI^+(\tau, \mu)}{d\tau} = -I^+(\tau, \mu) + \frac{1}{2} \int_0^1 [I^+(\tau, \mu) + I^-(\tau, \mu)] \, d\mu$$

$$-\mu \frac{dI^-(\tau, \mu)}{d\tau} = -I^-(\tau, \mu) + \frac{1}{2} \int_0^1 [I^+(\tau, \mu) + I^-(\tau, \mu)] \, d\mu$$

(5-54)

An approximate solution to this set of equations may be obtained by substitution of the Gaussian quadrature for the integral terms. This results in an approximation of Equations (5-54) by a set of $2n$ linear, homogeneous, first-order differential equations.

$$\mu_i \frac{dI^+(\tau, \mu_i)}{d\tau} = -I^+(\tau, \mu_i) + \frac{1}{2} \sum_{j=1}^n w_j [I^+(\tau, \mu_j) + I^-(\tau, \mu_j)]$$

$$-\mu_i \frac{dI^-(\tau, \mu_i)}{d\tau} = -I^-(\tau, \mu_i) + \frac{1}{2} \sum_{j=1}^n w_j [I^+(\tau, \mu_j) + I^-(\tau, \mu_j)]$$

(5-55)

The solution of Equations (5-55) will have an exponential form. It may be written

$$I^+(\tau, \mu_i) = X_i e^{\gamma \tau} \qquad i = 1, 2, \ldots, n$$

$$I^-(\tau, \mu_i) = X_{i+n} e^{\gamma \tau} \qquad i = 1, 2, \ldots, n$$

(5-56)

Here, X_i, X_{i+n}, and γ are values to be determined. Substitution of (5-56) into (5-55) results in the following matrix equation.

$$\left[\delta_{p,q}(1 + \gamma \mu_p) - \frac{w_p}{2} \right](X_q) = 0$$

(5-57)

In (5-57), the indices p and q range from 1 to $2n$; μ and w_p, of course, have only n distinct values and the following special relationship must be noted.

$$\mu_p = -\mu_{p-n} \qquad \text{for } n < p \leq 2n$$

$$w_p = w_{p-n} \qquad \text{for } n < p \leq 2n$$

Note that $\delta_{p,q}$ is again the Kronecker delta and has the values

$$\delta_{p,q} = 1 \qquad \text{when } p = q$$

$$\delta_{p,q} = 0 \qquad \text{when } p \neq q$$

The matrix Equation (5-57) represents a set of homogeneous, linear algebraic equations. For a nontrivial solution, the determinant of the coefficient matrix must be zero. It will be noted that the diagonal elements of this coefficient matrix each contain the unknown parameter γ and thus the determinant is essentially a polynomial of order $2n$ in γ. There must, therefore, be $2n$ values of γ that will satisfy the equation. These $2n$ values are called *Eigenvalues* of the matrix and are analogous to the natural frequencies in the multidegree of freedom vibrating system. For each γ_s $(s = 1, 2, \ldots, 2n)$ there exists a set of values X_p. These are called the *Eigenvectors* of the matrix. Since the equation is homogeneous, the values of X_p for each Eigenvalue may be determined only as ratio. Thus, the solution of (5-55) may be written

$$I^+(\tau, \mu_i) = \sum_{s=1}^{2n} C_s X_{i,s} \exp(\gamma_s \tau)$$

$$I^-(\tau, \mu_i) = \sum_{s=1}^{2n} C_s X_{i+n,s} \exp(\gamma_s \tau)$$

(5-58)

In Equations (5-58), the C_s represents constants of integration to be determined from the boundary conditions. Consider the problem of the plane-parallel atmosphere bounded by diffusely-reflecting surfaces. The boundary conditions may be written as

$$I^+(0, \mu_i) = \epsilon_1 I_b(T_1) + 2\rho_1 \sum_{j=1}^{n} w_j \mu_j I^-(0, \mu_j)$$

$$I^+(\tau_0, \mu_i) = \epsilon_2 I_b(T_2) + 2\rho_2 \sum_{j=1}^{n} w_j \mu_j I^+(\tau_0, \mu_j)$$

(5-59)

Substituting Equation (5-58) into Equation (5-59) results in the following set:

$$\sum_{s=1}^{2n} C_s X_{i,s} = \epsilon_2 I_b(T_1) + 2\rho_1 \sum_{j=1}^{n} w_j \mu_j \sum_{s=1}^{2n} C_s X_{j+n,s}$$

$$\sum_{s=1}^{2n} C_s X_{i+n,s} \exp(\gamma_s \tau_0) = \epsilon_2 I_b(T_2) + 2\rho_2 \sum_{j=1}^{n} w_j \mu_j \sum_{s=1}^{2n} C_s X_{j,s} \exp(\gamma_s \tau_0)$$

(5-60)

These equations may be arranged as follows.

$$\sum_{s=1}^{2n} C_s(X_{i,s} - 2\rho_1 \sum_{j=1}^{n} w_j \mu_j X_{n+j,s}) = \epsilon_1 I_b(T_1)$$

$$\sum_{s=1}^{2n} C_s(X_{i+n,s} - 2\rho_2 \sum_{j=1}^{n} w_j \mu_j X_{j,s})[\exp(\gamma_s \tau_0)] = \epsilon_2 I_b(T_2)$$

(5-61)

Equations (5-61) may be solved for the $2n$ values of C_s. It may be readily noted that the solutions for C_s may be expressed in the form

$$C_s = A_s I_b(T_1) + B_s I_b(T_2)$$

(5-62)

In (5-62), A_s and B_s are constants determined from the inversion of the coefficient matrix in Equation (5-61). Substitution into Equation (5-58) for any given optical depth results in a set of equations of the form

$$I^+(\tau_1, \mu_i) = D_i I_b(T_1) + E_i I_b(T_2)$$

$$I^-(\tau_1, \mu_i) = F_i I_b(T_1) + G_i I_b(T_2)$$

(5-63)

Here the D_i, E_i, F_i, and G_i are constants determined by the indicated substitution. The net flux is now obtained by utilizing the quadrature to integrate the intensities over the spherical solid angle. The result may be expressed as

$$Q_v = MI_b\,(T_1) - NI_b\,(T_2) \tag{5-64}$$

Where M and N are parameters resulting from the computation. It may be reasoned that M and N must be equal since the net flux must be zero when $T_1 = T_2$. The computations does indeed result in such an equality.

Thus, for the case of radiative equilibrium between two infinite parallel walls, the flux may be expressed in terms of a parameter times the difference of the black-body intensities corresponding to the temperatures of the two walls.

$$Q = M(\tau_0, \rho_1, \rho_2)\frac{\sigma}{\pi}\,(T_1^4 - T_2^4) \tag{5-65}$$

The parameter M depends only on the optical spacing of the two plates and on their respective reflectances.

Table 5-1 gives computed values of M for various optical depths and combinations of surface reflectance. These values are computed using $n = 4$ in the quadrature.

TABLE 5-1.

Parameter M for Radiative Equilibrium

Optical Spacing	Combinations of Surface Reflectance					
	0.1–0.1	0.1–0.5	0.1–0.9	0.5–0.5	0.5–0.9	0.9–0.9
0.1	2.3894	1.4256	0.3079	1.0159	0.2832	0.1646
0.2	2.2332	1.3726	0.3054	0.9887	0.2811	0.1638
0.3	2.1199	1.3251	0.3030	0.9638	0.2791	0.1631
0.4	2.0109	1.2817	0.3007	0.9406	0.2772	0.1625
0.6	1.8266	1.2043	0.2963	0.8982	0.2734	0.1612
0.8	1.6757	1.1368	0.2921	0.8602	0.2698	0.1599
1.0	1.5491	1.0772	0.2881	0.8256	0.2664	0.1587
1.5	1.3053	0.9534	0.2786	0.7508	0.2582	0.1558
3.0	0.8894	0.7108	0.2538	0.5918	0.2368	0.1477
5.0	0.6249	0.5313	0.2271	0.4619	0.2134	0.1383

5-6. An Isothermal Gas In A Diffuse Enclosure

An enclosure theory similar to that developed in Chapter 4 for evacuated enclosures may also be developed for enclosures containing an isothermal semidiathermanous medium such as an absorbing and emitting gas. Consider the intensity of radiation leaving a differential element of surface dA_j and incident on surface element dA_i.

$$I_{ji} = C \exp\,(-\rho\kappa_v r_{ij}) + I_{bv}(T_a) \tag{5-66}$$

In Equation (5-66), C is a constant of integration; ρ is the mass density of the absorbing gas; κ_v is the monochromatic mass absorption coefficient of the gas; r_{ij} is the distance between dA_i and dA_j; T_a is the temperature of the isothermal gas. It may be readily seen that C may be obtained in terms of the radiosity at the jth surface element.

$$C = \frac{R_j}{\pi} - I_{bv}(T_a) \tag{5-67}$$

Therefore, substitution of (5-67) into (5-66) gives

$$I_{ji} = \frac{R_{v,j}}{\pi} \exp\left(-\rho\kappa_v r_{ij}\right) + [1 - \exp\left(-\rho\kappa_v r_{ij}\right)]I_{bv}(T_a) \tag{5-68}$$

The integral equation for the radiosity within the enclosure may now be expressed in a similar form to that of the evacuated enclosure in Chapter 4.

$$R_{v,i} = \epsilon_{v,i} \pi I_{bv}(T_i)$$
$$+ \rho_{v,i} \iint_A \frac{\{[R_{v,j} - \pi I_{bv}(T_a)] \exp\left(-\rho\kappa_v r_{ij}\right) + \pi I_{bv}(T_a)\}\mu_i\mu_j \, dA_j}{\pi r_{ij}^2}$$
$$\tag{5-69}$$

The integration in (5-69) is taken over all of the enclosure directly visible from point i. As before, the enclosure may be divided into finite areas and the approximation is made that the radiosity is constant over each discrete area. With such a lumping of the surface areas, Equation (5-69) may be integrated over A_i and divided by A_i, resulting in the equation

$$R_{v,i} = \epsilon_{v,i} \pi I_{bv}(T_i) + \rho_{v,i} \sum_{j=1}^{n} [R_{v,j} - \pi I_{bv}(T_a)]\Phi_{ij} + \rho_{v,i} \pi I_{bv}(T_a) \tag{5-70}$$

where the Φ_{ij} is analogous to the F_{ij} of the evacuated enclosure and is determined by the expression

$$\Phi_{ij} = \frac{1}{A_i} \iiiint_{A_j \, A_i} \frac{\exp\left(-\rho\kappa_v r_{ij}\right)\mu_i\mu_j \, dA_j dA_i}{\pi r_{ij}^2} \tag{5-71}$$

Equation (5-70) may be rewritten in matrix notation as

$$(R_{v,i}) = (\delta_{ij} - \rho_{v,i}\Phi_{ij})^{-1}(G_i + D_i) \tag{5-72}$$

where δ_{ij} is the Kronecker delta, and the G_i and D_i have the form

$$D_i = \pi\rho_{v,i}I_{bv}(T_a)(1 - \sum_{j=1}^{n} \Phi_{ij})$$
$$\tag{5-73}$$
$$G_i = \pi\epsilon_{v,i}I_{bv}(T_i)$$

It should be noted that the Φ_{ij} obey the reciprocity rule and the rule of corresponding corners developed for the F_{ij} of the evacuated enclosure. However, the Φ_{ij} DOES NOT obey the summation rule.

A limited number of values of Φ_{ij} may be found in the literature. Hottel and Cohen (9) and also Rhodes (10) have published graphs of Φ_{ij}.

5-7.   Radiative Transfer in Gases

The preceding analyses have referred to the transfer of monochromatic energy in absorbing media. Most solids and liquids absorb energy in rather "broad" bands, in other words, over wavelength intervals of several microns. Gases, on the other hand, tend to absorb and emit energy in narrow bands that are only a few microns in width. The problem of integrating over frequency must, therefore, be treated in a slightly different fashion than in the surface problem.

From quantum theory it is recognized that the structure of a single molecule is such that it may emit and absorb only certain energy quanta corresponding to the allowable energy configurations of the molecule. Thus, one might expect that a gas composed of identical molecules would absorb and emit photons having exact frequencies corresponding to these allowable energies. Indeed, most of our knowledge of the structure of matter is the result of spectroscopic studies of the absorption and emission lines of gases.

In real gases, these emission lines must have finite width and are shaped as a probability function. This "line broadening," as it is called, is a result of a combination of phenomena. Penner (11) discusses this quantitatively in his book. Qualitatively, these phenomena are discussed briefly as follows:

(1)   Natural line broadening results from a variation of the emitted photons from many emitters. The exact frequency of any single emission may be determined only to within a narrow limit in accord with the Heisenberg uncertainty principle. Thus, for each transition, the emitted photons from a large number of molecules will have a probabalistic distribution.

(2)   Collision broadening results from the interaction of the force fields between molecules. Transition energies are affected by the proximity of colliding molecules and thus the frequency of the photon emitted or absorbed in the transition is influenced. The collision frequency is influenced by the pressure and temperature of the gas. As the gas pressure is increased, the emission lines broaden into bands.

(3)   Doppler broadening is the result of the movement of the molecules or atoms. The frequency of a photon emitted from a molecule moving away from the detector will be shifted slightly to the longer wavelengths, while a photon emitted from a molecule moving toward the detector will be shifted toward the shorter lengths. Since the gas is in a state of thermal agitation, photons will be emitted over a small range of frequencies as a result of this effect.

(4)   A Stark broadening occurs as a result of the interacting electrical

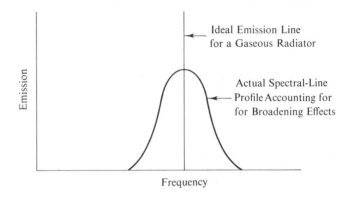

Figure 5-9.   The broadening effects on a spectral-line profile.

fields of ions and the free electrons present in high-temperature gases or plasmas.

Figure 5-9 illustrates schematically the result of the broadening of an emission line for a gaseous radiator.

5-8.   Computation of Total Flux from Monochromatic Flux in Gases

Since gases normally emit and absorb energy in relatively narrow bands, it is important to note in forming an enclosure theory that much of the exchange between the enclosing surfaces may occur in frequency regions in which the gas does not participate. In the computation of total flux for such a case, it is suggested that the radiant heat exchange be first computed for the enclosure as though the enclosure were evacuated. Then, that portion of the flux that falls within the frequency region in which the gas participates must be subtracted from this flux. The monochromatic flux determined from the solution of (5-72) must then be numerically integrated over each of the frequency intervals in which the gas participates. Next, this integrated value should be added to the flux computed for the evacuated enclosure less the subtracted amount. This may be stated in the form of the equation

$$Q = \int_0^\infty Q_{v,e}\, dv - \sum_{j=1}^n \int_{v_j}^{v_j + \Delta v_j} Q_{v,e}\, dv + \sum_{j=1}^n \int_{v_j}^{v_j + \Delta v_j} Q_{v,g}\, dv \qquad (5\text{-}74)$$

In this equation, $Q_{v,e}$ represents the monochromatic flux assuming that the enclosure is evacuated, and $Q_{v,g}$ represents the monochromatic flux accounting for an isothermal participating gas. The frequency intervals in which the gas emits and absorbs energy are denoted by the intervals v_j and $v_j + \Delta v_j$, with n being the number of bands in which the gas emits and absorbs energy.

Normally, a numerical quadrature formula as presented in Equation (4-140) would be utilized for the evaluation of the first integral on the right side of Equation (5-74) while a Gaussian quadrature, similar to Expression (4-75), would be used for the integrals in the second and third terms of (5-74).

It is obvious that the practicality of the method above depends on the availability of a sizeable, high-speed digital computer. Another serious limitation to this type of analysis is the lack of valid gas-absorption coefficients. The tabulation of this data is further complicated by the fact that these coefficients vary with pressure and temperature. D. K. Edwards (12) has presented graphs for carbon dioxide absorption. He reports the gas absorptance to be a function of wave number (the reciprocal of wavelength). The symbol α_v is utilized for this value and it is related to the monochromatic mass-absorption coefficient in the following manner.

$$\alpha_v = 1 - \exp\left(-\kappa_v \rho L\right) \qquad (5\text{-}75)$$

where ρ is the density of the gas and L is the path length of the attenuated ray through the gas. For Edwards' work, $\rho L = 0.5$ $(lb_m)(ft^{-2})$. Substitution into (5-75) results in the expression

$$\kappa_v = -\frac{1}{\rho L} \ln\left(1 - \alpha_v\right) \qquad (5\text{-}76)$$

A number of studies have been undertaken to determine α_v for gases normally found in the atmosphere. These gases are principally CO_2 and H_2O. Some of the more prominent works are by Howard, Burch, and Williams (13) and by Elsasser (14). These authors have developed the expressions below for the total absorption in a band.

$$\alpha = \int \alpha_v \, dv = Apr(P + p)^x \qquad \text{for weak absorption} \qquad (5\text{-}77)$$

$$\alpha = \int \alpha_v \, dv = B(\rho r)^{1/2}(P + p)^y \qquad \text{for medium absorption} \qquad (5\text{-}78)$$

$$\alpha = \int \alpha_v \, dv = C + D \ln(\rho r) + K \ln(P + p) \qquad (5\text{-}79)$$
$$\text{for strong absorption}$$

In the equations above, A, B, C, D, K, x, y are constants, ρ is the concentration of the absorbing constituent, r is the path length.

Bevans (15), (16) and Dunkle (17) have defined a geometrical absorption factor that utilizes these band absorption values in computing radiant heat transfer between surfaces. This absorption factor is defined as

$$\bar{\alpha}_{ij} = \frac{1}{F_{ij}A_i} \int_{A_i} \int_{A_j} \frac{\alpha(r_{ij})\mu_i\mu_j \, dA_j \, dA_i}{\pi r_{ij}^2} \qquad (5\text{-}80)$$

where F_{ij} is the configuration factor defined by Equation (4-8) and $\alpha(r_{ij})$ is one of the expressions of (5-77), (5-78) or (5-79). The relationship between the $\bar{\alpha}_{ij}$ and the effective $\bar{\Phi}_{ij}$ [defined by (5-73)] for the absorption band may be readily shown to be

$$\bar{\Phi}_{ij} = \left(1 - \frac{\bar{\alpha}_{ij}}{\Delta\nu}\right)F_{ij} \qquad (5\text{-}81)$$

In this expression $\Delta\nu$ is the frequency bandwidth. Thus, published values of $\bar{\alpha}_{ij}$ may be utilized for the determination of Φ_{ij}. Values of $\bar{\alpha}_{ij}$ and short-cut methods of computation may be found in Bevans (15) and Dunkle (17).

For optically small separations α_{ij} may be replaced by the product $\rho k L_{ij}$, where L_{ij} is called the *mean beam length*, and is defined as

$$L_{ij} = \frac{1}{F_{ij}A_j} \int_{A_i} \int_{A_j} \frac{\mu_i\mu_j \, dA_j \, dA_i}{\pi r_{ij}} \qquad (5\text{-}82)$$

This approximation may be seen to apply to $\bar{\alpha}_{ij}$ computed by the expression for weak absorption, Equation (5-77). It may also be seen to apply directly to the exponential form for small optical distances; thus the series expansion for the exponential may be written

$$\exp\left(-\rho\kappa_\nu r_{ij}\right) = 1 - (\rho\kappa_\nu r_{ij}) + \frac{(\rho\kappa_\nu r_{ij})^2}{2} - \frac{(\rho\kappa_\nu r_{ij})^3}{6} + \cdots \qquad (5\text{-}83)$$

Neglecting terms with exponents of 2 and higher, $\alpha_\nu(r_{ij})$ may be written as Equation (5-84).

$$\alpha_\nu(r_{ij}) \cong \rho\kappa_\nu r_{ij} \qquad \text{for } (\rho\kappa_\nu r_{ij}) \ll 1 \qquad (5\text{-}84)$$

The band approximation may be used for the integrals in the last terms of Equation (5-74). For such an approximation, it is feasible to assume that $Q_{\nu,e}$ would not vary significantly over an absorption band of the gas. The following expression becomes a substitute for (5-74).

$$Q = \int_0^\infty Q_{\nu,e} \, d\nu - \sum_{j=1}^{n} (Q_{\nu_j,e} - Q_{\nu_j,g}) \, \Delta\nu_j \qquad (5\text{-}85)$$

In (5-85) the $Q_{\nu_j,g}$ is computed by using the $\bar{\Phi}_{ij}$ determined by Equation (5-81) for each band. The $\Delta\nu_j$ should be determined as accurately as is possible for each band.

In general, the problem of radiative heat transfer through absorbing and emitting media still remains a complicated problem. Much work needs to be done both in the measurement of the radiative properties of matter and in the methods of computation.

5-9.   Radiative Heat Transfer in Flames

In the previous paragraphs we have generally assumed that thermodynamic equilibrium exists so that $J_\nu = \rho\kappa_\nu$ in Equation (5-5). In the case of a burning gas or flame, a chemical reaction is taking place and the photons emitted as the reaction progresses do not necessarily fit the spectral distribution that is predicted by the Planck expression. For flames, therefore, Equation (5-5) should be solved with two separate parameters. Letting $k_\nu = \rho\kappa_\nu$, the equation of transfer for flames may be written as:

$$\frac{dI_\nu}{dx} = -k_\nu I_\nu + J_\nu \qquad (5\text{-}86)$$

The problem is complicated because k_ν and J_ν may vary throughout the geometry of the flame. However, average values of k_ν and J_ν may be assumed for some cases without introducing large errors. Hood (18) has measured average values of these for small laboratory flames using the techniques described briefly in Chapter 8. Shahrokhi (19) and Tsai (20) have predicted fluxes from freely burning flames to targets using Hood's data and found good comparison with measurements made with a radiometer.

For a flame burning in an open area, Equation (5-86) may be integrated along geometric paths to the point of interest. The flame may be divided into sections and the flux from each section incident on a target would then be summed to give the final total flux. Figure 5-10 illustrates how this may be accomplished.

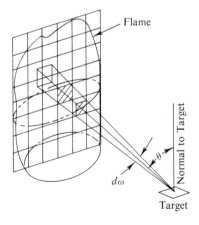

Figure 5-10.   Geometry for numerical integration of flames.

The integration of Equation (5-86) results in the expression

$$I_\nu = \frac{J_\nu}{k_\nu}(1 - e^{-k\nu a}) \tag{5-87}$$

In this expression, I_ν is the intensity emerging from the flame and a is the geometric thickness of the flame along the direction characterizing I_ν. The average intensity along the central direction for each solid angle subtended by the grid at the target is then multiplied by its solid angle, the cosine of the angle between the surface normal and the direction of the incident ray.

For flames in furnace enclosures with diffuse walls, an expression similar to Equation (5-70) may be developed with $I_{b\nu}(T_a)$ replaced by J_ν/k_ν.

PROBLEMS

1. Show that the emission of a surface into a medium of refractive index n is given by $n^2\epsilon_\nu(\mu, \phi)I_{b\nu}(T)$ where $\epsilon_\nu(\mu, \phi)$ is given by the relationship.

$$\epsilon_\nu(\mu, \phi) = 1 - \frac{1}{\pi}\int_0^{2\pi}\int_0^1 \kappa'\rho_\nu(\mu, \phi, \mu', \phi')\, d\mu'\, d\phi'$$

and $\rho_\nu(\mu, \phi, \mu', \phi')$ is the reflection function for the surface into the medium.

2. Develop an expression for the radiative heat transfer between two black, infinite, parallel-plane surfaces separated by an isothermal medium of optical thickness τ_0.

3. Two surfaces having a reflectance of 0.4 are separated by an isothermal gas having an optical thickness of 1.0.

   Temperature $1 = 100°F$, $\quad T_2 = 700°F \quad T_{gas} = 100°F$

   Compute the net flux at surface 1.

4. An infinite-plane diffuse surface is bounded by a semi-infinite isothermal gas. (a) Develop an expression for the radiative heat transfer at the surface by applying the correct boundary conditions to a solution of Equation (5-11). (b) Compare your answer with the result in Equation (5-21) when $\tau_0 \longrightarrow \infty$.

5. Compare the results in Problem 4(a) with those obtained for a specularly-reflecting surface by allowing $\tau_0 \longrightarrow \infty$ in Equation (5-25).

6. An isothermal semi-infinite material having a real-refractive index n is bounded by a semi-infinite vacuum. If the interface is perfectly smooth, the Fresnel reflection at the surface is given by $\rho_\nu(\mu)$. Starting with Equation (5-11), show that the directional emission from the surface is $\epsilon_\nu(\mu) = 1 - \rho_\nu(\mu)$, as would be expected from Kirchhoff's relation. Does Equation (5-36) agree with this as $\tau_0 \longrightarrow \infty$?

7. An infinite isothermal sheet of dielectric with smooth parallel faces, a real-refractive index of n, and an optical thickness of τ_0 is suspended in an infinite vacuum. Develop an expression for the directional emittance of this sheet.

8. Develop an expression for the reflected intensity form a diffuse surfacr coated with a dielectric coating having a refractive index of 1 and an optical depth of τ_0. Assume an incident monodirectional flux q_ν characterized by a small solid angle with a central direction of θ' with respect to surface normal.

9. Assume a gray gas bounded by two infinite-plane gray surfaces at temperatures of 100°F and 1000°F and diffuse reflectances of 0.1 and 0.9, respectively. If the optical spacing of the plates is 1.5 and radiative equilibrium exists, compute the net flux.

10. Develop an expression for Φ_{ij} for two infinite parallel plates separated by a uniformly absorbing medium.

11. Write out the development of Expression (5-81).

References

1. Planck, M., *The Theory of Heat Radiation*, Dover Publications, Inc., New York, 1959.

2. Kourganoff, V., *Basic Methods in Transfer Problems*, Oxford University Press, New York, 1952; Dover Publications, Inc., New York, 1963.

3. Hopf, E., *Mathematical Problems of Radiative Equilibrium*, Cambridge Tracts, 1934.

4. Sobolev, V. V., *A Treatise on Radiative Transfer*, D. Van Nostrand Company, Inc., New York, 1963.

5. Chandrasekhar, S., *Radiative Transfer*, Oxford University Press, New York; 1950; Dover Publication, Inc., New York, 1960.

6. Francis, J. E., and Love, T. J., "Radiant Heat Transfer Analysis of Isothermal Diathermanous Coatings on a Conductor," *A. I. A. A. Journal*, Vol. 4, No. 4 (April. 1966), p 643.

7. Love, T. J., *An Investigation of Radiant Heat Transfer in Absorbing, Emitting and Scattering Media*, Aeronautical Research Laboratories Report, ARL 63-3, January 1963.

8. Viskanta, R., *Heat Transfer in Thermal Radiation Absorbing and Scattering Media*, Argonne National Laboratory, ANL-6170, May 1960.

9.   Hottel, H. C. and Cohen, E. S., "Radiant Heat Exchange in a Gas-Filled Enclosure: Allowance for Nonuniformity of Gas Temperature," *A. I. Ch. E. Journal*, Vol. 4, No. 1 (March 1948).

10. Rhodes, M. S., "An Examination of Two Dimensional Heat Transfer Configuration Factors," *International Developments in Heat Transfer*, Part IV, 1961, International Heat Transfer Conference, Boulder, Colorado, August 1961.

11. Penner, S. S., *Quantitative Molecular Spectroscopy and Gas Emissivities*, Addison-Wesley Publishing Co., Inc., Reading, Massachusetts, 1959.

12. Edwards, D. K., "Absorption by Infrared Bands of Carbon Dioxide at Elevated Pressures and Temperatures," *Journal of the Optical Society of America*, Vol. 50 (1960).

13. Howard, J. N., Burch, D. L., and Williams, D., "Infrared Transmission of Synthetic Atmospheres," *Journal of the Optical Society of America*, Vol. 46 (1956) Part 1 P. 186, Part 2 P. 237, Part 3 P. 242, Part 4 P. 334.

14. Elsasser, W. M., "Atmospheric Radiation Tables," American Meteorological Society, *Meteorological Monographs*, Vol. 4, No. 23 (August 1960).

15. Bevans, J. T., and Dunkle, R. V., "Radiant Interchange Within An Enclosure," *Journal of Heat Transfer*, Vol. 82, Series C, No. 1 (February 1960).

16. Oppenheim, A. K., and Bevans, J. T., "Geometric Factors for Radiation Heat Trasfer Through on Absorbing Medium in Cartesian Coordinates," *Journal of Heat Transfer*, Vol. 82, Series C, No. 4 (November 1960).

17. Dunkle, R. V., "Geometric Beam Lengths for Radiant Heat Transfer Calculations," *Journal Heat of Transfer*, Vol. 86, Series C, No. 1 (February 1964).

18. Hood, J. D., "A Method For The Determination of The Radiative Properties of Flames," Ph. D. Dissertation, University of Oklahoma, Norman, Oklahoma (1966).

19. Shahrokhi, F., "Numerical Technique For Calculation of Radiant Energy Flux To Targets From Flames," Ph. D. Dissertation, University of Oklahoma, Norman, Oklahoma (1965).

20. Tsai, Y. W., "The Prediction of Radiative Heat Transfer From Flames," Master's Thesis, University of Oklahoma, Norman, Oklahoma (1966).

6   Absorbing, Emitting, and
Scattering Media

In the preceding chapter, the problem of radiative transfer through absorbing and emitting media of constant refractive index was considered. In many situations of interest to the engineer, the media through which the radiant energy propagates contains local inhomogeneities that divert some of the energy. Examples of such situations include radiative heat transfer through dusts, smoke, glass fiber insulation, plastics or ceramics that contain bubbles or pigment particles. In such media energy will be scattered as well as absorbed from a pencil of rays, resulting in a change of intensity along a given direction. This attenuation of the ray is called *extinction*. The extinction coefficient, β, must now replace the absorption coefficient in Equation (5-5). This monochromatic mass-extinction coefficient includes both scattering and absorption effects. In addition to the extinction or attenuation of a ray as it traverses a scattering and absorbing medium, there exists the possibility that a ray will be strengthened by radiation scattered into the ray from rays traversing the medium along other directions. The equation of transfer given in (5-5) must now be written as in (6-1) on page 140.

$$\frac{dI_v}{dx} = -\rho\beta_v I_v + J_{v,s} + J_{v,e} \qquad (6\text{-}1)$$

where I_v is the radiation intensity along the x direction, ρ is the mass density of the absorbing and emitting media, β_v is the mass-extinction coefficient, $J_{v,s}$ is the increased intensity resulting from radiation being scattered into the ray, and $J_{v,e}$ represents the increase in intensity of the ray from the thermal emission.

The increase in intensity $J_{v,s}$ due to energy scattered into the x direction from radiation traveling through the element of mass in the space increment dx in all other directions may be expressed in terms of an integration over the spherical solid angle. It should be noted that $J_{v,s}$ is the the coherent scattering and Raman scattering or other effects are not considered. The thermal re-emission of the absorbed energy is accounted for in the emission term $J_{v,e}$.

$$J_{v,s}(\mu, \Phi) = \frac{\rho}{4\pi} \int_0^{2\pi} \int_{-1}^{+1} I_v(\mu', \Phi') S_v^*(\mu', \Phi', \mu, \Phi) \, d\mu' d\Phi' \qquad (6\text{-}2)$$

Here, the function $S_v^*(\mu', \Phi', \mu, \Phi)$ is called the *scattering function*, and it is somewhat analogous to the reflection function of Chapter 3. It is that fraction of energy incident on a differential element of mass from the directions contained in the solid angle $d\mu' d\Phi'$ and scattered into the solid angle $d\mu d\Phi$.

For the case of radiative heat transfer through an isotropic medium, Equation (6-1) may be written

$$\frac{dI_v(\mu, \Phi)}{dx} =$$

$$-\rho\beta_v I_v(\mu, \Phi) + \frac{\rho}{4\pi} \int_0^{2\pi} \int_{-1}^{+1} I_v(\mu', \Phi') S_v^*(\mu', \Phi', \mu, \Phi) \, d\mu' d\Phi' \qquad (6\text{-}3)$$

$$+ n^2 \rho \kappa_v I_{bv}(T)$$

In this expression, κ_v is the mass-absorption coefficient as developed in the previous chapter.

Consider now, an isolated, isothermal enclosure containing an isotropic media that absorbs, scatters, and emits radiant energy. For such a case, (6-3) may be rewritten as:

$$0 = -\rho\beta_v n^2 I_{bv}(T) + \frac{\rho}{4\pi} \int_0^{2\pi} \int_{-1}^{+1} n^2 I_{bv}(T) S_v^*(\mu', \Phi', \mu, \Phi) \, d\mu' d\Phi'$$

$$+ \rho \kappa_v n^2 I_{bv}(T) \qquad (6\text{-}4)$$

Dividing out the $\rho n^2 I_{bv}(T)$ gives the relationship

$$\beta_v = \frac{1}{4\pi} \int_0^{2\pi} \int_{-1}^{+1} S_v^*(\mu', \Phi', \mu, \Phi) \, d\mu' d\Phi' + \kappa_v \qquad (6\text{-}5)$$

Thus, for an isotropic medium the integrated scattering function is independent of direction. This integral is defined as the monochromatic mass-scattering coefficient of the isotropic medium.

$$\sigma_\nu = \frac{1}{4\pi} \int_0^{2\pi} \int_{-1}^{+1} S_\nu^*(\mu', \Phi', \mu, \Phi) \, d\mu', \, d\Phi' \tag{6-6}$$

It is convenient in some forms of analysis to use a normalized scattering function or phase function.

$$S_\nu(\mu', \Phi', \mu, \Phi) = \frac{S_\nu^*(\mu', \Phi', \mu, \Phi)}{\sigma_\nu} \tag{6-7}$$

6-1.   The Scattering Function

The scattering of electromagnetic waves by localized inhomogenities has been extensively studied in such fields as astrophysics, meteorology, colloid chemistry, and radar engineering. An excellent review of the work prior to 1957 is given in Van De Hulst's book (1). The work through 1962 was summarized at the 1962 Interdisciplinary Conference on Electromagnetic Scattering. The proceedings of this conference were published under the editorship of Kerker (2).

The scattering function may be determined analytically for simple geometric shapes, such as spheres, by solving Maxwell's equations with the coordinate system and boundary conditions corresponding to an infinite plane wave incident on the object. This finding was first published by Gustav Mie in connection with his studies of colloidal suspensions of gold. The solution results in an expression involving an infinite series of Ricatti Bessel functions and developed in detail by Stratton (3). The development and results are reviewed by Van De Hulst (1). For uniform homogeneous spheres, the solutions may be expressed as a function of the size parameter α and the relative-refractive index m of the sphere with respect to the surrounding medium. The size parameter α is the dimensionless ratio of the particle circumference, πD, and the wavelength of the incident radiation, λ.

$$\alpha = \frac{\pi D}{\lambda} \tag{6-8}$$

Although the Mie theory holds for the full range of particle size parameters, a simpler formulation developed earlier by Rayleigh holds when $\alpha \ll 1$. This is based on the concept of an oscillating dipole. For large values of α, the Mie solution converges very slowly and the principles of geometric optics are often utilized in obtaining the scattering function. The computation of the scattering function is thus frequently classified as shown at the top of the next page.

$$\alpha \ll 1 \qquad \text{Rayleigh scattering}$$
$$\alpha \cong 1 \qquad \text{Mie scattering}$$
$$\alpha \gg 1 \qquad \text{Geometrical scattering}$$

It should be noted that if the particles have a real refractive index, there will be no absorption or emission of radiation by the particles. Such a case is called *conservative scattering* and, in symbolic terms, $\sigma_v = \beta_v$.

The scattering function that is derived for a single particle is called *independent single scattering*. Generally, when the particles are spaced more than three radii apart, the form of the scattering function is independent of the particle arrangement. If the optical dimensions of the particle cloud are less than 0.1, the scattering effect may usually be considered to be single scattering, that is, the energy that has undergone more than a single interaction may be neglected. For larger optical dimensions, the effects of multiple scattering must be considered.

For some problems where the exact form of the scattering function is unknown, isotropic scattering is assumed (this is not to be confused with scattering by an isotropic media). The normalized-scattering function becomes identically one for the case of isotropic scattering.

$$S_v(\mu', \Phi', \mu, \Phi) \equiv 1 \qquad \text{Isotropic scattering} \qquad \textbf{(6-9)}$$

The normalized-scattering function for Rayleigh scattering can be written in the form

$$S_v(\mu', \Phi', \mu, \Phi) = \tfrac{3}{4}(1 + \cos^2 \Theta) \qquad \text{Rayleigh scattering} \qquad \textbf{(6-10)}$$

Here Θ represents the polar angle between the incident ray and the scattered ray. It should be noted that scattering by an isotropic media will always be axially symmetric and thus there is no dependence on the azimuthal angle.

As in the case of reflection, scattering is accompanied by a polarization. The expression given in Equation (6-10) is the sum of the intensity of each polarization resulting from a circularly-polarized incident ray. In most heat transfer computations, the diffuse emission and multiple reflections tend to obscure polarization effects and for this reason will be neglected.

Many computer programs for the computation of the Mie solutions of the scattering function have been written. Some of these programs are available through various sharing libraries. Churchill, Clark, and Chu (4) have published a table of coefficients to be used in a Legendre polynomial representation of the scattering function for spheres having real-refractive indices ranging from $m = 0.9$ to $m = 2.0$ and $m = \infty$, and for values of α from 1 to 18. In their representation, the scattering function is expressed as

$$S_v(\mu, \Phi, \mu', \Phi') = \sum_{n=1}^{\infty} a_n P_n(\cos \Theta) \qquad \textbf{(6-11)}$$

where a_n are coefficients tabulated for various values of α and m; $P_n(\cos \Theta)$ are Legendre polynomials of order n. The argument of the polynomial is the cosine of the polar angle between the scattered ray and the incident direction.

In the usual engineering situation, the scattering media is not composed of uniform-diameter, spherical particles, although many situations do involve mists of spherical droplets with a dispersion of sizes. Deirmendjian (5) has superimposed Mie solutions for droplet size distributions found in clouds. A similar procedure may be utilized for mists in other situations.

In the case where the cloud of particles is formed from a dispersion of random size, shape, and orientation, as well as of unknown refractive index, it becomes necessary to measure the scattering function. Love and Beattie (6) have presented measurements of clouds of aluminum particles, carbonyl iron, glass, carbon, and silica particles. Because of the random orientation such clouds may be considered to scatter radiation in an axially-symmetric fashion. A typical plot of such scattering functions is given in Figure 6-1.

The value of β_v and σ_v are also functions of the refractive index and size of the particles. While we have given these the name of mass-extinction coefficient and mass-absorption coefficient, it should be noted that these quantities have dimensions of area per unit mass and could well be

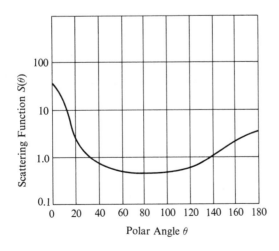

Figure 6-1.

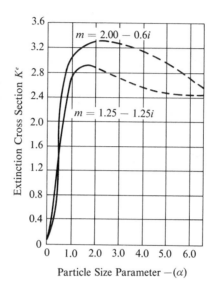

Figure 6-2a. Extinction cross section for spherical particles.

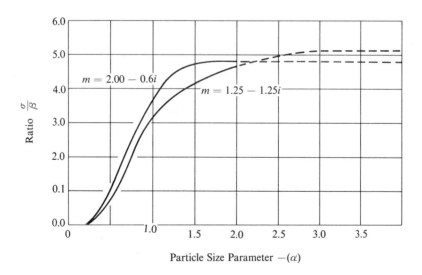

Figure 6-2b. Scattering to extinction ratio of spherical particle.

144

called *cross sections*. Usually, the data given in the literature will be in terms of cross-section ratios, defined as *the ratio of the mass-extinction or scattering coefficient to the actual projected area of a unit mass of particles.* A typical plot of the extinction cross-section ratio and the scattering cross-section ratio is given in Figure 6-2.

6-2. Radiative Heat Transfer between Parallel Plates Separated by Scattering Media

For an example of radiative heat transfer in an enclosure, consider the problem of two infinite, diffuse, parallel plates separated by a uniform, isotropic cloud of particles that scatter in an axially-symmetric fashion. In this case, Equation (6-3) may be written as

$$\mu \frac{dI^+(\mu, \tau)}{d\tau} = -I^+(\mu, \tau) + \frac{\sigma}{2\beta} \int_0^1 [I^+(\mu', \tau)S(+\mu, +\mu')$$

$$+ I^-(\mu', \tau)S(+\mu, -\mu')] \, d\mu' + \frac{\kappa}{\beta} I_{bv}(\tau)$$

$$-\mu \frac{dI^-(\mu, \tau)}{d\tau} = -I^-(\mu, \tau) + \frac{\sigma}{2\beta} \int_0^1 [I^+(\mu', \tau)S(-\mu, +\mu')$$

$$+ I^-(\mu', \tau)S(-\mu, -\mu')] \, d\mu' + \frac{\kappa}{\beta} I_{bv}(\tau) \qquad \textbf{(6-12)}$$

In this expression, again, the plus sign indicates the intensity in any differential solid angle contained in the hemisphere containing the positive τ direction. The minus signs indicate the intensity in those directions contained in the hemisphere containing the negative τ direction. The functions of the type $S(\mu, \mu')$ may be defined as

$$S(\mu, \mu') = \frac{1}{2\pi} \int_0^{2\pi} S(\mu, 0; \mu', \Phi') \, d\Phi' \qquad \textbf{(6-13)}$$

As noted earlier in this chapter for the case of the isotropic medium, the scattering function may be expressed in terms of a single polar angle between the incident ray and the scattered ray. Most tabulations of either analytically or experimentally determined scattering functions will be expressed as a function of this single polar angle. It can be shown from solid geometry that the polar angle Θ between an incident ray characterized by $(\mu, 0)$ and a scattered ray characterized by (μ', Φ') is given by the expression

$$\cos \Theta = \mu\mu' + (1 - \mu^2)^{1/2}(1 - \mu'^2)^{1/2} \cos \Phi' \qquad \textbf{(6-14)}$$

In those cases where the scattering function may be represented by a Legendre series as in Expression (6-11), the scattering function may be expressed in the form of (6-15).

$$S(\mu, \mu') = \sum_{n=1}^{\infty} a_n P_n(\mu, \mu') \tag{6-15}$$

In this case $P_n(\mu, \mu')$ represents the integrated Legendre polynomial.

$$P_n(\mu, \mu') = \frac{1}{2\pi} \int_0^{2\pi} P_n(\cos \Theta) \, d\Phi' \tag{6-16}$$

The plus and minus signs given in the form of the scattering function used in Equation (6-12) represent the scattering from a ray traversing the space in a positive direction into a ray in the positive direction or negative direction as the sign indicates. It may be reasoned intuitively from the isotropic nature of the medium that the following reciprocal relations must hold.

$$\begin{aligned} S(+\mu, +\mu') &\equiv S(-\mu, -\mu') \\ S(+\mu, -\mu') &\equiv S(-\mu, +\mu') \end{aligned} \tag{6-17}$$

An approximate solution to Equation (6-12) may be obtained by use of a Gaussian quadrature for the representation of the integral. In this case, the integrodifferential equation may be reduced to a set of first-order, ordinary, linear nonhomogeneous equations.

$$\mu_i \frac{dI^+(\tau, \mu_i)}{d\tau} = -I^+(\tau, \mu_i) + \frac{\sigma}{2\beta} \sum_{j=1}^{n} a_j [I^+(\tau, \mu_j) S(+\mu_i, +\mu_j)$$

$$+ I^-(\tau, \mu_j) S(+\mu_i, -\mu_j)] + \frac{\kappa}{\beta} I_{bv}(\tau)$$

$$-\mu_i \frac{dI^-(\tau, \mu_i)}{d\tau} = -I^-(\tau, \mu_i) + \frac{\sigma}{2\beta} \sum_{j=1}^{n} a_j \{I^+(\tau, \mu_j)[S(-\mu_i, +\mu_j)]$$

$$+ I^-(\tau, \mu_j) S(-\mu_i, -\mu_j)\} + \frac{\kappa}{\beta} I_{bv}(\tau) \tag{6-18}$$

where the a_j are the weight factors, and μ_j are the ordinates of the quadrature formula.

A solution for the homogeneous portion of the set of equations above will have the form

$$\begin{aligned} I^+(\tau, \mu_i) &= X_i e^{\gamma \tau} \\ I^-(\tau, \mu_i) &= X_{i+n} e^{\gamma \tau} \end{aligned} \tag{6-19}$$

Substitution of Expression (6-19) into the homogeneous part of (6-18) leads to the following set of algebraic equations.

$$\left(b_{p,q} - \frac{\delta_{pq}}{\mu_p} - \gamma \right)(X_p) = 0 \tag{6-20}$$

where

$$b_{p,q} = \frac{\sigma}{2\beta} \left(\frac{a_q S_{p,q}}{\mu_p} \right)$$

The indices of the subscripts on the quadrature weight factors and ordinates have been changed as follows.

$$a_q = a_j \quad \text{when} \quad j = q \qquad\qquad q = 1, 2, \ldots, n$$
$$a_q = a_j \quad \text{when} \quad j = q - n \quad\ \ q = n + 1, n + 2, \ldots, 2n$$
$$\mu_p = \mu_j \quad \text{when} \quad j = p \qquad\qquad p = 1, 2, \ldots, n$$
$$\mu_p = \mu_j \quad \text{when} \quad j = p - n \quad\ \ p = n + 1, n + 2, n + 3, \ldots, 2n$$

The $S_{p,q}$ is the scattering function evaluated at the corresponding quadrature points.

There exist $2n$ values of γ for which the determinant of the coefficient matrix in Equation (6-20) will equal zero. These values are called the *Eigenvalues of the matrix* and are equivalent to the $2n$ roots of the polynomial obtained by expanding the matrix. Associated with each Eigenvalue there will be $2n$ values of X_p known as *Eigenvectors*. Since the equations given in (6-20) are homogeneous, the Eigenvectors are obtained only as a ratio. The homogeneous solution set for Equations (6-18) may be given as

$$I^+(\tau, \mu_i) = \sum_{p=1}^{2n} C_p X_{i,p} \exp{(\gamma_p \tau)}$$
$$I^-(\tau, \mu_i) = \sum_{p=1}^{2n} C_p X_{(i+n),p} \exp{\gamma_p \tau}$$

(6-21)

The C_p are constants to be determined from the boundary conditions.

The particular solution is very complicated for the case of a nonisothermal cloud of particles. However, for the case in which the cloud of particles is isothermal, the particular solution may be readily obtained. For the isothermal cloud, the solution may be written

$$I^+(\tau, \mu_i) = \sum_{p=1}^{2n} C_p X_{i,p} \exp{(\gamma_p \tau)} + I_b(T_a)$$
$$I^-(\tau, \mu_i) = \sum_{p=1}^{2n} C_p X_{(i+n),p} \exp{(\gamma_p \tau)} + I_b(T_a)$$

(6-22)

In the equations above, T_a is the temperature of the particle cloud.

The boundary conditions to be utilized in determining the C_p are the radiosities of the bounding surfaces. These bounding conditions for diffuse surfaces may be written

$$I^+(0, \mu_i) = \epsilon_1 I_b(T_1) + 2\rho_1 \sum_{j=1}^{n} a_j \mu_j I^-(0, \mu_j)$$
$$I^-(\tau_0, \mu_i) = \epsilon_2 I_b(T_2) + 2\rho_2 \sum_{j=1}^{n} a_j \mu_j I^+(\tau_0, \mu_j)$$

(6-23)

In (6-23), the ϵ_1, ϵ_2 are the emittance of Surface 1 and 2, respectively, and ρ_1, ρ_2 are the corresponding surface reflectances. Substitution of the expressions for intensity given in Equation (6-22) (evaluated at $\tau = 0$ and $\tau = \tau_0$) into (6-23) results in $2n$ equations for the $2n$ C_p's.

$$\sum_{p=1}^{2n} C_p[X_{i,p} - 2\rho_1 \sum_{j=1}^{n} a_j\mu_j X_{(j+n),p}] = \epsilon_1 I_b(T_1) - \epsilon_1 I_b(T_a)$$

$$\sum_{p=1}^{2n} C_p[X_{(i+n),p} \exp(\gamma_p\tau_0) - 2\rho_2 \sum_{p=1}^{2n} a_j\mu_j X_{j,p} \exp(\gamma_p\tau_0)]$$
$$= \epsilon_2 I_b(T_2) - \epsilon_2 I_b(T_a) \qquad \textbf{(6-24)}$$

The C_p may thus be determined as a linear combination of $I_b(T_1)$, $I_b(T_2)$ and $I_b(T_a)$. Substitution of these values of C_p into the expression for intensity in Equation (6-22) provides an expression for intensity of the radiation in the directions corresponding to the ordinates of the quadrature formula. This permits the use of the quadrature for an integration over the spherical solid angle. Thus the net monochromatic flux may be written in terms of the Planck intensity corresponding to the temperatures of each surface and the particle cloud.

$$Q_\nu = MI_{b\nu}(T_1) - NI_{b\nu}(T_2) - PI_{b\nu}(T_a) \qquad \textbf{(6-25)}$$

where M, N, and P are dimensionless parameters computed in the manner described above. It should be noted that these parameters are indepen-

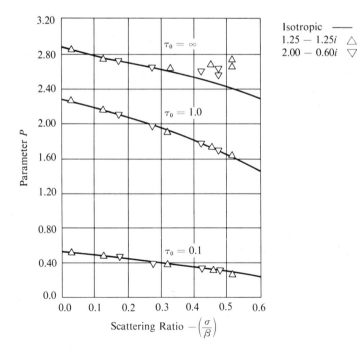

Figure 6-3. Comparison of results of multiple-scattering computations for anisotropic and isothropic scattering.

dent of temperature and depend on the reflectance of each surface, the optical spacing of the plates, the scattering function, and the ratio of scattering to extinction.

The results of computations by Love (7) are given for spheres having refractive indices of 1.25–1.25i and 2.60–0.60i and for isotropic scattering. It will be noted that in Figure 6-3 for low α/β ratio and/or optical spacing less than 1.0, the results for isotropic scattering are essentially the same as for the two anisotropic scattering cases.

Figures 6-4 and 6-5 give an example of the parameters M, N and P for spheres having a refractive index of 1.25–1.25i that corresponds roughly to iron in the visible range. These graphs are for $\rho_1 = 0.1$ and $\rho_2 = 0.9$.

In order to compute the total net heat flux, it is necessary to integrate Expression (6-25) over all wavelengths. This may be accomplished numerically by utilization of the quadrature technique given by Expression (3-24). In this case, the integration may be written as

$$Q = T_1^4 \sum_{j=1}^{5} A_j M_j - T_2^4 \sum_{j=1}^{5} A_j N_j - T_a^4 \sum_{j=1}^{5} A_j P_j \qquad \text{(6-26)}$$

In the equation above, the A_j are given by Table 3-1 and the M_j, N_j, and P_j are determined from the results of the analysis. These must be

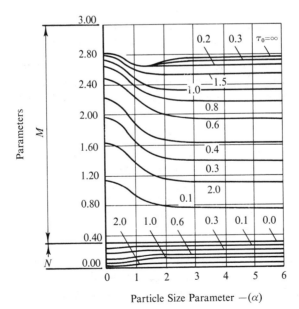

Figure 6-4. Dimensionless parameters M and N for heat transfer computation through scattering media.

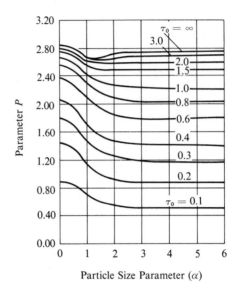

Figure 6-5. Dimensionless parameters P for heat transfer computation through scattering media.

determined at the particle size parameter, α, corresponding to the frequencies or wavelengths specified by the formula and tabulated in Table 3-1. These may be computed and tabulated as shown in Table 6-1.

TABLE 6-1.

Particle Size Parameter Corresponding to Quadrature Frequency

$$\alpha_1 = (0.320 \times 10^{-4})DT$$
$$\alpha_2 = (1.714 \times 10^{-4})DT$$
$$\alpha_3 = (4.362 \times 10^{-4})DT$$
$$\alpha_4 = (8.595 \times 10^{-4})DT$$
$$\alpha_5 = (15.334 \times 10^{-4})DT$$

In Table 6-1, D is the particle diameter in microns and T is the temperature that characterizes the radiation in degrees Rankine (°R).

The use of these charts can be best discussed through a numerical example.

Example

Statement of Problems Two infinite, plane-parallel walls are spaced 0.2 ft apart. A uniform cloud of iron particles occupies the intervening space. The apparent density of the cloud is 0.01 $(lb_m)(ft^{-3})$. The particles are assumed to be spheres with a diameter of $2\,\mu$ and a refractive index of 1.25–1.25i for all frequencies. The cloud moves past the area of interest in a rapid turbulent fashion such that the cloud may be considered isothermal. The following conditions of temperature and wall properties exist.

Wall 1:	Temperature, 2000°R, Reflectance, 0.10
Wall 2:	Temperature, 500°R, Reflectance, 0.90
Particles:	Temperature, 1000°R

Information Desired   Find the net radiant flux at Wall 1.

Solution   (a) Compute the three sets α_j corresponding to the 2-micron particle diameter and the respective temperatures of Wall 1, Wall 2, and the atmosphere. This is accomplished by using Table 6-1.

(b) From the graph in Figure 6-2, read K_j^e corresponding to each α_j computed above.

(c) Compute $(\tau_0)_j$ corresponding to each K_j^e determined above. The K^e is a cross section ratio, that is, it is the ratio of the apparent cross sectional area as determined by the extinction of a ray penetrating the cloud to the actual cross sectional area of the particles. The K^e is related to the mass-extinction coefficient β_v by the relationship

$$\beta_v = \frac{3K^e}{3D\rho_a}$$

In this equation, D is the particle diameter, and ρ_a is the density of the individual particles. Since K^e is dimensionless, if β_v is to be expressed in square feet per pound mass, the dimensional units of D and ρ_a must be selected accordingly.

$$(\tau_0)_j = \rho\beta_v L = (0.01)(\beta_v)_j(0.2)$$

(d) Read M_j, N_j, P_j from the graphs in Figures 6-4 and 6-5. The values of M_j should correspond to the values of α_j and $(\tau_0)_j$ computed using the temperature of Wall 1. The values of N_j should correspond to the temperature of Wall 2, and P_j should correspond to the temperature of the particles. These values should be read from the graphs corresponding to $\rho_1 = 0.10$ and $\rho_2 = 0.90$, and the refractive index of the particles, $m = 1.25–1.25i$.

The results of the operations for this problem are found in Table 6-2.

TABLE 6-2.

Computed Values for the Example

Corresponding to Wall 1 temperature of 2000°R

j	α_j	K_j^e	$(\tau_0)_j$	M_j
1	0.13	0.38	0.353	2.17
2	0.69	2.21	2.051	2.71
3	1.74	2.92	2.710	2.68
4	3.44	2.64	2.45	2.69
5	6.13	2.44	2.26	2.71

TABLE 6-2 (Continued).

Corresponding to Wall 2 temperature of 500°R

j	α_j	K_j^e	$(\tau_0)_j$	N_j
1	0.032	0.08	0.074	0.265
2	0.171	0.52	0.483	0.130
3	0.436	1.35	1.253	0.050
4	0.860	2.62	2.431	0.019
5	1.530	2.89	2.682	0.021

Corresponding to particle temperature of 1000°R

j	α_j	K_j^e	$(\tau_0)_j$	P_j
1	0.064	0.19	0.176	1.17
2	0.340	1.05	0.974	2.60
3	0.872	2.63	2.440	2.65
4	1.72	2.91	2.700	2.64
5	3.07	2.69	2.500	2.65

(e) The values M_j, N_j, P_j are then multiplied by the corresponding value A_j presented in Table 3-1. The resulting terms are summed and multiplied by the fourth power of the corresponding temperature.

$A_j M_j \times 10^{11}$	$A_j N_j \times 10^{11}$	$A_j P_j \times 10^{11}$
0.75	0.09	0.41
33.77	1.62	22.46
81.68	1.52	80.77
29.05	0.20	28.46
1.07	0.01	1.05
146.32	3.44	143.15

$q_{net} = (10^{-11})[(146.32)(16 \times 10^{12}) - (3.44)(0.0625)(10^{12}) - (143.14)(10^{12})]$

$q_{net} = 21,960 \ (BTU)(hr^{-1})(ft^{-2})$

6-3. The Scattering Problem with an Incident Flux

There are many problems in which a surface coating, a planetary atmosphere, or a scattering boundary layer are subjected to an essentially monodirectional incident flux. The analysis presented in this chapter may be modified slightly and the net radiative flux computed in a similar fashion. In order to preserve the axial symmetry, this analysis is limited to normal incident rays for the case of anisotropic scattering. For isotropic scattering, however, it may be modified to include any angle of incidence. Although the analysis may be used for scattering particles in a coating

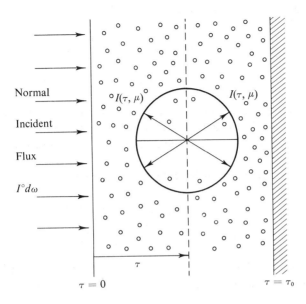

Figure 6-6.   Coordinate scheme for problem of normal incident flux.

having a relative-refractive index differing from unity, it is considerably more complicated. In this book, we will consider only the problem of the particles suspended in a medium having a relative-refractive index of unity with respect to the surrounding.

Consider a monodirectional flux normal to a plane-parallel cloud of particles of finite optical thickness, bounded by a diffuse surface on the side opposite the incident flux (Figure 6-6). It is assumed that the temperature of the particles is uniform.

The intensity of the unabsorbed, unscattered incident radiation will be accounted for separately from the scattered radiant flux.

Let I^0 be the intensity of the incident flux and $d\omega$ be the solid angle subtended by the flux. Then $I^0 e^{-\tau}$ will be the intensity of the attenuated flux at optical depth τ. The contribution to the scattered radiation field in the direction μ is $\sigma I^0 d\omega e^{-\tau}[S(\mu, 1)]/4\pi$ and the equation of transfer becomes

$$+\mu_i \frac{dI^+(\tau, \mu_i)}{d\tau} = -I^+(\tau, +\mu_i) + \frac{\sigma}{2\beta} \sum_{j=1}^{n} a_j S(\mu_i, +\mu_j) I^+(\tau, +\mu_j)$$

$$+ \frac{\sigma}{2\beta} \sum_{j=1}^{n} a_j S(\mu_i, -\mu_j) I^-(\tau, -\mu_j)$$

$$+ \frac{\sigma}{4\pi\beta} S(+\mu_i, 1) I^0 d\omega e^{-\tau} + \frac{\kappa}{\beta} I_{b\nu}(T_a)$$

$$-\mu_i \frac{dI^-(\tau, \mu_i)}{d\tau} = -I^-(\tau, -\mu_i) + \frac{\sigma}{2\beta} \sum_{j=1}^{n} a_j S(-\mu_i, +\mu_j) I^+(\tau, +\mu_j) \quad \text{(6-28)}$$

$$+ \frac{\sigma}{2\beta} \sum_{j=1}^{n} a_j S(-\mu_i, -\mu_j) I^-(\tau, -\mu_j)$$

$$+ \frac{\sigma}{4\pi\beta} S(-\mu_i + 1) I^0 d\omega e^{-\tau} + \frac{\kappa}{\beta} I_{bv}(T_a)$$

The homogeneous solution for this set of equations will be the same as Equation (6-19). In order to find the particular solution associated with the scattered attenuated flux, the method of undetermined coefficients is used.

A solution of the following from is assumed.

$$I_p^+(\tau, \mu_i) = \xi_i \left[\frac{\sigma}{4\pi\beta} S(+\mu_i, 1) I^0 d\omega e^{-\tau} \right]$$

$$I_p^-(\tau, \mu_i) = \xi_{(i+n)} \left[\frac{\alpha}{4\pi\beta} S(-\mu_i, 1) I^0 d\omega e^{-\tau} \right]$$

$$\text{(6-29)}$$

where ξ is the coefficient to be determined by substitution into the equation of transfer. This gives the following set of simultaneous algebraic equations.

$$-\mu_i \xi_i S(+\mu_i, 1) =$$

$$-\xi_i S(+\mu_i, 1) + \frac{\sigma}{2\beta} \sum_{j=1}^{n} \xi_j a_j S(+\mu_i, \mu_j) S(+\mu_j + 1)$$

$$+ \frac{\sigma}{2\beta} \sum_{j=1}^{n} \xi_{(j+n)} a_j S(+\mu_i, -\mu_j) S(-\mu_j, 1) + S(+\mu_i, 1)$$

$$\mu_i \xi_{(i+n)} S(-\mu_i, 1) =$$

$$\text{(6-30)}$$

$$-\xi_{(i+n)} S(-\mu_i, 1) + \frac{\sigma}{2\beta} \sum_{j=1}^{n} \xi_j a_j S(-\mu_i, +\mu_j) S(+\mu_j, 1)$$

$$+ \frac{\sigma}{2\beta} \sum_{j=1}^{n} \xi_{(j+n)} a_j S(-\mu_i, -\mu_j) S(-\mu_j, 1) + S(-\mu_i, 1)$$

This set of linear equations must now be solved for ξ_i, and may be written in matrix form. Let

$$b_{p,q} = \frac{\sigma a_q S_{p,q} S_q}{2\beta} \quad \text{(6-31)}$$

where the subscripts have the same meaning as for Equation (6-20).

$$S_p, S_q = S(+\mu_i, 1) \quad i,j = p,q \quad p,q = 1, 2, \ldots, n$$
$$S_p, S_q = S(-\mu_i, 1) \quad i,j = (p-n), (q-n)$$
$$p,q = n+1, n+2, \ldots, 2n$$

The matrix form of the equation is

$$[(S_p - \mu_p S_p)\delta_{pq} - b_{pq}](\xi_p) = (S_p) \quad \text{(6-32)}$$

Thus

$$(\xi_p) = [(S_p - \mu_p S_p)\delta_{pq} - b_{pq}]^{-1}(S_p) \tag{6-33}$$

The inversion may be performed by numerical techniques.

The equations for the intensities at the discrete directions may now be written as

$$I^+(\tau, \mu_i) = \sum_{\alpha=1}^{2n} C_\alpha x_{i,\alpha} e^{\gamma_\alpha \tau} + I_{bv}(T_a) + \varphi_i I^0 d\omega e^{-\tau}$$

$$I^-(\tau, \mu_i) = \sum_{\alpha=1}^{2n} C_\alpha x_{(i+n),\alpha} e^{\gamma_\alpha \tau} + I_{bv}(T_a) + \varphi_{(i+n)} I^0 d\omega e^{-\tau} \tag{6-34}$$

where

$$\varphi_i = \xi_i\left[\frac{\sigma}{4\pi\beta}S(+\mu_i, 1)\right]$$

$$\varphi_{(i+n)} = \xi_{(i+n)}\left[\frac{\sigma}{4\pi\beta}S(-\mu_i, 1)\right] \tag{6-35}$$

The constants C_α remain to be evaluated by the boundary conditions.

$$I^+(0, \mu_i) = 0$$

$$I^-(\sigma_0, \mu_i) = R/\pi \tag{6-36}$$

where R represents the radiosity of the diffuse surface bounding one side of the plane-parallel dispersion of optical thickness τ_0.

$$R = (1 - \rho)\pi I_{bb}(T) + 2\pi\rho \int_0^1 \mu I(\tau_0, \mu)\, d\mu + \rho e^{-\tau_0} I^0 \, d\omega \tag{6-37}$$

where ρ is the monochromatic reflectivity of the diffuse surface, and T is the temperature of the surface. Utilizing the quadrature formula to replace the integral as before, (6-36) is written

$$0 = \sum_{\alpha=1}^{2n} C_\alpha x_{i,\alpha} + I_{bv}(T_a) + \varphi_i I^0 \, d\omega$$

$$\sum_{\alpha=1}^{2n} C_\alpha x_{(i+n),\alpha} e^{\gamma_\alpha \tau_0} + I_{bv}(T_a) + \varphi_{(i+n)} I^0 d\omega e^{-\tau_0}$$

$$= (1 - \rho)I_{bb}(T_1) + 2\rho \sum_{j=1}^{n} a_j\mu_j[\sum_{\alpha=1}^{2n} C_\alpha x_{i,\alpha} e^{\gamma_\alpha \tau_0} + I_{bv}(T_a) \tag{6-38}$$

$$+ \varphi_i I^0 d\omega e^{-\tau_0}] + \frac{\rho}{\pi}I^0 d\omega e^{-\tau_0}$$

Rearrangement of these equations gives

$$\sum_{\alpha=1}^{2n} C_\alpha x_{i,\alpha}$$

$$= -I_{bb}(T_a) - \varphi_i I^0 d\omega \sum_{\alpha=1}^{2n} C_\alpha e^{\gamma_\alpha \tau_0}[x_{(i+n),\alpha} - 2\rho \sum_{j=1}^{n} a_j\mu_j x_{j,\alpha}]$$

$$= (1 - \rho)[I_{bv}(T) - I_{bv}(T_a)] + \left[2\rho \sum_{j=1}^{n} a_j\mu_j\varphi_j - \varphi_{(i+n)} + \frac{\rho}{\pi}\right]e^{-\tau_0}I^0 d\omega \tag{6-39}$$

The C_α's may be determined by utilizing matrix techniques. Let $a_{p,\alpha}$, represent the terms of a matrix where

$$a_{p,\alpha} = X_{i,\alpha}, \qquad\qquad p = 1, 2, \ldots, n$$

$$a_{p,\alpha} = [X_{(i+n),\alpha} - 2\rho \sum_{j=1}^{n} a_j \mu_j x_{j,\alpha}] e^{\gamma_\alpha \tau_0}, \qquad (6\text{-}40)$$

$$p = (1 + n) = n + 1, n + 2, \ldots, 2n$$

Let

$$(B_\alpha) = (a_{p,\alpha})^{-1}(b_p) \qquad (6\text{-}41)$$

where

$$b_p = -1, \qquad\qquad p = 1, 2, \ldots, n$$
$$b_p = (\rho - 1), \qquad p = n + 1, n + 2, \ldots, 2n$$

and

$$(D_\alpha) = (a_{p,\alpha})^{-1}(d_p) \qquad (6\text{-}42)$$

where

$$d_p = -\varphi_i \qquad p = 1, 2, \ldots, n = 1$$
$$d_p = \left[2\rho \sum_{j=1}^{n} a_j \mu_j \varphi_j + \frac{\rho}{\pi} - \varphi_p \right] e^{-\tau_0} \qquad (6\text{-}43)$$

and

$$(E_\alpha) = (a_{p,\alpha})^{-1}(e_p)$$

where

$$e_p = 0 \qquad\qquad p = 1, 2, \ldots, n$$
$$e_p = 1 - \rho, \qquad p = n + 1, n + 2, \ldots, 2n$$

The equation for intensity may thus be written

$$I^+(\tau, \mu_i) = (\sum_{\alpha=1}^{2n} E_\alpha x_{i,\alpha} e^{\gamma_\alpha \tau}) I_{bv}(T) + (1 + \sum_{\alpha=1}^{2n} B_\alpha x_{i,\alpha} e^{\gamma_\alpha \tau}) I_{bv}(T_a)$$

$$+ (\varphi_i e^{-\tau} + \sum_{\alpha=1}^{2n} D_\alpha x_{i,\alpha} e^{\gamma_\alpha \tau}) I^0 \, d\omega$$

$$\qquad\qquad (6\text{-}44)$$

$$I^-(\tau, \mu_i) = [\sum_{\alpha=1}^{2n} E_\alpha x_{(i+n),\alpha} e^{\gamma_\alpha \tau}] I_{bv}(T) + [1 + \sum_{\alpha=1}^{2n} B_\alpha x_{(i+n),\alpha} e^{\gamma_\alpha \tau}] I_{bv}(T_a)$$

$$+ [\varphi_{(i+n)} e^{-\tau} + \sum_{\alpha=1}^{2n} D_\alpha x_{(i+n),\alpha} e^{\gamma_\alpha \tau}] I^0 \, d\omega$$

Again utilizing the quadrature formula to integrate the intensity over all directions in order to obtain the flux gives

$$Q = M^n I_{bb}(T) + N^n I_{bb}(T_a) + P^n I^0 \, d\omega \qquad (6\text{-}45)$$

where

$$M^n = 2\pi \sum_{j=1}^{n} a_j \mu_j \{ \sum_{\alpha=1}^{2n} E_\alpha e^{\gamma_\alpha \tau} [x_{i,\alpha} - x_{(i+n),\alpha}] \}$$

$$N^n = 2\pi \sum_{j=1}^{n} a_j \mu_j \{ \sum_{\alpha=1}^{2n} B_\alpha e^{\gamma_\alpha \tau} [x_{i,\alpha} - x_{(i+n),\alpha}] \} \qquad \text{(6-46)}$$

$$P^n = 2\pi \sum_{j=1}^{n} a_j \mu_j \{ \sum_{\alpha=1}^{2n} D_\alpha e^{\gamma_\alpha \tau} (x_{i,\alpha} - x_{(i+n),\alpha}) + [\varphi_i - \varphi_{(i+n)}] e^{-\tau_0} \} + e^{-\tau_0}$$

The final term in the expression for P^n is the result of the attenuated incident flux. The reflection of the incident flux is accounted for in the diffuse boundary condition (6-37) for the radiosity at τ_0. The integration over all frequencies of radiation may be accomplished in the same way as in the previous problems.

For the case of isotropic scattering, the equations for ξ_i, can be solved readily and an insight into the behavior of ξ_i, may be gained. With the scattering functions taken as identically 1, the equations of transfer become

$$\mu_i \frac{dI(\tau, +\mu_i)}{d\tau} = -I(\tau, +\mu_i) + \frac{\sigma}{2\beta} \sum_{j=1}^{n} a_j [I^+(\tau, \mu_j) + I^-(\tau, \mu_j)]$$

$$+ \frac{\sigma}{4\pi\beta} I^0 \omega e^{-\tau} + \frac{\kappa}{\beta} I_{bb}(T_a)$$

$$\qquad \text{(6-47)}$$

$$-\mu \frac{dI(\tau, -\mu_i)}{d\tau} = -I(\tau, -\mu_i) + \frac{\sigma}{2\beta} \sum_{j=1}^{n} a_j I^+(\tau, \mu_j) + I^-(\tau, \mu_j)$$

$$+ \frac{\sigma}{4\pi\beta} I^0 d\omega e^{-\tau} + \frac{\kappa}{\beta} I_{bb}(T_a)$$

Assume the particular integral associated with the attenuated flux to be of the form

$$I_p^+(\tau, \mu_i) = \xi_i \left(\frac{\sigma}{4\pi\beta} I^0 d\omega e^{-\tau} \right)$$

$$I_p^-(\tau, \mu_i) = \xi_{(i+n)} \left(\frac{\sigma}{4\pi\beta} I^0 d\omega e^{-\tau} \right) \qquad \text{(6-48)}$$

Substituting this into the differential equations gives

$$-\xi_i \mu_i = -\xi_i + \frac{\sigma}{2\beta} \sum_{j=1}^{n} a_j [\xi_j + \xi_{(j+n)}] + 1$$

$$\xi_{(i+n)} = -\xi_{(i+n)} + \frac{\sigma}{2\beta} \sum_{j=1}^{n} a_j [\xi_j + \xi_{(j+n)}] + 1 \qquad \text{(6-49)}$$

Therefore,

$$\xi_i(1 - \mu_i) = \xi_{(i+n)}(1 + \mu_i) \qquad \text{(6-50)}$$

Thus,

$$\xi_i(1 - \mu_i) = \frac{\sigma}{2\beta} \sum_{j=1}^{n} a_j \xi_j \left(\frac{1}{1 + \mu_j}\right) + 1$$

$$\xi_i = \frac{C}{1 - \mu_i}$$

(6-51)

where C does not vary with the index 1. Solving for C gives

$$C = \frac{1}{1 - (\sigma/\beta) \sum_{j=1}^{n} a_j/(1 - \mu_j)^2}$$

(6-52)

It is important to note that since σ/β varies between 0 and 1 that if the summation in the denominator is greater than 1, (which it is for all orders of approximation), then C will have a singularity for some value of σ/β.

Chandrasekhar (8) in *Radiative Transfer* (p. 82, Equation 90), develops a similar expression for the case of isotropic scattering in a semi-infinite atmosphere with an incident flux. No mention of the singularity is made in *Radiative Transfer* although C (designated γ in *Radiative Transfer*) is utilized for all values of the albedo of single scattering (σ/β) in numerous cases.

The analysis, however, should not be influenced by this pole except for values of σ/β that give large values of C as will be found in the neigh-

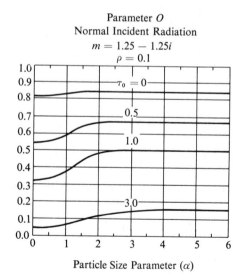

Parameter O
Normal Incident Radiation
$m = 1.25 - 1.25i$
$\rho = 0.1$

Particle Size Parameter (α)

Figure 6-7.

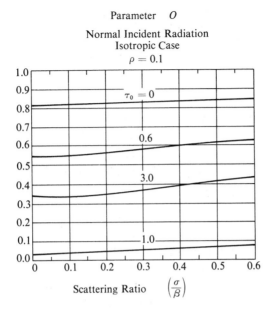

Parameter O

Normal Incident Radiation
Isotropic Case

$\rho = 0.1$

$\tau_0 = 0$

0.6

3.0

1.0

Scattering Ratio $\left(\dfrac{\sigma}{\beta}\right)$

Figure 6-8.

borhood of the singularity. In this region, numerical round-off errors may be expected to give erratic results.

Some values of the parameter P^n at $\tau = \tau_0$ are given in the graphs in Figures 6-7 and 6-8. It should be noted that this parameter corresponds to the fraction of the incident flux that would be absorbed by the opaque surface protected by the cloud of scattering particles having an optical thickness of τ_0.

6-4.   The Problem of Radiative Equilibrium

The problem of radiative equilibrium in a scattering atmosphere may be approached in a manner similar to the problem of radiative equilibrium in a pure absorbing atmosphere. First, write Equation (6-3) in the axially-symmetric form.

$$\mu\frac{dI\,(\mu, \tau)}{d\tau} = -I(\mu, \tau) + \frac{1}{2\beta}\int_{-1}^{+1} I(\mu', \tau)S^*(\mu', \mu)\,d\mu' + \frac{\kappa}{\beta}I_{b\nu}(\tau) \qquad \text{(6-53)}$$

Recall the condition required for radiative equilibrium in such an atmosphere given by Equation (5-52).

$$\int_{-1}^{+1}\left[\mu\frac{dI\,(\mu, \tau)}{d\tau}\right]d\mu = 0 \qquad \text{(5-52)}$$

Integrating Equation (6-53) and replacing the left side of the equation by zero gives the relationship

$$\int_{-1}^{+1} -I(\mu, \tau)\, d\mu + \frac{1}{2\beta} \int_{-1}^{+1} \int_{-1}^{+1} I(\mu', \tau) S^*(\mu', \mu)\, d\mu'd\mu$$
$$+ 2\frac{\kappa}{\beta} I_{bv}(\tau) = 0 \tag{6-54}$$

By virtue of the symmetry of the scattering function, (6-54) may be rewritten as

$$2\frac{\kappa}{\beta} I_{bv}(\tau) = \int_{-1}^{+1} \left[1 - \int_{-1}^{+1} \frac{S^*(\mu', \mu)}{2\beta}\, d\mu \right] I(\mu', \tau)\, d\mu' \tag{6-55}$$

Recognizing the equality

$$\sigma = \tfrac{1}{2}\int_{-1}^{+1} S^*(\mu', \mu)\, d\mu \tag{6-56}$$

and remembering that $\beta = \sigma + \kappa$, results in rewriting Equation (6-55) in the form

$$2\frac{\kappa}{\beta} I_{bv}(\tau) = \int_{-1}^{+1} \frac{\kappa}{\beta} I(\mu', \tau)\, d\mu' \tag{6-57}$$

Thus, for the case of radiative equilibrium, the transport equation may be written as

$$\mu\frac{dI(\mu, \tau)}{d\tau} = -I(\mu', \tau) + \frac{1}{2}\int_{-1}^{+1}\left[\frac{\sigma S(\mu', \mu)}{\beta} + \frac{\kappa}{\beta} \right] I(\mu', \tau)\, d\mu' \tag{6-58}$$

It can be readily seen that for the case of isotropic scattering, the problem reduces to that of a pure absorbing and emitting medium. For the case of anisotropic scattering in an isotropic media, one may argue intuitively that the integral in Equation (6-58) represents the sum of the scattered and absorbed radiation and must therefore equal the integral of the incident radiation. The problem then again reduces to that of a pure absorbing and emitting atmosphere.

In this chapter, only one method for computing radiative heat transfer has been presented. For isotropic scattering or simple scattering functions Chandrasekhar (8) and others have presented more exact and more sophisticated approaches. A diffusion approximation presented by Chu, Churchill, and Pang (9) appears to have considerable merit, particularly for geometries other than the plane-parallel case presented above. However, the problem of reflecting boundaries remains to be solved.

The entire field of radiative heat transfer through media that scatters radiation is a very fertile and important area for continuing analytical and experimental research. It should be pointed out that there are many similarities to the problem of radiative heat transfer in a scattering media and neutron transport theory and investigators should check the literature in neutron transport theory as well as other areas of electromagnetic scattering.

PROBLEMS

1. From a handbook, find typical particle sizes of some industrial dusts and smokes. What range of particle size parameter α do these represent for thermal radiation analyses.

2. Demonstrate that $I_b(\tau_a)$ is the particular solution for the set of differential equations (6-18) for an isothermal plane-parallel atmosphere.

3. Find the net monochromatic flux at Wall 1 for a radiation wavelength of 3 microns if Wall 2 is 1 ft in distance and separated by a cloud of iron spheres 0.8 μ in diameter. The cloud is turbulent and is assumed isothermal at 500°R. There are 0.002 (lbm) (ft^{-3}) of iron particles uniformly dispersed in the stream.

    Wall 1 has a reflectance of 0.1 and a temperature of 1000°R.
    Wall 2 has a reflectance of 0.9 and a temperature of 500°R.

4. Rewrite Equation (6-28) for an isotropically scattering cloud and an incident flux of $I_0 d\omega$ having an angle of incidence of θ with the normal to the cloud.

5. Show that

$$\sigma = \tfrac{1}{2} \int_{-1}^{+1} S^*(\mu', \mu) \, d\mu$$

References

1. Van De Hulst, H. C., *Light Scattering by Small Particles*, John Wiley & Sons, Inc., New York, 1957.

2. Kerker, M., *Proceedings of the Interdisciplinary Conference on Electromagnetic Scattering*, Potsdam, N. Y., August 1962, Pergamon Press, New York, 1963.

3. Stratton, J. A., *Electromagnetic Theory*, McGraw-Hill Book Co., New York, 1941.

4. Chu, C. M., Clark, C. C., Churchill, S. W., *Tables of Angular Distribution Coefficients for Light Scattering by Spheres*, University of Michigan Press, Engineering Research Institute, Ann Arbor, Mich., 1947.

5. Deirmendjian, D., *Scattering and Polarization of Polydispersed Suspensions with Partial Absorption.* Kerker, p. 171. See above.

6. Love, T. J., and Beattie, J. F., *Experimental Determination of Thermal Radiation Scattering by Small Particles,* Aerospace Research Laboratories Report ARL 65-110, Office of Aerospace Research, United States Air Force, June 1965.

7. Love, T. J., *An Investigation of Radiant Heat Transfer in Absorbing, Emitting and Scattering Media,* Aerospace Research Laboratories Report ARL 63-3, Office of Aerospace Research, United States Air Force, January 1963.

8. Chandrasekhar, S., *Radiative Transfer,* Oxford University Press, New York, 1950; Dover Publications, Inc., New York, 1960.

9. Chu, C. M., Churchill, S. W., and Pang, S. C., *A Variable-Order Diffusion Type Approximation for Multiple Scattering.* Kerker, p. 407. See reference on the previous page.

7 Combined Radiation, Conduction and Convection

In the previous chapters, the temperature field over the region of interest was assumed to be a known function—with the exception of the problem of radiative equilibrium. In most design cases, the temperature field is not known. This distribution must be predicted on the basis of an energy balance that involves the effects of radiation, conduction, and convection.

In the evacuated enclosure problem the net radiation flux at the surface of the enclosure is actually a boundary condition for the conduction problem within the surface. In problems involving radiative transfer in partially transparent solids, the radiative transport and the conductive transport are coupled in a more complicated fashion. If the problem concerns radiative transfer in fluids, the convective effects make the problem even more complex.

It is the purpose of this chapter to discuss the formulation of some of these coupled problems. In most instances the solution of such problems involves lengthy numerical processes that will not be discussed in detail.

7-1. The Conduction Problem with Radiative Boundary Conditions

Consider first the radiative cooling of a plane slab of opaque material. The problem may be posed in terms of the one-dimensional partial-differential equation for the temperature distribution within the slab and the radiative flux at the bounding surface.

$$\frac{\partial T}{\partial t} = \frac{k}{\rho C} \frac{\partial^2 T}{\partial x^2} \tag{7-1}$$

where T = the temperature as a function of the normal distance x and the time t; k is the thermal conductivity, ρ the density, and C the specific heat of the solid. The initial and boundary conditions are

$$T(x, 0) = T_0$$

$$-k \frac{\partial T}{\partial x}\bigg|_{\substack{x=\pm L \\ \text{All } t}} = \frac{\epsilon}{1 - \epsilon} [\sigma T^4(L, t) - R(t)] \tag{7-2}$$

In (7-2), ϵ is the total emittance of the slab and $R(t)$ is the radiosity of the surface of the slab corresponding to either $+ L$ or $- L$ as a function of time. Thus, the boundary condition involves the solution of the radiative enclosure problem. When the incident radiation is zero, the problem simplifies somewhat to the expression

$$k \frac{\partial T}{\partial x}\bigg|_{x=\pm L} = \epsilon \sigma T^4(L, t) \tag{7-2a}$$

However, even in this situation the nonlinear term in the boundary condition prevents the use of the usual methods of solution.

It is of some interest to consider the dimensionless parameters of the problem above. Such parameters are useful in experimental modeling and in presentation of results of computations. By making the following substitutions into Equations (7-1) and (7-2a), the equations may be made dimensionless.

$$\theta = \frac{T}{T_0}$$

$$\xi = \frac{x}{L} \tag{7-3}$$

$$\eta = \frac{t}{t_0}$$

The Fourier number results from the substitution in Equation (7-1) and a form of the Biot number is derived from (7-2a).

$$F_0 = \frac{\alpha t_0}{L^2}, \qquad B_i = \frac{\epsilon \sigma T_0^3 L}{k} \tag{7-4}$$

In (7-4), $\alpha = (k/\rho C)$ is the thermal diffusivity. These two dimensionless numbers thus become the basis of comparison for problems involving the radiative cooling of a slab. With these substitutions, the dimensionless form of Equation (7-1) and its boundary conditions is written below.

$$\frac{\partial \theta}{\partial \eta} = F_0 \frac{\partial^2 \theta}{\partial \xi^2}$$

$$\theta(\xi, 0) = 1 \qquad \frac{\partial \theta}{\partial \xi}\Big|_{\xi = \pm 1} = B_i \theta^4$$

(7-1a)

Fairall, Wells, and Belcher (1) present some results of a numerical integration of the equation above.

7-2. The Problem of the Radiating Fin

Consider now the problem of a one-dimensional radiating fin as illustrated in Figure 7-1.

The differential equation governing the temperature distribution $T(x)$ for a steady-state condition in a fin of uniform thickness with the incident flux neglected may be written as

$$kt \frac{d^2 T}{dx^2} - 2\epsilon\sigma T^4 = 0$$

(7-5)

The boundary conditions for this problem are

$$T = T_b \qquad \text{at } x = 0$$

$$\frac{dT}{dx} = 0 \qquad \text{at } x = L$$

(7-6)

Again using the substitutions of Equation 7-3, the dimensionless par-

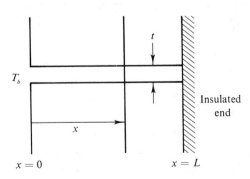

Figure 7-1.

ameter associated with the radiative fin problem may be written as

$$N = \frac{2\epsilon\sigma L^2 T_b^3}{kt} \qquad (7\text{-}7)$$

Equation (7-5) may thus be expressed utilizing this dimensionless form as

$$\frac{d^2\theta}{d\xi^2} - N\theta^4 = 0 \qquad (7\text{-}8)$$

where

$$\theta = 1 \qquad \text{at } \xi = 0$$
$$\frac{d\theta}{d\xi} = 0 \qquad \text{at } \xi = 1$$

Liu (2) has suggested the following solution for this problem. In order to integrate (7-8), multiply the equation by $d\theta/d\xi$ and rewrite the equation in the form

$$\frac{1}{2}\frac{d}{d\xi}\left(\frac{d\theta}{d\xi}\right)^2 = \frac{N}{5}\frac{d}{d\xi}\theta^5 \qquad (7\text{-}9)$$

Equation (7-9) may now be integrated directly.

$$\left(\frac{d\theta}{d\xi}\right)^2 = \frac{2N}{5}\theta^5 + C \qquad (7\text{-}10)$$

Application of the boundary condition at $\xi = 1$ gives C in terms of the unknown temperature at the end of the fin, which is designated θ_e.

The first-order equation is then integrated as follows after the variables have been separated.

$$\int_0^1 d\xi = \left(\frac{5}{2N\theta_e^5}\right)^{1/2}\int_1^{\theta_e}\frac{d\theta}{(\theta/\theta_e)^{5/2}\,[1 - (\theta_e/\theta)^5]^{1/2}} \qquad (7\text{-}11)$$

Substitution of $Z = (\theta_e/\theta)^5$ transforms the integral on the right side of the equation into a form that may be written in terms of the complete and incomplete Beta function. (See Erdélyi, *Higher Transcendental Functions* (3), p. 87.)

$$\left(\frac{2N\theta_e^5}{5}\right)^{1/2} = -\frac{\theta_e}{5}\int_{\theta_e^5}^1 Z^{-7/10}(1 - Z)^{-1/2}\,dZ \qquad (7\text{-}12)$$

In terms of the complete Beta function and the incomplete Beta function, (7-12) is thus written

$$(10N\theta_e^3)^{1/2} = B_{\theta_e^5}\left(\tfrac{3}{10}, \tfrac{1}{2}\right) - B\left(\tfrac{3}{10}, \tfrac{1}{2}\right) \qquad (7\text{-}13)$$

This transcendental equation must then be solved for θ_e. This may be computed utilizing identities and series found in Abramowitz and Stegun, (4). Reynolds (5) has tabulated values of θ_e for various values of N. The fin effectiveness, E, is equal to the ratio of the energy radiated from the fin to the energy that would be radiated if the entire fin was at a uniform temperature equal to the base temperature. Reynolds (5) also develops optimization techniques that may be utilized in fin design. MacKay (6) also provides curves and methods that may be utilized in radiative fin design.

TABLE 7-1.

Tabulation of θ_c and Thin Effectiveness

N	θ_e	E
∞	0	0
3.247	0.631	0.335
1.567	0.724	0.451
0.938	0.786	0.545
0.611	0.833	0.626
0.409	0.871	0.700
0.272	0.903	0.765
0.174	0.931	0.831
0.101	0.956	0.890
0.045	0.979	0.944
0	1.000	1.000

*Taken from Reynolds, W. C., Reference (5).

7-3.   Combined Conductive and Radiative Equilibrium

In ceramics, plastics, and other semitransparent matter, the transport of thermal energy by conduction and radiation may be of the same order of magnitude. For steady-state heat transfer through such a medium without internal heat generation, the divergence of the combined conductive and radiative net flux must equal zero.

$$\nabla \cdot (-k \operatorname{Grad} T + Q) \tag{7-14}$$

In the equation above, k is the thermal conductivity, T the local temperature, and Q the total net radiative flux. For a one-dimensional system, such as a sheet of glass or a ceramic coating, in which the thermal conductivity is assumed constant, (7-14) may be reduced to the equation

$$k\frac{d^2T}{dx^2} = \frac{dQ}{dx} \tag{7-15}$$

Utilizing Equations (5-38), Q may be expressed in the following manner.

$$Q(\tau) = 2\pi \int_0^\infty \int_0^1 \mu[I^+(\tau, \mu) - I(\tau, \mu)]\, d\mu\, d\nu \tag{7-16}$$

$$Q(\tau) = 2\pi \int_0^\infty \int_0^1 [C_1\mu e^{-(\tau/\mu)} - C_2\mu e^{(\tau-\tau_0)/\mu} + n^2 \int_0^\tau e^{(t-\tau)/\mu} I_{b\nu}(t)\, dt$$
$$-n^2 \int_\tau^{\tau_0} e^{-(t-\tau)/\mu} I_{b\nu}(t)\, dt]\, d\mu d\nu \tag{7-17}$$

Here, C_1 and C_2 must be determined from the boundary conditions. For a sheet of dielectric material with smooth surfaces, the reflection at the boundaries will be specular and C_1 and C_2 will be functions of μ in accordance with Fresnel's equations. If the surfaces are roughened, as would be the case with many ceramic materials, a diffuse reflection may be assumed, and C_1 and C_2 become constants.

Example. Consider a typical problem that involves the effect of a ceramic coating on a metal subsurface. The temperature of the metal-ceramic interface is known. The coated plate radiates freely to space. Determine the radiative flux leaving the coating surface. Neglect scattering within the coating and assume the coating to act as a gray absorber.

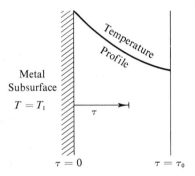

Figure 7-2.   Schematic coating problem for conductive and radiative equilibrium.

Solution. For such a system C_1 and C_2 must first be determined. It is assumed that diffuse reflections occur at both interfaces. As in Chapter 5, C_1 and C_2 are determined by the radiosities of the boundaries.

$$I^+(0, \mu) = n^2 \frac{\epsilon_1 \sigma T_1^4}{\pi} + 2\rho_1 \int_0^1 \mu I^-(0, \mu)\, d\mu$$

$$I^-(\tau_0, \mu) = 2\rho_2 \int_0^1 \mu I^+(\tau_0, \mu)\, d\mu$$

(7-18)

Substituting Equations (5-13) into Equations (7-18) give the following.

$$C_1 = \frac{n^2 \epsilon_1 \sigma T_1^4}{\pi} + 2\rho_1 \int_0^1 \left[\mu C_2 e^{-\tau_0/\mu} + \frac{n^2}{\pi} \int_0^{\tau_0} e^{-t/\mu} \sigma T(t)^4\, dt \right] d\mu$$

$$C_2 = 2\rho_2 \int_0^1 \left[\mu C_1 e^{-\tau_0/\mu} + \frac{n^2}{\pi} \int_0^{\tau_0} e^{-(t-\tau_0)/\mu} \sigma T(t)^4\, dt \right] d\mu$$

(7-19)

Collecting terms yields (7-20) on the next page.

$$C_1 = \frac{n^2 \epsilon_1 \sigma T_1^4}{\pi} + 2\rho_1 C_2 E_3(\tau_0) + \frac{2\sigma\rho_1 n^2}{\pi} \int_0^{\tau_0} T(t)^4 E_2(t)\, dt$$

$$C_2 = 2\rho_2 C_1 E_3(\tau_0) + \frac{2\sigma\rho_2 n^2}{\pi} \int_0^{\tau_0} T(t)^4 E_2(\tau_0 - t)\, dt$$

(7-20)

Now C_1 and C_2 may be determined in terms of the unknown function $T(t)^4$. For this problem, $Q(\tau)$ in Equation (7-17) may be written as

$$Q(\tau) = 2\pi C_1 E_3(\tau) - 2\pi C_2 E_3(\tau_0 - \tau)$$
$$+ 2n^2\sigma \int_0^{\tau} E_2(\tau - t)T(t)^4\, dt - 2n^2\sigma \int_{\tau}^{\tau_0} E_2(t - \tau)T(t)^4\, dt$$

(7-21)

Differentiating Equation (7-21) with respect to τ gives

$$\frac{dQ}{d\tau} = -2\pi C_1 E_2(\tau) - 2\pi C_2 E_2(\tau_0 - \tau)$$
$$+ 4n^2\sigma T(\tau)^4 - 2n^2\sigma \int_0^{\tau} E_1(\tau - t)T(t)^4\, dt$$
$$- 2n^2\sigma \int_{\tau}^{\tau_0} E_1(t - \tau)T(t)^4\, dt$$

(7-22)

Equation (7-15) may now be rewritten for this case.

$$Ka^2 \frac{d^2 T}{d\tau^2} = 4n^2\sigma T^4(\tau) - 2\left[\pi C_1 E_2(\tau) + \pi C_2 E_2(\tau_0 - \tau)\right.$$
$$\left. + n^2\sigma \int_0^{\tau_0} E_1(|t - \tau|)T^4(t)\, dt\right]$$

(7-23)

where a is the volume-absorption coefficient of the dielectric.

Viskanta and Grosh (7) have solved a problem similar to (7-23) with somewhat less complicated functions of C_1 and C_2 and for known temperatures at each interface. However, at present, the author knows of no solution for Equation (7-23). Presumably, a satisfactory solution could be obtained by a lengthy numerical procedure.

7-4. Rosseland Approximation for Optically Thick Layers

For optically thick systems a radiation diffusion model may be developed. The model visualizes the travel of a photon between successive emission and absorption in much the same manner that kinetic theory of gases refers to the free path of a molecule of gas. This analogy is frequently utilized in such diffusion approximations and an optically thick system is one in which the characteristic length is much greater than the "radiation mean free path." This diffusion approximation is named after Rosseland, an astrophysicist who first developed the analogy.

The Rosseland flux approximation is given in Equation (7-24)

$$Q = -\frac{4}{3}\sigma \frac{dT^4}{d\tau} = -\frac{16}{3}\sigma T^3 \frac{dT}{d\tau}$$

(7-24)

Cess (8) has shown this to be the limiting case for Equation (7-17) as $\tau \to \infty$.

The equation for combined radiative and conductive flux in such a system may be written as

$$Q_T = -k\frac{dT}{dx} - \frac{16\sigma T^3}{3a}\frac{dT}{dx} \qquad (7\text{-}25)$$

Noting that Q_T is equal to a constant for the combined conductive and radiative equilibrium, Equation (7-4) may be integrated directly if the temperatures of the interfaces are known.

$$Q_T = \frac{k}{x_0}(T_1 - T_2) + \frac{4\sigma}{3ax_0}(T_1^4 - T_2^4) \qquad (7\text{-}26)$$

It should be noted that Equation (7-24) makes no allowance for reflections at the interfaces. Cess (8) demonstrates that (7-26) is a good approximation when the reflection at the boundaries is negligible.

In general, the problem of combined conduction and radiation is a very difficult nonlinear problem. Only a few solutions have been published with a limited number of boundary conditions utilized. Much additional work needs to be done.

7-5.   Combined Convection and Radiation

The problem of the interaction of radiation and convection is of particular interest in the case of the high-temperature boundary layer. The starting point for the solution of such a problem must begin with the expression for the energy transport equation. Equation (7-27) is presented essentially as developed by Schlichting (9).

$$\rho C_p \frac{DT}{Dt} = \beta T \frac{Dp}{Dt} + \nabla \cdot (k\nabla T) + \mu\Phi - \nabla \cdot Q \qquad (7\text{-}27)$$

In this equation, ρ is the fluid density, C_p the specific heat of the fluid. The operator D/Dt is the substantial derivative, T is the temperature, β is the coefficient of thermal expansion, p is the pressure, k is the thermal conductivity of the fluid, μ is the viscosity of the fluid, Φ is the viscous dissipation term, and Q is the net radiative flux vector.

For an incompressible boundary layer without viscous dissipation, (7-27) may be reduced to the form

$$\rho C_p\left(u\frac{\partial T}{\partial x} + v\frac{\partial T}{\partial y}\right) = k\frac{\partial^2 T}{\partial y^2} - \frac{\partial Q_y}{\partial y} \qquad (7\text{-}28)$$

In Expression (7-28), u is the x component of the velocity vector and v is the y component; Q_y is the total net radiative flux perpendicular to the plate. It should be noted that the change in the x component of the radiative flux is neglected. This assumption follows for an isothermal plate. For some instances, particularly with high-speed flow $\partial Q_x/\partial_x$ may not be neglected.

Equation (7-28) may be expressed in integral form as

$$\rho C_p \frac{d}{dx} \int_0^{\delta_t} [u(T - T_\infty)]\, dy = -k \left(\frac{\partial T}{\partial y}\right)_{y=0} + (Q_y)_{y=0} - (Q_y)_{y=\delta_T} \quad (7\text{-}29)$$

where δ_T is the thermal boundary-layer thickness and $(Q_y)_{y=0}$ and $(Q_y)_{y=\delta_T}$ are given by integrating Equations (5-42) over all wavelengths. Of course, in order to determine Q, the temperature profile must be known. It can be demonstrated that the net radiative flux at the wall and at the outer edge of the thermal boundary layer are relatively insensitive to the exact shape of the temperature profile. Thus, as in the case of purely convective transfer, a profile may be assumed and the left-hand side of the equation may be integrated with respect to y. A method developed by H. B. Squire is presented in *Boundary Layer Theory*, Schlicting (9), p. 321.

The following polynomial profiles are assumed.

$$\begin{aligned} u &= U_\infty (2\eta - 2\eta^3 + \eta^4) \\ T - T_\infty &= (T_w - T_\infty)(1 - 2\eta_T + 2\eta_T^3 - \eta_T^4) \end{aligned} \quad (7\text{-}30)$$

where $\eta = y/\delta$, and $\eta_T = y/\delta_T$. Also, δ is the momentum boundary-layer thickness and δ_T the thermal boundary-layer thickness.

The effect of radiation is to increase the thermal boundary-layer thickness, and hence for gases with a Prandtl number less than one, the thermal boundary-layer thickness is greater than the momentum boundary layer. Substitution of (7-30) into (7-29) gives the expression

$$\rho C_p \frac{d}{dx} [(\delta_T)(U_\infty)(T_w - T_\infty)(H)] = 2 \frac{k}{\delta_T}(T_\omega - T_\infty) + Q(0) - Q(\delta_T) \quad (7\text{-}31)$$

where

$$H = \frac{3}{10} - \frac{3}{10}\frac{\delta}{\delta_T} + \frac{2}{15}\left(\frac{\delta}{\delta_T}\right)^2 - \frac{3}{140}\left(\frac{\delta}{\delta_T}\right)^4 + \frac{1}{180}\left(\frac{\delta}{\delta_T}\right)^5$$

The momentum boundary-layer thickness δ may be determined at any x from the momentum and continuity equations. Equation (7-31) is thus one equation with a single unknown δ_T. The determination of δ_T along the boundary layer may be determined by a trial and error procedure utilizing a numerical integration along the boundary. It should be noted that the numerical integration of Equations (5-42) requires the knowledge of the radiative property of the gas and the value of δ_T. Equation (7-31) is rewritten below in terms of the finite difference equation that must be solved point by point along the boundary.

$$\rho C_p \left[\delta_T U_\infty H(T_w - T_\infty) \right]_{x_i}^{x_i + \Delta x}$$
$$= \left[2 \frac{k}{\delta_T} (T_\omega - T_\infty) + Q(0) - Q(\delta_T) \right]_{x_i + (\Delta x/2)} \Delta x \tag{7-32}$$

The solution of (7-32) requires the use of a high-speed digital computer. The computation starts at $x = 0$. A trial and error procedure is choosing a δ_T and computing the left- and right-hand sides of the above equation, then repeating until the two values are within an acceptable error. This must then be repeated for each Δx increment along the boundary layer.

The advantage of the foregoing procedure is that it provides an opportunity to take into account the radiative properties of the gas. It may also be utilized with various geometries. The obvious disadvantage is the comparatively large amount of computer time required.

Viskanta (11), (12), Cess (8), (10), and others have studied the problem of boundary-layer radiation. Their approach has been to simplify the radiation term through a gray-gas approximation and to develop similarity transformations for the differential equation by reducing the equations to ordinary differential equations that are then integrated numerically.

Olfe and Zakkay (13) gives a good summary of the studies that were made prior to 1964 in the area of radiative heat transfer problems in hypersonic flow. It is beyond the scope of our book to elaborate on this complex problem. A considerable amount of work has been done in this area but much more work, both analytical and experimental, is needed.

PROBLEMS

1.   Develop a possible linear approximation for boundary condition (7-2a) that will permit a bounding solution for unsteady conduction problem 7-1, valid for small time. Is your solution an upper or lower limit for the nonlinear solution?

2.   Calculate the heat transfer from an aluminum fin radiating freely to space. The fin has a base temperature of $1000°R$, a total hemispherical emittance of 0.6, a thickness of 0.05 in. and extends 3 in. from its base.

3.   The radiative flux leaving a coating that is transmitting energy by conduction and radiation may be expressed in terms of the net radiative flux at $\tau = \tau_0$. Write the expression for this flux, simplifying where possible.

4.   Derive the energy equation for Couette flow with radiative transfer, utilizing the Rosseland approximation for the radiative term.

References

1. Fairall, R. S., Wells, R. A., and Belcher, R. L., "Unsteady-State Heat Transfer in Solids with Radiation at One Boundary, *Journal of Heat Transfer*, Vol. 84, Series C, No. 3 (August 1962), p. 266.

2. Liu, Chen-Ya, "On Minimum Weight Rectangular Fins," *Journal of the Aerospace Science*, Vol. 27 (November 1960), p. 871.

3. Erdélyi, Magnus, Oberhettinger, Tricomi, *Higher Transcendental Functions*, Vol. 1, McGraw-Hill Book Company, New York, 1953.

4. Abramowitz, M., and Stegun, I. A., *Handbook of Mathematical Functions*, National Bureau of Standards Applied Mathematics Series, No. 55, June 1964.

5. Reynolds, W. C., "A Design-Oriented Optimization of Simple Tapered Radiating Fins," *Journal of Heat Transfer*, Vol. 82, Series C, No. 3 (August 1960), p. 193.

6. Mackay, D. B., *Design of Space Powerplants*, Prentice-Hall Inc., Englewood Cliffs, New Jersey, 1963

7. Viskanta, R., and Grosh, R. J., "Heat Transfer by Simultaneous Conduction and Radiation in an Absorbing Medium," *Journal of Heat Transfer*, Vol. 84, Series C, No. 1 (February 1962), p. 63.

8. Cess, R. D., *The Interaction of Thermal Radiation with Conduction and Convection Heat Transfer*, Advances in Heat Transfer, Vol. 1, Academic Press, New York, 1964.

9. Schlichting, Hermann, *Boundary Layer Theory*, McGraw-Hill Book Company, 4th ed., New York, 1960.

10. Cess, R. D., "Radiation Effects Upon Boundary Layer Flow of an Absorbing Gas," *Journal of Heat Transfer*, Vol. 86, Series C, No. 4 (November 1964), p. 469.

11. Viskanta, R., *Heat Transfer in Thermal Radiation Absorbing and Scattering Media*, Argonne National Laboratory Report ANL-6170, May 1960.

12. Viskanta, R., and Grosh, R. J., "Boundary Layer in Thermal Radiation Absorbing and Emitting Media," *International Journal of Heat and Mass Transfer*, Vol. 5, (1962), p. 795.

13. Olfe, D. B., and Zakkay, V., *Supersonic Flow Chemical Processes and Radiative Transfer*, The MacMillan Comany, New York, (1964).

8 Experimental Methods

The accuracy of any prediction of radiative heat transfer must depend on a knowledge of the radiative properties of the matter involved in the energy exchange. It was pointed out in Chapter 3 that for most surfaces, the complications or surface roughness and contamination require an experimental determination of the radiative properties. Although the reflection function is required to completely describe the radiative characteristics of a surface, it is, in general, too complicated for practical use. The properties that are usually measured are total hemispherical emittance or reflectance by the measurement either of the reflection, of a diffuse incident flux into a specific direction, or of the total reflection of an incident flux. The α/ϵ of surfaces is also frequently determined directly by experiment.

The experimental methods utilized for surface properties may be classified in two general categories: calorimetric methods and optical methods. Most of the important techniques have been discussed in some detail in Clauss (1), Blau and Fisher (2), Richmond (3), and Katzoff (4). These references are to the proceedings of symposia held specifically to discuss measurement of radiative properties of surfaces and the effects of the space environment. In general, meaningful measurement of surface radiation properties is difficult and little progress has been made toward standardized techniques.

Before discussing in detail the various methods, it is desirable to first examine the basic components utilized in radiative property measurements.

The importance of infrared and optical instrumentation to various military applications such as IR photography for reconnaissance, IR scopes for surveillance, and IR tracking of missiles, as well as interest in astronomical observations and the well-developed fields of spectroscopy in physics and chemistry, has led to significant developments. The basic components of any experimental apparatus for radiative property determination may be similar to instruments developed in the aforementioned fields. Smith, Jones, and Chasmar (5), and Kruse, McGlauchlin, and McQuistan (6) are two of several excellent works dealing with infrared techniques.

8-1. Radiation Sources

The Hohlraum (heated cavity). The standard source for thermal radiation measurements is an isothermal cavity. A small aperture allows the radiation to be emitted from the cavity without disturbing the radiation field inside. The radiation leaving the opening will correspond to the emission of a black body at the temperature of the enclosure. Such an enclosure is normally constructed from a heavy metal block that is heated electrically. The exterior is well insulated and the interior is roughened and allowed to oxidize to provide a nearly diffuse surface of high emittance. Such a body is shown schematically in Figure 8-1.

Because the radiation from the cavity is very nearly black, such a cavity is normally used as a radiation standard. The main disadvantages of the hohlraum are listed at the top of the next page.

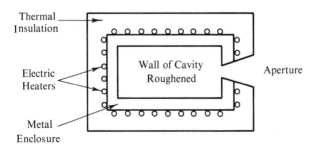

Figure 8-1.   Schematic of heated cavity.

1. The temperature limitation of the metal walls limits the power output, particularly at short wavelengths.
2. The cavity is usually large, bulky, and difficult to maintain at a uniform desired temperature.

The Globar. A very practical source that is widely used in spectroscopy is the silicon carbide rod. An electric current is passed through the rod from water-cooled terminals at either end of it. The rod is about $\frac{1}{4}$ in. in diameter and about 2 in. in length. The life of the globar depends on the temperature at which it is operated. It will operate at temperatures up to 2400°R.

The emittance of the globar is approximately constant over a wide spectral range. The emittance, however, will vary to some extent between rods and with the age and surface condition of the globar. In general, the globar would be used in exprimental procedures in which relative measurements are being made (in other words, when a transmitted or reflected flux is compared with the incident flux). However, the emittance of the globar changes slowly and normally, and will not change significantly during the course of an experiment. Voltage fluctuations will directly affect the output power and should be guarded against.

Tungsten Filament Lamp. The tungsten filament lamp may be used for higher power outputs at shorter wavelengths than the globar. The glass envelope, however, limits the wavelength to less than 3 μ because of the glass envelope filtering out the longer wavelengths.

Other sources that have been used include the Nernst glower, consisting of an electrically-heated tube of zirconium and yttrium oxides, carbon rods, and carbon arcs. The Welsbach mantel, similar to the gasoline lantern or gas light, has also been used.

The Laser provides an essentially monochromatic, monodirectional flux of very high intensity. The primary drawbacks to the Laser, in addition to its high cost, are the limited number of wavelengths at which any one Laser can operate. Mercury vapor lamps and other metallic vapor arcs have been used for radiation sources at the short wavelengths. In general, these sources do not furnish a continuous spectrum but radiate in certain narrow bands characteristic of the atomic structure of the vapor.

8-2.   Windows, Prisms, and Mirrors

In most experiments, windows are required to shield the detector from convective currents, to contain a sample of gas, or to, in some way, isolate a portion of the experiment. Window materials are selected on the basis of spectral transmission characteristics, structural properties, and affinity for water vapor. For some special cases the effects of temperature and other adverse conditions must be considered.

Smith, Jones, and Chasmar (5) list the following choices for window materials from 1 to 2 mm thick on the grounds of high transparency combined with mechanical strength and resistance to deterioration by the atmosphere.

Materials	For Wavelengths
1. Pyrex-type glass	$\leq 2.5\mu$
2. Quartz	$\leq 4.0\mu$
3. Sapphire	$\leq 5.5\mu$
4. Periklase	$\leq 9.5\mu$
5. Fluorite	$\leq 11\mu$
6. Diamond (Type II)	$> 11\mu$
7. Polyethylene	$> 100\mu$

In addition, rocksalt is a widely used material because of its relatively low cost and good transmission characteristics out to about 15μ. Sodium chloride, however, is very hygroscopic and special care must be taken to avoid moisture.

Prisms are utilized for the purpose of separating a beam of radiation into a spectral band. They are utilized in obtaining essentially monochromatic radiation in monochromators and spectrometers. Filters and gratings are also utilized for this purpose. The materials suitable for prism

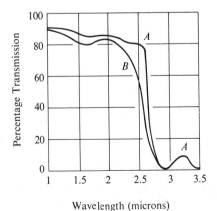

Wavelength (microns)

Figure 8-2.   Transmission of crown and flint glass. *A,* transmission of crown glass 3 mm thick. *B,* transmission of flint glass 3 mm thick. Smith, Jones, and Chasmar (5).

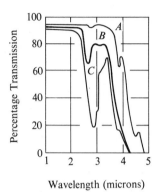

Figure 8-3.   Transmission curves of fused and crystalline quartz. A, fused quartz 0.25 cm thick. B, fused quartz 1.0 cm thick. C, natural quartz (ordinary ray) 1.0 cm thick. Smith, Jones, and Chasmar (5).

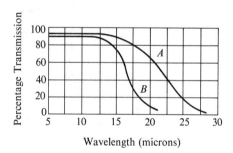

Figure 8-4.   Transmission of rocksalt. Sample A, 1 mm thick. Sample B, 1 cm thick. Smith, Jones, and Chasmar (5).

use must be transparent, and consideration must be given to the dispersive property of the material. In general, the window materials given above are also suitable for prisms (for wavelengths in which the transmission is high). The two most widely used prism materials in radiative heat-transfer applications are probably fused quartz for wavelengths below 2μ, and rocksalt for wavelengths from 2μ out to 15μ. The NaCl is hygroscopic and must be protected from moisture while in use and stored in a sealed jar with a desicant while not in use.

Mirrors are normally utilized for focusing and collimating of infrared

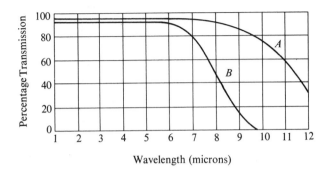

Wavelength (microns)

Figure 8-5. Transmission of CaF$_2$. Sample A, 1 mm thick. Sample B, 1 cm thick. Smith, Jones, and Chasmar (5).

radiation. These mirrors are front surface mirrors of ground glass with a vacuum-deposited metal-reflecting surface. Aluminum and silver are the most widely used metals. Respectively, they reflect 94 and 97 per cent of the incident energy. These mirrors are commercially available from various optical manufacturing firms. Special care must be taken to avoid contact with the reflecting surface of the mirrors. Cleaning may be accomplished by pouring undenatured ethyl alcohol over the surface of the mirrors and allowing the alcohol to drain and evaporate naturally.

The use of mirrors in directing and concentrating radiant energy in radiative property measurement apparatus may be planned using geomet-

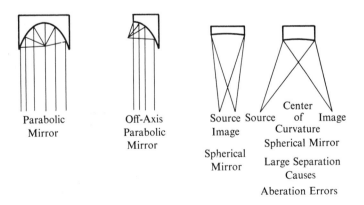

Figure 8-6. Example of mirror optics.

rical optics. Plane mirrors are utilized for changing the direction of the radiation. Parabolic mirrors are used for collimating radiation or for concentrating energy from a distant source. Spherical mirrors are generally inexpensive and may be used for focusing radiation from a small source onto a detector. However, care must be taken to avoid large angular separation that causes aberration and, subsequently, possible error in energy accounting. Figure 8-6 illustrates the geometrical optics for each of these cases.

8-3.　Detectors

Detectors for thermal radiation fall in three general categories:

1. Thermal elements in which a measurement of temperature corresponds to the amount of absorbed flux.
2. The semiconductor detectors that undergo a radical change in electrical conductivity when subjected to an incident flux.
3. The photocell that depends on the photoelectric effect at a metal surface.

The thermal detectors are generally more sensitive in the long wavelength regions beyond approximately 2μ. The semiconductors are normally used in the intermediate wavelength range of $1–2\mu$, and the photocell is utilized in the visible and shorter-wavelength regions.

The thermocouple or thermopile detector, shown in Figure 8-7, is probably the most widely used of the thermal detectors. The detector consists essentially of an enclosure with a window that admits the radiation on a target. This target is usually a blackened gold foil leaf. One junction of the

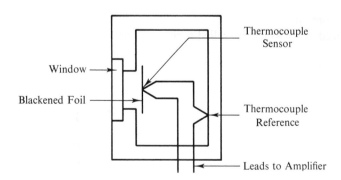

Figure 8-7.　Schematic diagram of a thermocouple radiation detector.

thermocouple circuit is attached to the leaf and the other is located in the enclosure in a position shielded from the radiation and attached to a "heat sink." The thermocouple voltage output is then amplified to give a reading of the temperature difference between the target and ambient temperature. In some cases, more than one set of thermocouple junctions are used in series. This increases the output signal, but because the signal-to-noise ratio is not improved, this does not increase the minimum detectable signal.

The bolometer is a similar device in which the electrical resistance of the thermal element is an indication of the absorbed flux. It consists of an electrical bridge circuit that contains two platinum strips of nearly equal resistance. One of the strips is blackened and receives the incident flux. The other is shielded from the radiation and a balance of the bridge circuit indicates the heating of the element receiving the radiation. Bolometers may also be constructed by utilizing thermistors or semiconducting elements. Cryogenic cooling may also be utilized. Its advantages are noise reduction and improved sensitivity.

In order to supply an alternating signal that can be easily amplified, the radiation incident on the thermal detector is often "chopped." That is, the beam is interrupted at a regular frequency by a rotating shutter. The fluctuating response of the detector is then amplified, and the amplified signal is usually rectified and then supplied to the output meter or recorder.

A semiconductor detector may be visualized as a material in which the annihilation of the incident photons produces free electrons or free "hole," or both, in the material. If the signal-detection mechanism is based upon measuring the conductivity change in the material, it is known as a *photoconductive effect*. If the photon annihilation imparts enough energy to the electrons to excite them to a higher energy level so that they make a quantum jump over a potential barrier in the material, a voltage is produced. This would be called a *photovoltaic effect*.

Lead sulphide, P_bS, is widely used as a semiconductor detection element and is used out to wavelengths of 3μ. It is generally used as a photoconductive detector.

For visible and shorter wavelengths, the photomultiplier is normally utilized. In the photomultiplier, when a photon impinges on a metal target, it emits an electron into the surrounding vacuum. These electrons are accelerated by an electric potential onto secondary emitting stages where a single incident electron will cause the emission of several electrons which in turn cascade to a third surface. In such a manner the photoeffect is multiplied and very small fluxes may be detected.

It is sometimes necessary to change optics and detectors in the course of an experiment where radiation is to be measured over a wide range of wavelengths. The summary above is intended to be only a brief introduction. Investigators planning experiments should consult Smith, Jones, and Chasmar (5), and Kruse, McGlauchlin, and McQuistan (6) as well as other similar sources for detailed information. Manufacturers of optical, infrared, and spectrometer equipment should be consulted for availability and comparative prices.

8-4.   Monochromators

The purpose of the monochromator is to separate a beam of radiation into its spectral components. This may be accomplished with instruments utilizing prisms, gratings, interference mechanisms, or filters. For work involving property determinations in radiative heat transfer, the prism type instruments have been most widely used. Figure 8-8 gives a schematic drawing of a prism monochromator. This particular schematic is of one type of the several monochromators manufactured by the Perkin-Elmer Corporation.

In Figure 8-8, the beam of radiation to be analyzed enters the instrument through the window and adjustable slit $S1$. This beam is usually focused on the slit by external mirrors. The entering radiation is collimated by an off-axis parabolic mirror $M1$ through the prism PR onto a plane mirror $M2$. The beam is reflected back through the prism and focused by $M1$ onto the exit slit $S2$ after undergoing a change of direction in mirror $M5$. The energy may then exit the monochromator through the window or may be redirected along the alternate path onto a detector that is integral to the instrument.

Mirror $M2$ is called a *Littrow mirror*. It pivots at one edge and its position is controlled by the micrometer hand setting MW. The position of the Littrow mirror determines which part of the spectrum, created by the prism refraction, exits the instrument and is detected. The micrometer adjustment MS provides a means of varying the width of the slit $S1$. A wider slit provides for more energy on the detector, but also reduces the resolution (that is, it allows a wider spectral range to be incident on the detector).

The wavelength settings must be calibrated each time a prism is changed or the instrument is moved. This should also be checked periodically during normal use. Calibration is accomplished by passing the incoming beam through various media with known, well-defined, absorption spectra. The dial setting of MW is noted as the detector senses the absorption peak. A plot is made of the dial readings versus wavelength for a calibration curve.

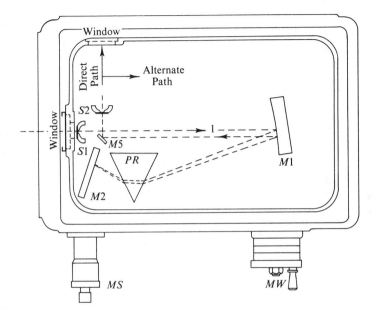

Figure 8-8. Schematic diagrams of a Perkin-Elmer prism monochromator.

8-5. Calorimetric Property Measurements

The measurement of total hemispherical emittance of surfaces is normally accomplished by calorimetric methods. Best (7) presented a method that has also been discussed in Clauss (1). A small metal sphere is suspended in a large, blackened, hollow sphere. The container is immersed in a cold bath and evacuated to about 10^{-5} torr. The small metal sphere is then heated by an internal electric heater. The power consumed is measured, and thermocouples measure the sphere temperatures.

Such an apparatus may be classified as a steady-state device. It is generally suitable for use in determining emittance of metal surfaces, although it may be very difficult to obtain a spherical surface identical to a rolled-sheet metal surface. The apparatus may be used to study coatings of paint applied to metal surfaces and is perhaps more practical for this type application. Figure 8-9 is a schematic illustration of such an apparatus.

A transient calorimetric apparatus has been developed by Wood and Coffin (8). A diagram of this is shown in Figure 8-10. In this apparatus

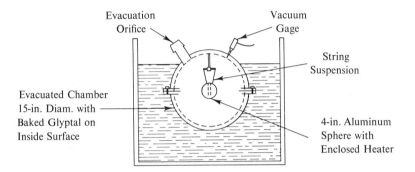

Figure 8-9.   Diagram of a steady-state calorimetric apparatus for emittance determinations.

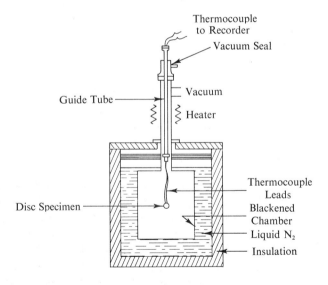

Figure 8-10.   Transient, calorimetric apparatus for hemispherical total-emittance measurements. See Wood and Coffin (8).

the specimen is a disc supported only by thermocouple leads. The procedure is to suspend the specimen in a guide tube in a heated region above a blackened chamber that is cooled with liquid nitrogen.

The hot specimen is then dropped into the cooled chamber below and allowed to cool by radiation. The temperature of the specimen is recorded as a function of time. Utilizing the known heat capacity of the specimen, the hemispherical total emittance may then be computed as a function of specimen temperature.

A third type of calorimetric device is utilized in the direct determination of α/ϵ ratios. Such a device is illustrated in Figure 8-11. The specimen is suspended in front of a window in an evacuated container that is cooled by liquid nitrogen or other means. A solar simulator irradiates the specimen through the window and the resulting equilibrium temperature is measured. Gaumer and Stewart discuss this technique in Richmond (3), *Measurement of Thermal Radiation Properties of Solids*, p. 127.

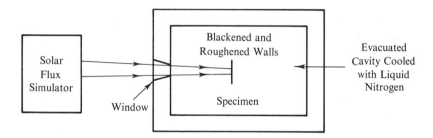

Figure 8-11.   A schematic diagram of apparatus for α/ϵ determination.

There are a number of errors that must be considered in calorimetric determinations. A detailed discussion of these errors is given by Nelson and Bevans in Richmond (3), p. 55. The errors consist of

1. Errors in temperature of the sample. This is especially a problem in a specimen having a low thermal conductivity with a subsequent variation in temperature over the specimen surface.
2. Possible reflections of the specimen back onto itself. Usually this may be minimized by making sure that walls of the cavity are roughened and have a much larger area than the specimen.
3. Conduction of heat by power leads and thermocouple leads serves as a loss of energy that is difficult to predict.
4. The edges of a sample will usually differ from the major surface being investigated. This is an additional error source.
5. The convection of heat from the surface by free molecule flow may be significant if the vacuum in the chamber is not sufficient.
6. Errors in the electric heater power measurements are difficult to

eliminate since lead size is usually minimized to reduce heat conduction loss. Power fluctuations naturally complicate the measurements.

7. There are, of course, errors that arise from sample size determinations and the preparation of the sample surface to assure duplication of the material to be used in an engineering application.

8-6. Direct Measurement of Directional Emittance

The direct measurement of normal emittance of metals and coated-metal surfaces at higher than room temperatures has been made by Richmond in Clauss, *First Symposium—Surface Effects on Spacecraft Materials* (1), p. 182. These measurements are accomplished by mounting a black-body furnace and the electrically-heated specimen on a lathe bed. A spherical mirror and a plane mirror are utilized to focus the flux from the black body onto the monochromator for a reference. A plot of the emission of the black body versus wavelength is made. The traversing mechanism of the lathe bed moves the black body out of the way and moves the specimen into the viewing area. The plot of the specimen emission at the same temperature as the black body is made as a function of wavelength. The computed ratio gives the monochromatic directional emission in the direction of measurement. Figure 8-12 is a schematic diagram of the apparatus. The aperture in the shield assures the same solid angle for the flux for all measurements. Caution should be taken at lower temperatures with specimens having relatively high reflectance to eliminate the effect of the reflection of the incident flux. This may be done

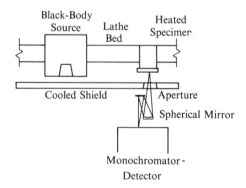

Figure 8-12. Schematic of apparatus for direct measurement of directional emittance.

by making measurements at two different specimen temperatures and holding the environment temperature constant. The assumption must be made that the emittance is the same for both measurements. The difference of the two measurements divided by the difference in the black-body intensity corresponding to the two temperatures gives the value of the emittance.

8-7. Heated-cavity Reflectometer

In many instances the temperature limitations on a specimen will prohibit the use of the direct methods described above. The heated-cavity reflectometer was developed by Gier, Dunkle, and Bevans (9) for the purpose of measuring the reflection of a diffuse incident flux. Figure 8-13 illustrates the configuration of their apparatus. The specimen is mounted on a water-cooled fixture inside an isothermal hohlraum. The specimen is cooled in order to minimize the effects of emission. The radiation leaving the specimen is viewed through the opening in the cavity by means of external optics and a monochromator with a suitable detector. This energy is compared with the energy radiation from other parts of the cavity. The intensity is assumed constant in the small solid angle viewed by the detector and is expressed in Equation 8-1.

$$[I_\nu(u, \phi)]_{\text{measured}} = \epsilon_\nu(u, \phi)I_{b\nu}(T_s)$$
$$+ \frac{1}{\pi} \int_0^{2\pi} \int_0^1 I_{b\nu}(T_e)\rho_\nu(\mu, \phi, \mu', \phi')\mu' \, d'\mu' d\phi' \quad (8\text{-}1)$$

If the temperature of the specimen T_s is small compared to the temperature of the enclosure T_e, the first term on the right may be neglected. If

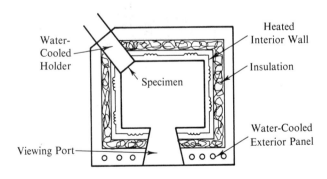

Figure 8-13. Gier-Dunkle heated-cavity reflectometer.

the emission term is significant, measurement may be taken at two different enclosure temperatures and a constant specimen temperature. This results in the two following relationships.

$$[I_v^1(\mu, \phi)]_{\text{measured}} = \epsilon_v(\mu, \phi)I_{bv}(T_s)$$
$$+ \frac{1}{\pi} \int_0^{2\pi} \int_0^1 I_{bv}'(T_{e,1})\rho_v(\mu, \phi, \mu', \phi')\mu' \, d\mu' \, d\phi'$$

$$[I_v^2(\mu, \phi)]_{\text{measured}} = \epsilon_v(\mu, \phi)I_{bv}(T_s) \tag{8-2}$$
$$+ \frac{1}{\pi} \int_0^{2\pi} \int_0^1 I_{bv}'(T_{e,2})\rho_v(\mu, \phi, \mu', \phi')\mu' \, d\mu' \, d\phi'$$

Subtracting the two Equations (8-2), eliminates the effect of specimen emission. Since the intensity incident on the specimen from inside the cavity is isotropic (except for the energy from the direction of the opening), the integral of the reflection function may be factored and the resulting expression gives the value of the integrated reflection function in terms of the measured quantities.

$$\frac{1}{\pi} \int_0^{2\pi} \int_0^1 \rho_v(\mu, \phi, \mu', \phi')\mu' \, d\mu' \, d\phi'$$
$$= \frac{I_v^1(\mu, \phi)_{\text{measured}} - I_v^2(\mu, \phi)_{\text{measured}}}{I_{bv}(T_{e,1}) - I_{bv}(T_{e,2})} \tag{8-3}$$

Application of Equation (3-6), which equates the directional emittance to the integral of the reflection function, shows that the effective result of the measurement is to give the directional emittance.

$$\epsilon_v(\mu, \phi) = 1 - \frac{I_v^1(\mu, \phi)_{\text{measured}} - I_v^2(\mu, \phi)_{\text{measured}}}{I_{bv}(T_{e,2}) - I_{bv}(T_{e,1})} \tag{8-4}$$

A correction may be made to this for the effect of the very small flux incident on the specimen from the solid angle subtended by the aperture. This correction is left as an exercise for the reader.

8-8.   Coblentz Hemispherical Reflectometer

The hemispherical reflectometer was developed by W. W. Coblentz of the National Bureau of Standards early in this century. It consists essentially of a hemispherical front surface mirror with a small aperture that provides for an incident beam of radiant energy onto a small sample located near the center of the hemisphere. The energy that is reflected from the sample strikes the surface of the mirror and is reflected back onto a detector located beside the sample. Figure 8-14 is a schematic illustration of the reflectometer.

The Coblentz hemispherical reflectometer must be calibrated using a specimen of known reflectance. It, in effect, gives the fraction of energy reflected in all directions from a ray of a given solid angle and direction

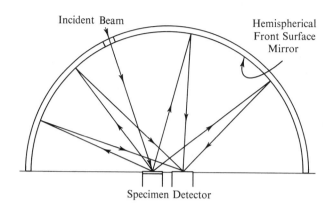

Figure 8-14. Coblentz hemispherical reflectometer.

of incidence. Errors are introduced by the aberration because the specimen and detector are displaced from the focus of the mirror. These are minimized somwhat if the specimen has the same general type of reflection function as the standard. Spectral properties are obtained by utilizing a monochromator to provide an incident beam of a narrow spectral width.

The meaning of the measurement made by the Coblentz hemisphere in terms of emittance may be examined by referring to the integration of the reflection function if the emitted energy is neglected.

Energy detected

$$= \frac{1}{\pi} \int_0^{2\pi} \int_0^1 I_v(\mu', \phi') \rho_v(\mu, \phi, \mu', \phi') \mu' \, \Delta\mu' \Delta\phi' \, \mu \, d\mu \, d\phi \qquad (8\text{-}5)$$

Dividing both sides of (8-5) by the incident flux gives the reaction

$$\frac{\text{Energy detected}}{\text{Incident flux}} = \frac{1}{\pi} \int_0^{2\pi} \int_0^1 \rho_v(\mu, \phi, \mu', \phi') \mu \, d\mu \, d\phi \qquad (8\text{-}6)$$

By application of the reciprocity law and Equation (3-6), the measurement made by the Coblentz hemisphere reduces to the following relationship in terms of emittance data.

$$\epsilon_v(\mu, \phi) = 1 - \frac{\text{Energy detected}}{\text{Incident flux}} \qquad (8\text{-}7)$$

8-9. The Integrating-hemisphere Reflectometer

Janssen and Torborg—in Richmond (3), P. 169—utilized a specularly-reflecting hemisphere similar to the Coblentz hemisphere. However, in place of the detector a surface with a near-diffuse reflectance characteristic was substituted. This diffuse surface is irradiated by a monodirectional beam. The diffuse reflection is focused onto the specimen by the hemispherical mirror. The reflection of the diffuse irradiation by the specimen is focused into a monochromator with a detector. It can be easily seen that, ideally, the resulting measurement should be the same as with the heated-cavity reflectometer since the specimen is irradiated by a diffuse incident flux. Janssen and Torborg report results in good agreement with other methods of measurement. In their method, the measurement is made relative to a standard specimen. The aberration errors and other inaccuracies inherent in the previous systems are also problems in this system.

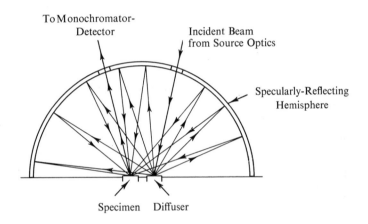

Figure 8-15.   Schematic of Janssen and Torborg's integrating hemisphere.

8-10.   The Integrating-sphere Reflectometer

The integrating-sphere reflectometer was originally devised by A. H. Taylor of the National Bureau of Standards as an instrument for the measurement of the optical reflectance of materials used in illuminating engineering. It has since been widely utilized as an instrument for reflectance measurements. The basic instrument consists of a hollow metal sphere with three openings. The openings provide for the admission of a beam of radiant energy from an external source, the specimen mounting, and a radiation detector. The interior of the sphere is coated with an optically thick layer having a diffuse and highly-reflective characteristic. Magnesium oxide or magnesium carbonate has been widely used for this application.

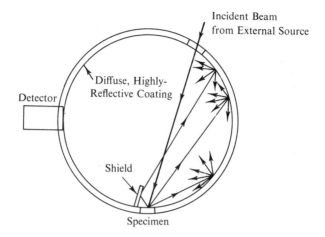

Figure 8-16. Integrating-sphere reflectometer.

The operation of the integrating-sphere reflectometer requires a calibration of the instrument with a specimen of known reflectance. The incident beam of radiation impinging on the specimen is reflected onto the walls of the sphere where it undergoes multiple reflections. The detector senses the radiosity of the walls of the sphere which should be proportional to the energy reflected in all directions by the specimen. Again, it can be shown that the measurement is proportional to $1 - \epsilon_v(\mu, \Phi)$.

The integrating-sphere reflectometer has been constructed as a portable instrument in some cases and has provided a relatively fast and simple determination of surface properties. Richmond, Dunn, Dewitt, and Hayes (10) of the National Bureau of Standards have recently utilized a Laser source with a precisely constructed sphere for accurate determination of properties.

Some of the inaccuracies inherent in the integrating-sphere reflectometer include the losses from openings in the sphere, and, perhaps a more serious problem, the degradation of the interior surface of the sphere with age. It should also be noted that the coatings are never absolutely diffuse and this also leads to a certain amount of error.

8-11. Goniometric Reflectometer

It was pointed out in Chapter 3 that the reflection function is needed for a complete specification of the radiative properties of surfaces. There are relatively few instances of such a property reported in the literature.

It was suggested in Chapter 3 that the complexity of obtaining, reporting, and utilizing such a function makes it generally impractical for the present. However, as applications dictate increasing accuracy in the prediction of radiative heat transfer, a need for more exact information will be required. It is obvious that the apparatus for such measurements has not been standardized at this point. In general, provision must be made for a complete traverse of the detector over the hemisphere bounded by the plane of the specimen surface for each orientation of the incident beam over the same hemisphere. In such measurements special care must be taken to properly account for the solid angles of the incident and detected fluxes and the specimen areas illuminated and observed at the detector. Special caution must also be taken to minimize aberration errors that may become very significant in this type of measurement.

8-12.   Measurement of Gas-absorption Coefficient

The measurement of the absorption coefficient of gases may be made with the use of an absorption cell. Special problems may exist in the selection of the window and mirror materials for these cells. Most of the cells that are commercially available are primarily used for spectroscopic observation of absorption lines for the purpose of identification of various

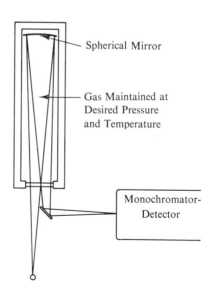

Figure 8-17.   Schematic of gas-absorption cell.

components. The heat transfer specialist is usually interested in obtaining a mass-absorption coefficient or volume-absorption coefficient for a gas at various pressures and temperatures. Provisions must thus be made for maintaining the gas at a constant temperature and pressure. One type of gas-absorption cell is a long cylinder with a window in one end and a front surface spherical mirror in the other. The radius of curvature of the mirror should be longer than the cell so that the focal point is sufficiently outside the cell to permit a convenient optical arrangement. A calibration measurement should be made with the cell evacuated. If the gas temperature is such that emission may be neglected, the optical path length of the beam is determined by taking the logarithm of the ratio of the flux reading with the gas in the cell and with the cell evacuated.

With the determination of the optical path, the mass-absorption coefficient may then be determined from the dimensions of the cell and density of the gas.

8-13.   Measurement of Flame Parameters

The determination of the volume emission of flames J_v and the absorption coefficient requires two measurements. The radiation from the flame is first focused onto the monochromator-detector system. The radiation from a source brighter than the flame is then focused on the monochromator-detector through the flame. These two measurements provide a means of obtaining the required parameters as shown in the following analysis. The transport equation, (5-5), may be integrated along the axis of the optical system that is focused on the monochromator.

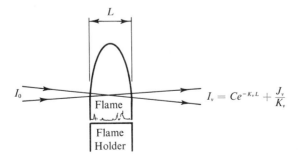

$$I_v = Ce^{-K_v L} + \frac{J_v}{K_v}$$

Figure 8-18.   Diagram of flame geometry for parameter measurements.

The integral of Equation (5-5) gives the intensity leaving the flame and may be expressed as Equation (8-8).

$$\frac{dI_\nu}{dx} = -k_\nu I_\nu + J_\nu \tag{5-5}$$

$$I_\nu = Ce^{-k_\nu L} + \frac{J_\nu}{k_\nu} \tag{8-8}$$

where L is the thickness of the flame and C is the constant of integration. For the flame alone, I_0 is zero, and for the observation with the external source, I_0 is the source intensity. The resulting equations for each condition are shown in (8-9).

$$I_\nu \text{ (flame only)} = \frac{J_\nu}{k_\nu}(1 - e^{-k_\nu L})$$

$$I_\nu \text{ (source attenuated by flame)} = I_0 e^{-k_\nu L} + \frac{J_\nu}{k_\nu}(1 - e^{-k_\nu L}) \tag{8-9}$$

The two measurements represented by the left of Equations (8-9) thus provide information that permits these equations to be solved for k_ν and J_ν.

A schematic plan for the optical layout for these determinations is shown in Figure 8-19. The flame that burns on the flame holder must be protected from stray air currents during the testing.

An apparatus of this type has been developed by Hood (11). Details of the construction and flame parameters for a number of different fuels are presented in his doctoral dissertation.

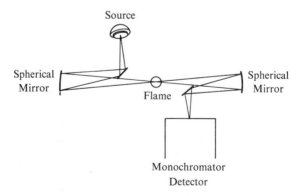

Source

Spherical Mirror

Flame

Spherical Mirror

Monochromator
Detector

Figure 8-19.   Schematic plan of apparatus for flame parameter measurements.

8-14.   Measurement of Scattering Parameters

The extinction coefficient and the angular distribution of scattered energy for dusts may be measured utilizing a cloud generator, source optics that rotate around the cloud, collecting optics, and a monochromator-detector system. The cloud generator must be designed to disperse the particles uniformly into an air stream that flows vertically through an open region for observation. Then the particle stream is collected in a vacuum system, and the particle cloud density is determined by taking weight samples for measured time intervals and is computed based on the particle stream size and velocity. A radiation source is mounted so that it may rotate around the column of dust. The radiation scattered by the dust particles is collected by a spherical mirror and focused onto the mono-chromator-detector.

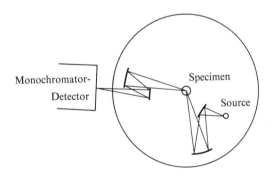

Figure 8-20.   Schematic of apparatus for measurement of scattering parameters.

The particle cloud must have an optical thickness of less than 0.1 in order to provide single scattering data. Special care must be taken to avoid reflections from surrounding objects from entering the monochromator. The device is also limited to measurements at angles at least 10° away from the 0° or 180° directions because of the optical system. More detailed information on a device of this type is given in Love and Wheasler (12), and Love and Beattie (13).

8-15.   Optical Pyrometry

Although the optical pyrometer is not basically involved in radiative property measurements, it does use the radiation emitted by a surface as a means of surface temperature determination. Thus, it seems appropriate to discuss briefly the operating principles of these devices.

A schematic of an optical pyrometer is shown in Figure 8-21. The radiant energy from the surface is focused onto the eye piece through a red filter that permits wavelengths of about 0.65μ to 0.665μ to be transmitted. Superimposed on the field of view is a tungsten filament lamp. The lamp power is adjusted until it is the same brightness as the surface under observation. At the red wavelength, the Planck function for the intensity of the radiating surface is given as

$$\epsilon_\lambda I_{b,\lambda}(T) \approx \epsilon_\lambda \lambda^{-5} e^{-C/\lambda T} \qquad (8\text{-}10)$$

where ϵ_λ is the spectral normal emittance of the surface. The emittance for the tungsten filament is very nearly one at this wavelength. When the lamp temperature is adjusted so that the filament disappears, the two intensities are equal and the following equality holds.

$$\epsilon_\lambda \lambda^{-5} e^{-C/\lambda T} = \lambda^{-5} e^{-C/\lambda T_L} \qquad (8\text{-}11)$$

In this equation, T_L is the known temperature of the lamp. Equation (8-11) reduces to

$$\frac{1}{T} = \frac{1}{T_L} - \frac{\lambda}{C} \ln \epsilon_\lambda \qquad (8\text{-}12)$$

It can be seen from Equation (8-12) that as $\epsilon_\lambda \to 1$, the lamp temperature more closely represents the surface temperature. For this reason, an observation of a groove or hole in the surface will usually give a more accurate temperature reading.

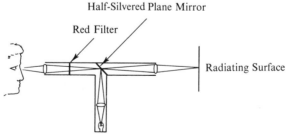

Half-Silvered Plane Mirror

Red Filter

Radiating Surface

Tungsten Filament Lamp with
Adjustable Power Input

Figure 8-21.   Schematic of an optical pyrometer.

8-16.   Radiometers

While the radiometer is an instrument that has already been discussed in Section 8(c) as a radiation detector, there are certain aspects that appear worthy of separate discussion. The most common type of radiometer used in detecting total radiation flux has a relatively large thermopile-detecting element. The radiation is admitted to the detector through a quartz window. The radiometer is usually calibrated at the factory using a blackbody source and relating millivolts output to the known diffuse incident flux. Care must be taken in the measurement of nongray radiative flux and in the measurement of directional flux so that the reflection and transmission characteristics of the radiometer window and the absorption of the hot junction do not invalidate the calibration.

8-17.   General Comments on Experimentation

There is still a great need for work to develop meaningful property measurements of surfaces, as well as gases, dusts, and other matter forms. There is also a need for experiments that can verify methods of radiative heat-transfer predictions. Although there has been considerable work in testing full-scale spacecraft and satellites in huge vacuum chambers with cryogenically cooled walls, little has been reported in the way of experiments with simple geometric relations. At the time of this writing, radiative heat transfer is still largely a theoretical and highly speculative subject. Computation is complicated but valid and meaninfgul experiments are even more difficult and expensive to perform.

PROBLEMS

1.   Based on the relations developed in Chapter 3, show that a measurement of $\epsilon_v(\mu, \Phi)$ may be used to determine the reflection of a perfectly-diffuse incident flux, but may not be used to accurately describe the reflection of a flux having other distributions.

2.   If the interior of a hohlraum is perfectly diffuse, but has a reflectance of ρ, derive an expression for the effective emittance based on the inside surface area and the opening area.

3.   Compute the per cent of normal incident energy transmitted through a window of crown glass 3 mm thick. Assume the frequency distribution of the energy to correspond to black radiation characterized by a temperature of 1500°F.

4. In a device for the calorimetric determination of the hemispherical total emittance, the flat disc-shaped specimen is suspended parallel to a flat specularly-reflecting wall. Derive an expression for the flux incident on the specimen as a result of its own reflection in the calorimeter wall.

5. Derive an expression for the α/ϵ ratio for a specimen subjected to test in an apparatus similar to that shown in Figure 8-11. What assumptions must be made? What factors do you think will influence the accuracy of the determination?

6. Explain why it would be impossible to obtain the equivalent of normal emittance from a polished specimen in a heated-cavity reflectometer.

7. Write an expression for the approximate error introduced in the directional emittance determined by the heated-cavity reflectometer resulting from the essentially negligible flux incident on the specimen from the solid angle subtended by the viewing port.

8. Consider an integrating sphere of radius R with a diffuse specimen having a diameter of d. Derive an exact expression based on an integral equation solution developed in Chapter 4 for the irradiation incident on the walls of the sphere. Present an argument, based on the result above, for a specimen of arbitrary reflection function; the irradiation of the interior of the sphere will vary only in the amount of the radiation incident directly from the specimen.

9. Write out the expressions that would be used to determine the absorption coefficient for a gas from the measurements taken using the gas-absorption cell. Account for the attenuation of the radiation through the windows.

References

1. Clauss, F. J., *First Symposium-Surface Effects on Spacecraft Materials*, John Wiley and Sons, Inc., New York, 1960.

2. Blau, H., and Fischer, H., *Radiative Transfer from Solid Materials*, McMillan Company, New York, 1962.

3. Richmond, J. C., *Measurement of Thermal Radiation Properties of Solids*, NASA Sp. 31, 1963.

4. Katzoff, S., *Symposium on Thermal Radiation of Solids*, NASA Sp. 55, 1965.

5. Smith, R. A., Jones, F. E., and Chasmar, R. P., *The Detection and Measurement of Infra-Red Radiation*, Oxford University Press, New York, 1957.

6. Kruse, P. W., McGlauchlin, L. D., and McQuistan, R. B., *Elements*

of Infra-Red Technology; Generation, Transmission and Detection, John Wiley and Sons, Inc., New York, 1962.

7. Best, G., "Emissivities of Copper and Alumimum, *Journal of the Optical Society of America,* Vol. 39, No. 12 (December 1949).

8. Wood, W. D., and Coffin, C. L., *Hemispherical Total-Emittance Measurement in the Temperature Range 175 to 350 k for Selected Thermal-Control and Corrosion-Protection Coatings,* AIAA Paper 66-18, Presented at the 3rd Aerospace Sciences Meeting, January 1966.

9. Gier, J. T., Dunkle, R. V., and Bevans, J. T., "Measurement of Absolute Spectral Reflectivity from 1.0 to 15 Microns," *Journal of the Optical Society of America,* Vol. 44, No. 7 (July 1954).

10. Richmond, J. C., Dunn, S. T., Dewitt, D. P., and Hayes, W. D., *Procedures for the Precise Determination of Thermal Radiation Properties,* Air Force Materiels Laboratory, Technical Documentary Report ML-TDR-64-257, Part II, April 1965.

11. Hood, James D., *Parameters for Prediction of Radiative Flux from Flames,* Ph. D. Dissertation, University of Oklahoma, 1966.

12. Love, T. J. and Wheasler, R. A., *An Experimental Study of Infrared Scattering by Clouds of Particles,* Aerospace Research Laboratories Report ARL 64-109, Office of Aerospace Research, United States Air Force, June 1964.

13. Love, T. J., and Beattie, J. F., *Experimental Determination of Thermal Radiation Scattering by Small Particles,* Aerospace Research Laboratories Report ARL 65-110, Office of Aerospace Research, United States Air Force, June 1965.

APPENDIX I Radiative Properties of Surfaces

Although the radiative properties of surfaces vary considerably with the exact condition of the surface, property tables are presented for approximate computations. The properties presented have been measured by various investigators using several different techniques. The sources of the properties quoted in this appendix are two very excellent collections that have been recently published.

References

1. Gubareff, Janssen, and Torborg, *Thermal Radiation Properties Survey*, Honeywell Research Center, Minneapolis-Honeywell Regulator Company, Minneapolis, Minnesota, 1960.

2. Wood, Deem, and Lucks, *Thermal Radiative Properties*, Plenum Press Handbooks of High-Temperature Materials, No. 3, Plenum Press, New York, 1964.

Total Normal Mean Effective Emittance
of Building Materials—Reference (1)

Temperature, °F* Wavelength, μ†	100 9.3	250 7.6	500 5.4	1000 3.6	5000 0.95	Solar 0.60
(A) _Building materials_						
Gravel	0.28	–	–	–	–	–
Dolomite lime	0.40	–	0.40	–	–	–
Marble, smooth, not shiny	0.56	–	0.56	–	–	–
Marble, polished, light gray	0.93	–	–	–	–	–
Granite	0.44	–	–	–	–	–
White marble	0.95	–	–	0.93	–	0.46
Red sand stone	0.59	–	–	–	–	–
Sand stone	0.83	–	0.92	–	–	–
Slate	0.67	–	0.67	–	–	–
Slate	0.80	–	–	–	–	–
Stonework	0.93	–	–	–	–	–
Limestone	0.95	–	–	0.80	–	–
Mica	0.75	–	–	–	–	–
Sand	0.76	–	–	–	–	–
Plaster of Paris	0.79	–	–	–	–	–
Plaster of Paris.	0.92	–	–	–	–	–
Gypsum, 0.02 in. thick on smooth or blackened plate	0.90	–	–	–	–	–
Plaster, rough lime	0.91	–	–	–	–	–
Plaster	0.93	–	–	–	–	–
Lime mortar	0.92	–	0.92	–	–	–
Quartz	0.89	–	–	0.58	–	–
Quartz, rough, fused	0.93	–	–	–	–	–
Polished glass	0.90	–	–	–	–	–
Glass	0.90	–	–	–	–	–
Glass, smooth	0.94	–	–	–	–	–
Polished glass	0.95	–	–	–	–	–
White paper	0.80	–	–	–	–	–
Paper, thin:						
Pasted on thin iron plate	0.92	–	–	–	–	–
Pasted on rough iron plate	0.93	–	–	–	–	–
Pasted on black lacquered plate	0.94	–	–	–	–	–
White paper	0.95	–	–	0.82	0.25	0.28
White, two thicknesses	–	–	–	–	–	0.27
White bond	–	–	–	–	–	0.25
Writing paper	0.98	–	–	–	–	–
Procelain, glazed	0.92	–	0.99	–	–	–
Asbestos, board	0.96	–	–	–	–	–
Abestos, paper	0.93	–	–	–	–	–

| Temperature, °F* | 100 | 250 | 500 | 1000 | 5000 | Solar |
Wavelength, μ†	9.3	7.6	5.4	3.6	0.95	0.60
(A) *Building Material, (Cont'd)*						
Asphalt pavement, dust free	–	–	–	–	–	0.93
Granolyte pavement	–	–	–	–	–	0.83
Asphalt	–	–	–	–	–	0.85
Oak, planed	0.91	–	–	–	–	–
Sawdust	0.75	–	–	–	–	–

| Temperature, °F | 100 | 2000 | 2500 | 5000 | Solar | 10,000 |
Wavelength, μ	9.3	2.1	1.8	0.95	0.60	0.50
(B) *Slates*						
Silver gray, Norwegian	–	–	0.78	0.79	0.79	0.81
Blue gray	–	–	0.80	0.87	0.87	0.88
Mauve	–	–	0.86	0.84	0.87	0.90
Greenish gray, rough	–	–	0.84	0.88	0.88	0.87
Dark gray, rough	–	–	0.90	0.89	0.90	0.91
Dark gray, smooth	–	–	0.91	0.89	0.89	0.89
Dark clay	–	–	–	–	0.93	–
(C) *Roofing materials*						
Galvanite iron, whitewashed	–	–	0.37	0.22	0.21	0.24
Aluminum surfaces	0.22	–	–	–	–	–
Aluminized felt	–	–	0.33	0.39	0.39	0.43
Enameled steel, white	–	–	0.65	0.45	0.47	0.43
Asbestos cement, white	–	–	0.65	0.59	0.60	0.64
Asbestos cement, red	–	–	0.67	0.67	0.66	0.66
Roofing lead, old	–	–	0.54	0.77	0.81	0.85
Galvanized iron, new	–	–	0.42	0.67	0.66	0.66
Enameled steel, blue	–	–	0.77	0.73	0.83	0.82
Enameled steel, red	–	–	0.76	0.74	0.83	0.92
Enameled steel, green	–	–	0.87	0.81	0.88	0.88
Roofing sheet, brown	–	–	0.80	0.85	0.89	0.93
Roofing sheet, green	–	–	0.87	0.89	0.88	0.88
Weathered asphalt	–	–	0.88	0.88	0.89	0.91
Bituminous felt	–	–	0.90	0.88	0.89	0.89
Galvanized iron, very dirty	–	–	0.90	0.89	0.89	0.89
Slate	0.67	–	–	–	–	–
Slate	0.80	–	–	–	–	–‡

*High temperature values were probably calculated from reflectivities. They are valid absorptivities for black-body radiation at indicated temperature when the surface is at room temperatures.

†Wavelength refers to the maximum emission of a black body.

‡The data given above were gathered and analyzed by the group of scientific workers of the Engineering Department of the University of California. Some of the values were rounded off by them to two decimal places for uniformity of tabulation. For the same reason, some of the values were listed under temperatures a little different from the test temperatures, and in some cases a linear interpolation was applied, but that does not affect the results in any serious way.

Total Normal Mean Effective Emittance
of Building Materials—Reference (1)*

	Temperature, °F	100	2000	2500	5000	Solar	
	Wavelength, μ	9.3	2.1	1.8	0.95	0.60	0.50
(A)	*Brick*						
	Red, rough, no gross irregularities	0.93	–	–	–	–	–
	Silica, unglazed, rough	–	0.80	–	–	–	–
	Silica, glazed, rough	–	0.88	–	–	–	–
	Grog brick, glazed	–	0.75	–	–	–	–
	Gault, cream	–	–	0.26	0.30	0.38	0.57
	Fletton, light portion	–	–	0.33	0.38	0.45	0.65
	Light buff	–	–	–	–	0.52	–
	Darker buff	–	–	–	–	0.60	–
	Lime clay (French)	–	–	0.43	0.38	0.50	0.71
	Wine cut (red)	–	–	0.44	0.51	0.61	0.85
	Stock, light fawn	–	–	0.44	0.52	0.64	0.81
	Fletton, dark portion	–	–	0.46	0.53	0.65	0.85
	Sandlime, red	–	–	0.59	0.63	0.72	0.89
	Red	–	–	–	–	0.70	–
	Red	–	–	–	–	0.77	–
	Mottled purple	–	–	0.67	0.73	0.79	0.85
	Stafford blue	–	–	0.79	0.87	0.90	0.92
	Fireclay	–	–	0.75	–	–	–
	Refractories: (40 kinds, from 1110°F to 1830°F)	–	–	–	0.65	Poor radiators	
					0.70–0.75		
		–	–	–	0.80–0.85	Good radiators	
					0.85–0.90		
(B)	*Roofing materials*						
	Clay tiles:						
	Dutch, light red	–	–	0.32	0.34	0.47	0.49
	Hand made, red	–	–	0.40	0.51	0.65	0.88
	Machine made, red	–	–	0.22	0.55	0.68	0.89
	Machine made, red	–	–	0.45	0.60	0.71	0.89
	Machine made, lighter red	–	–	0.48	0.59	0.70	0.87
	Hand made, red-brown	–	–	0.45	0.65	0.74	0.87
	Machine made, dark purple	–	–	0.78	0.78	0.82	0.87
(C)	*Concrete tiles*						
	Uncolored	–	–	0.63	0.62	0.65	0.73
	Brown	–	–	0.87	0.83	0.85	0.91
	Brown, very rough	–	–	0.92	0.88	0.87	0.90
	Black	–	–	0.94	0.91	0.91	0.91

*See footnotes to previous table.

Paints, Total Emittance—Reference (1)

Material	Temperature, °C	Emittance
Paints, oil		
16 different colors	100	0.92–0.96
All colors	0–93	0.92–0.96
Any type including lithopone	0–200	0.89–0.96
Black	93	0.92
Black, gloss	*	0.90
Black, on galvanized iron	*	0.90
Cream, on galvanized iron	*	0.90
Dark	0–93	0.92
Green	93	0.95
Green, gray	*	0.95
Nonmetallic, any color	*	0.97
Red	93	0.97
Red, on galvanized iron	*	0.90
White	93	0.94
White, enamel on iron	0–93	0.897
White, on galvanized iron	*	0.90
Paints, Aluminum	100	0.27–0.67
Aluminum	*	0.3–0.5
Aluminum	*	0.55
Aluminum	*	0.3–0.4
Aluminum on galvanized iron	*	0.52
Aluminum, 1 coat	93	0.27
Aluminum, 1 coat	100	0.70
Aluminum, 2 coats	100	0.5–0.7
Al—10 per cent, lacquer body 22 per cent	100	0.52
Al—26 per cent, lacquer body 27 per cent	100	0.30
Al with lacquer body	0–200	0.34–0.42
Rubbed with fine sandpaper	100	0.80
Paints,		
Bronze (Al, Au, Cu, etc.) with gum varnish liquid, any color, 2 coats	*	0.53
Bronze (Al, Au, Cu, etc.) with gum varnish liquid, any color, 3 coats	*	0.50
Al, Au, Cu, etc. cellulose prepared liquid, any color, 3 coats	*	0.34
Al, Au Cu, etc. cellulose prepared liquid, any color, covered with 2 coats copal varnish	*	0.92

	Temperature, °C	Emittance	Number of Measurements
Paints			
Flat white paint on polished aluminum	17.8–29.7	0.91	3
Flat black paint on polished aluminum	13.5–24.4	0.88	3
Enamel, vitreous, white	19	0.897	
	*	0.95	

*The temperature is not given, so it must be near room temperature, 20°C.

205

Parachute Cloth, Total Absorptance, Reflectance, and Transmittance—Reference (1)

Material	Absorptance*	Reflectance	Transmittance
Dacron, 100 lb	0.75	0.08	0.17
Dacron, 300 lb	0.79	0.07	0.14
Dacron, 600 lb	0.86	0.07	0.07
Dacron, 800 lb	0.90	0.07	0.03
Nylon rip-stop (orange) 1.1 oz per sq yd, MIL-C-7020	0.76	0.05	0.19
Nylon rip-stop 1.1 oz per sq yd (white) MIL-C-7020	0.73	0.06	0.21
Nylon rip-stop 1.6 oz per sq yd (white) MIL-C-7020B Type III	0.72	0.07	0.21
Nylon cloth 2.25 oz per sq yd, MIL-C-7350B Type I	0.88	0.07	0.05
Nylon cloth 4.30 oz per sq yd, MIL-C-8021 Type I	0.87	0.07	0.06
Nylon cloth 7.0 oz per sq yd, MIL-C-8021 Type II	0.85	0.10	0.05
Nylon cloth 14.0 oz per sq yd, MIL-C-8021 Type III	0.86	0.10	0.04

*This value is equal to the emittance of the material at 350°F when the monochromatic absorptance is considered independent of temperature.

Cloth, Miscellaneous Kind, Diffuse Reflectance
—Reference (1)

Wavelength	0.54	0.60	0.95	4.4	8.8	24.0
(A) *Cloth*						
Black felt	–	0.139	0.212	–	–	–
(For packing)	–	0.225	0.256	–	–	–
Black velvet	–	0.018	–	0.037	0.027	–
Blue flannel	–	0.175	–	–	–	–
Woolen cloth, lanacyl blue B.N.	–	0.251	–	–	–	–
Salacine blue-black A.B.	–	0.146	0.178	–	–	–
Salacine black P.B.	–	0.118	0.151	–	–	–
Cotton cloth:						
Diamine fast, red 8 B.L.	–	0.438	–	–	–	–
Diamine fast, black C.B.	–	0.331	–	–	–	–
Columbia fast, black R.	–	0.287	–	–	–	–
Diamine aldehyde black	–	0.295	–	–	–	–
Sulphur black A.W.L.	–	0.243	0.026	–	–	–
Linen:						
Starched, dull finish	–	0.812	–	–	–	–
Deep blue cloth (Navy Dept.)	–	0.170	–	–	–	–
The same, lighter shade	–	0.182	–	–	–	–

(B) *Cloth, white light*

	Reflectance
Cloth, black	0.01
Cloth, tracing	0.35
Cloth, white	0.60–0.70
Velvet black	0.004

Miscellaneous Materials, Reflectance—Reference (1)*

Materials	Reflectance	Materials	Reflectance
Magnesium oxide used for coating surfaces	0.97	Paper, white	0.70 to 0.80
		Camouflage paint:	
Snow	0.93	F_1 red-brown	0.064
Boric acid	0.94	F_2 red-brown	0.065
Aluminum oxide	0.94	A_1 green	0.320
$CaCO_3$	0.95	A_2 green	0.324
		C_1 blue	0.196
$HSbO_2$	0.89	C_2 blue	0.191
Zinc oxide	0.91	B_1 red-purple	0.248
$BaSO_4$	0.88	B_2 red-purple	0.246
China clay (Kaolin)	0.84		
Flat white X	0.71	Venetian red	0.11
		Vermillion (American)	0.14
Gloss white X	0.65	Burnt sienna	0.11
Lithopone	0.91	Chrome, yellow	0.55
Titanium oxide	0.91	Chrome, green	0.20
White lead (basic carbonate)	0.90		
		Cobalt, blue	0.07
Gray, light	0.49	Airship fabric, aluminum coated	0.33
Gray, medium	0.30	Airship fabric, black rubber coating	0.06
Pink, light	0.67		
Red (paint)	0.13	Print	0.60
Yellow, light	0.65	Science abstracts	0.62
Cream, light	0.74		
		AZO A (matte) photographic paper	0.72
Green, dark	0.12		
Green, light	0.47	AZO C (glossy) photographic paper	0.74
Blue, light	0.61		
Blue, medium	0.36	Plaster, raw	0.45
Ink, various kinds	0.01 to 0.04	Plaster, finished	0.65
Black velvet	0.01		
Brown soil	0.32		
Green leaves	0.25		

*A plain surface was coated with the material mentioned above and uniformly illuminated with white light. In some cases water was used for preparing the paint, but the adhesion of the powdery material to the surface (after water evaporated) was sufficiently good.

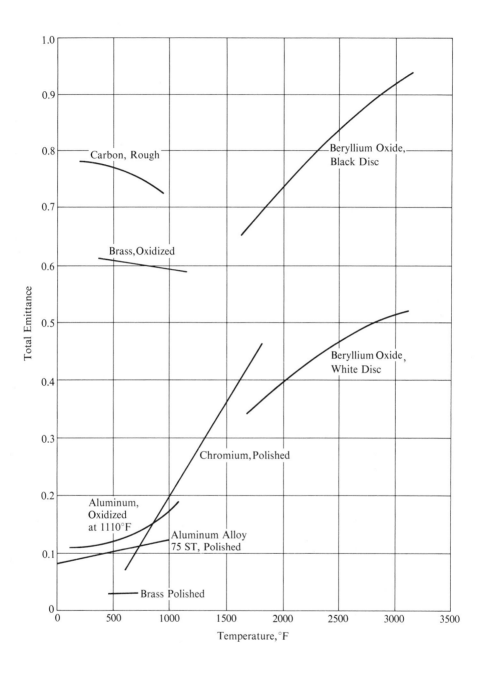

Figure I-1. A-C, total emittance (1).

209

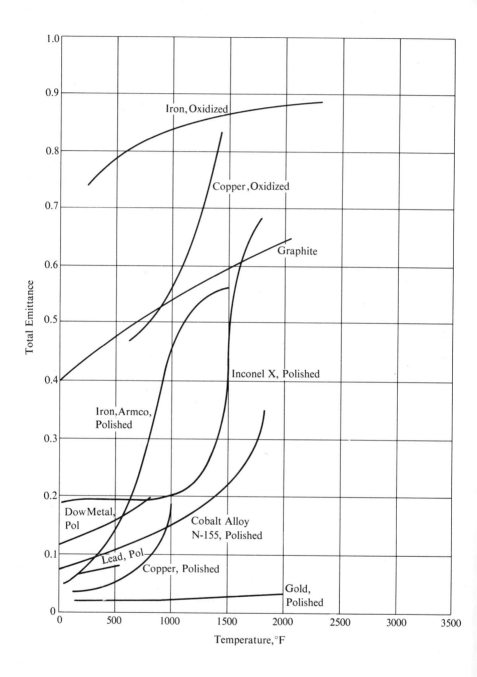

Figure I-2. C-L, total emittance (1).

210

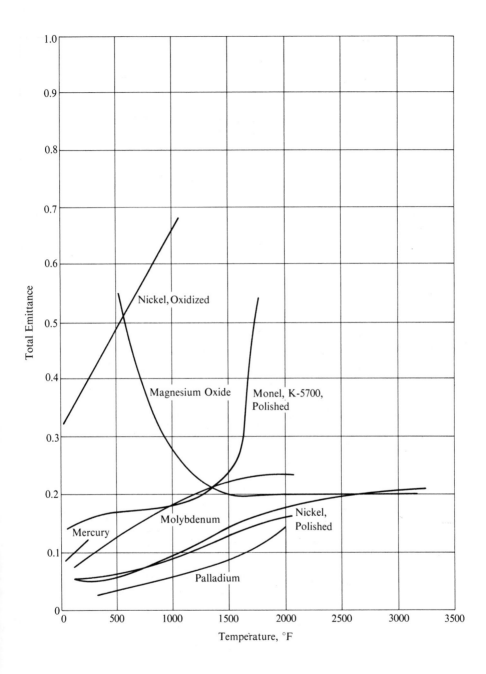

Figure I-3. *M-P,* total emittance (1).

211

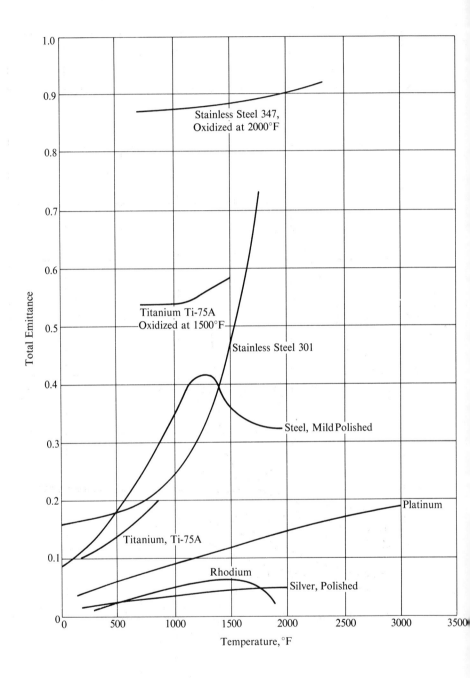

Figure I-4. *P-T,* total emittance (1).

212

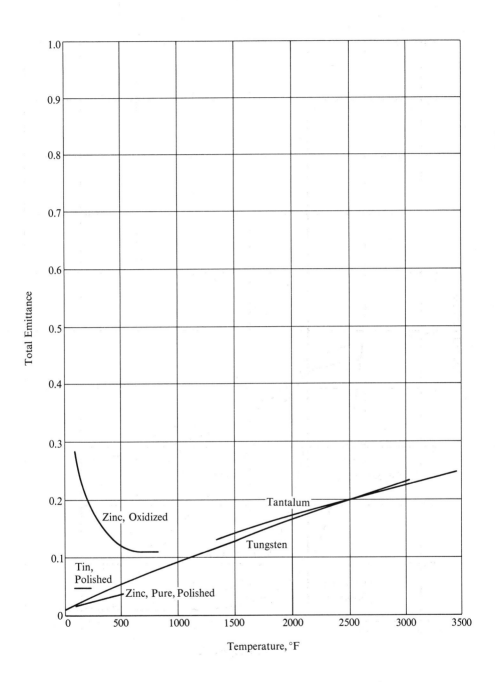

Figure I-5. *T-Z*, total emittance (1).

213

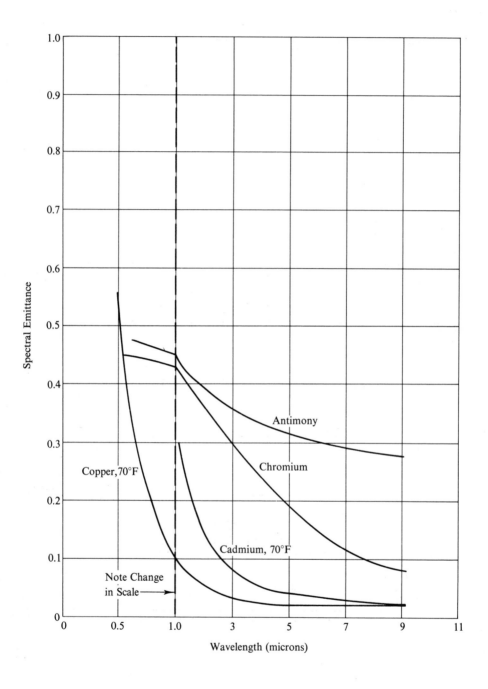

Figure I-6. A-C, spectral emittance (1).

214

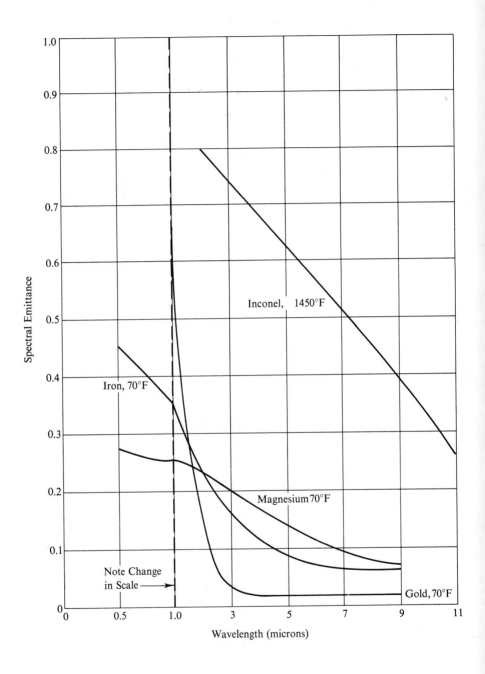

Figure I-7. *D-M,* spectral emittance (1).

215

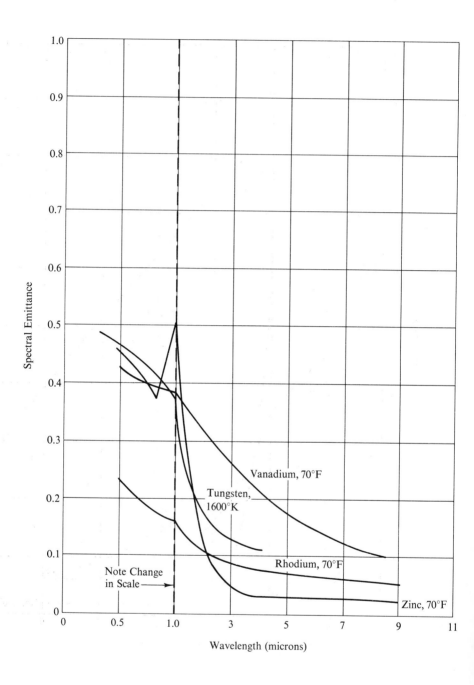

Figure I-8. *N-Z,* spectral emittance (1).

216

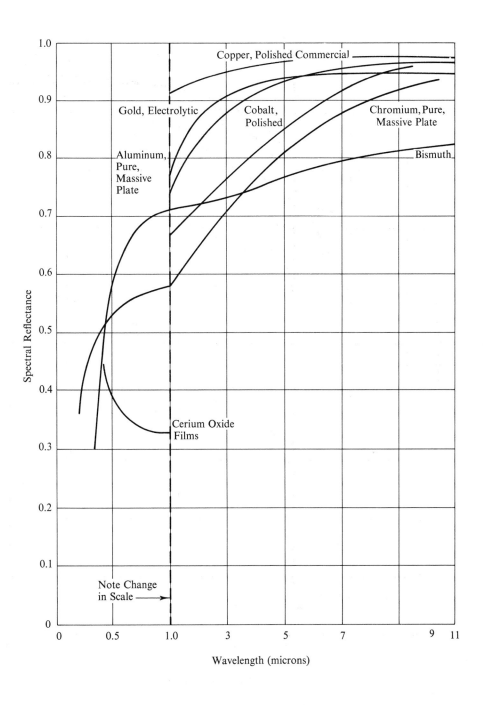

Figure I-9. A-C, spectral reflectance (1).

217

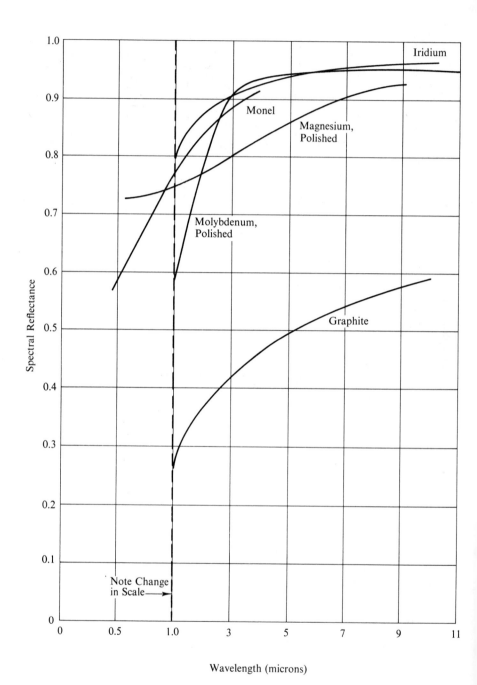

Figure I-10. G-M, spectral reflectance (1).

218

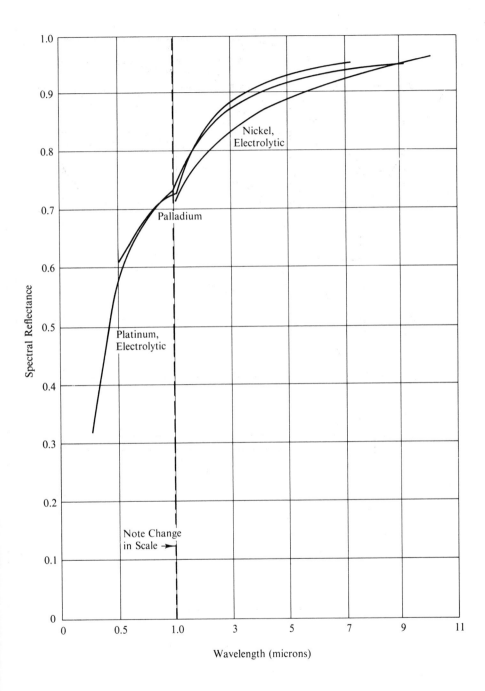

Figure I-11. *N-P,* spectral reflectance (1).

219

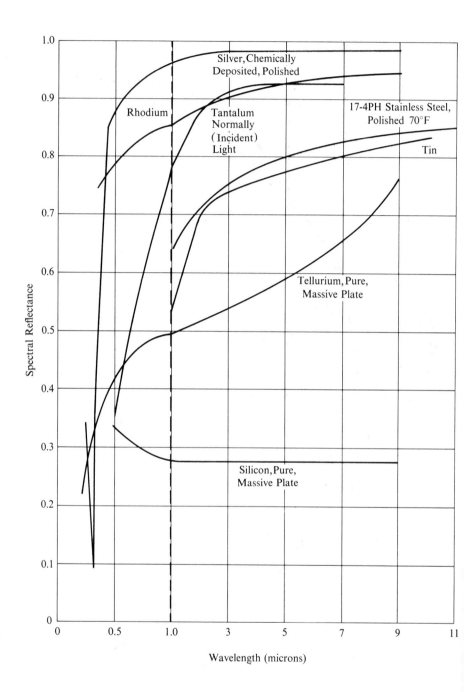

Figure I-12. *O-T,* spectral reflectance (1).

220

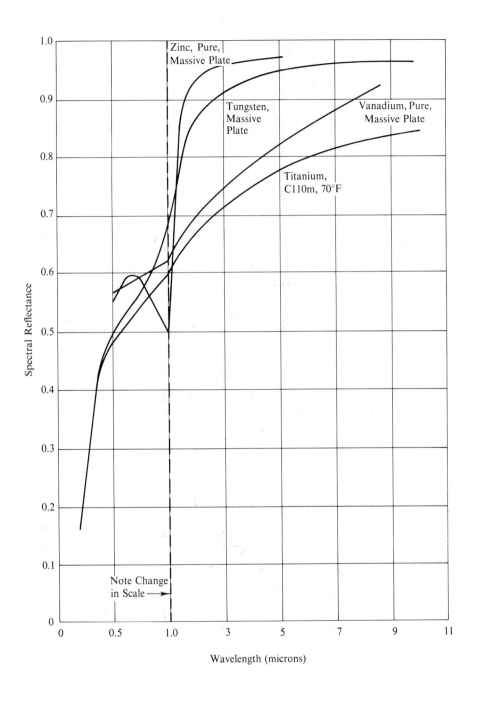

Figure I-13. *T-Z,* spectral reflectance (1).

221

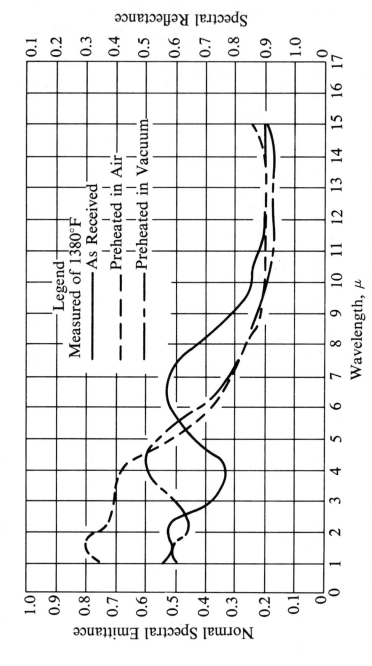

Figure I-14. Normal spectral emittance of titanium at 1380°F (2).

222

Normal Spectral Emittance of Titanium at 1380°F—Reference Information for Figure I-14

Investigator—J. G. Adams

Composition and Surface Condition	Test Method	Remarks
As received	Normal spectral	Measured in air.
Heated 30 min in air at 800°F	emittance. Furnace-heated disc	
Heated 30 min at 2.8×10^{-5} mm Hg at 800°F	specimen. Comparison black body (Hohlraum).	
	Spectrometer-monochromater with photomultiplier, lead sulphide, and thermocouple detectors.	
	Temperatures measured with thermocouples.	

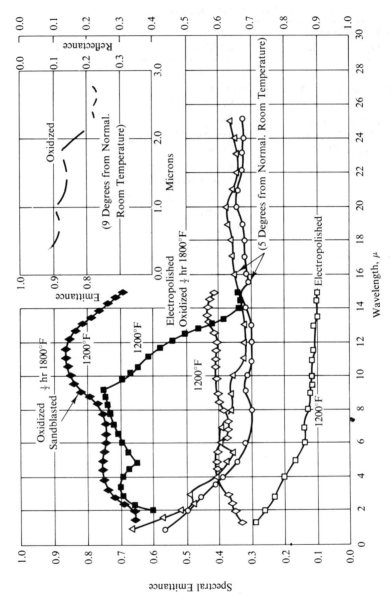

Figure I-15. Spectral emittance of stainless steel type 321 [2].

224

Spectral Emittance of Stainless Steel Type 321—Reference Information for Figure I-15

Investigator	Symbol	Composition and Surface Condition	Test Method	Remarks
Olson and Morris	×	Oxidized	Spectral reflectance at 9° from the normal. Monochromator, integrating sphere reflectometer, and lead sulphide detector. "Normal" illumination, hemispherical viewing.	Measured in air at room temperature. Data taken from reflectance curve.
Bevans, Gier, and Dunkle	△ ○	No thermal treatment 1000 hr at 705°F	Spectral reflectance at 5° from the normal. Gier-Dunkle reflectometer. Monochromator. Temperatures measured with thermocouples. Diffuse illumination, "normal" viewing.	Measured in air. Data taken from reflectance curves.
Richmond and Stewart	□ ◇ ■ ◆	Electropolished Sandblasted Electropolished, oxidized $\frac{1}{2}$ hr at 1800°F Sandblasted, oxidized $\frac{1}{2}$ hr at 1800°F (All measurement at 1200°F)	Normal spectral emittance. Recording, double-beam spectrophotometer. Comparison black body. Temperatures measured with thermocouples.	Measured in air. Data taken from table. Measured at 1200°F.

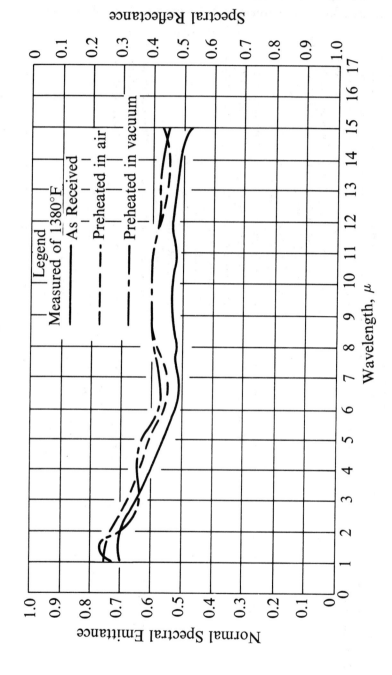

Figure 1-16. Normal spectral emittance of stainless steel type AM-350 at 1380°F (2).

Legend
Measured of 1380°F.
—— As Received
---- Preheated in air
—·—· Preheated in vacuum

Spectral Reflectance

Normal Spectral Emittance

Wavelength, μ

Normal Spectral Emittance of Stainless Steel Type AM-350 at 1380°F—Reference Information for Figure I-16

Investigator—J. G. Adams

Composition and Surface Condition	Test Method	Remarks
As received Heated 30 min in air at 900°F Heated 30 min in 4.4 $\times$ 10^{-5} mm Hg pressure at 900°F	Normal spectral emittance. Furnace-heated disc specimen. Comparison black body (Hohlraum). Spectrometer-monochromator with photomultiplier, lead sulphide, and thermocouple detectors. Temperatures measured with thermocouples.	Measured in air.

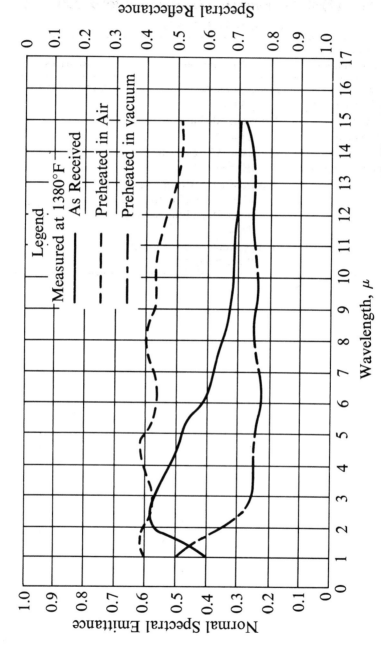

Figure 1-17. Normal spectral emittance of inconel X at 1380°F (2).

Normal Spectral Emittance of Inconel X at 1380°F—Reference Information for Figure I-17

Investigator—J. G. Adams

Composition and Surface Condition	Test Method	Remarks
As received	Normal spectral emittance.	Measured in air.
Heated 30 min in air at 1500°C	Furnace-heated disc specimen.	
Heated 30 min in 6.8 $\times$ 10^{-5} mm Hg pressure at 1500°C	Comparison black body (Hohlraum).	
	Spectrometer-monochromator with photomultiplier, lead sulphide, and thermocouple detectors.	
	Temperatures measured with thermocouples.	

Configuration Factors

The following formulae and graphs for configuration factor determination have been taken from the references noted. The formulae may be utilized directly in computer programs or values from the graphs may be used as direct input data for programs computing the exchange matrix elements. These tabulated formulae together with the configuration-factor algebra can serve a wide range of geometries.

Configuration P-1—Reference (1)

A differential area dA_1 and a plane rectangle A_2 perpendicular to the
the normal to dA_1. The normal to dA_1 passes through the corner of A_2.

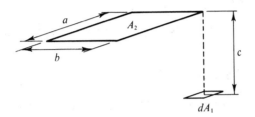

Figure II-1.

$$F_{12} = \frac{1}{2\pi}\left[\frac{x}{\sqrt{1+x^2}}\tan^{-1}\left(\frac{y}{\sqrt{1+x^2}}\right) + \frac{y}{\sqrt{1+y^2}}\tan^{-1}\left(\frac{x}{\sqrt{1+y^2}}\right)\right]$$

See Figure II-1.   A Graph of F_{12} is given in Figure II-17.

Configuration P-2—Reference (1)

A differential area dA_1 and a plane rectangle A_2, the planes of dA_1
and A_2 intersecting at an angle ϕ ($0° < \phi < 180°$).

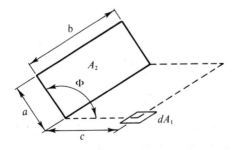

Figure II-2.

$$F_{12} = \frac{1}{2\pi} \left\{ \tan^{-1}\left(\frac{1}{L}\right) + V(N\cos\phi - L)\tan^{-1}(V) \right.$$
$$\left. + \frac{\cos\phi}{W}\left[\tan^{-1}\left(\frac{N - L\cos\phi}{W}\right) + \tan^{-1}\left(\frac{L\cos\phi}{W}\right)\right] \right\}$$

where

$$N = \frac{a}{b}, \qquad L = \frac{c}{b}, \qquad W = \sqrt{1 + L^2\sin^2\phi}$$

$$V = \frac{1}{\sqrt{N^2 + L^2 - 2NL\cos\phi}}$$

See Figure II-2. A graph of F_{12} is given in Figures 18a, 18b, and 18c.

Configuration P-3—Reference (1)

Figure II-3 gives a differential area dA_1, and any cylindrical surface A_2 generated by a line of infinite length moving parallel to itself and parallel to the plane of dA_1.

$$F_{12} = \tfrac{1}{2}(\sin\phi_2 - \sin\phi_1)$$

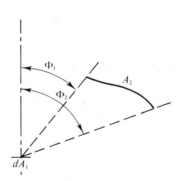

Figure II-3.

Configuration P-4—Reference (1)

Figure II-4 gives a differential area dA_1 and any infinite plane A_2 that intersects the plane of dA_1 with an angle θ.

$$F_{12} = \tfrac{1}{2}(1 + \cos\theta)$$

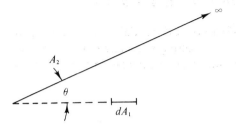

Figure II-4.

Configuration P-5—Reference (1)

A differential area dA_1 and a plane circular disc A_2 of radius r_2. The plane of dA_1 is parallel to the plane of A_2. The distance from dA_1 to the normal to the center of A_2 is r_1.

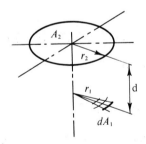

Figure II-5.

$$F_{12} = \frac{1}{2}\left(1 - \frac{x - 2E^2D^2}{\sqrt{x^2 - 4E^2D^2}}\right)$$

where

$$E = \frac{r_2}{D}, \qquad D = \frac{d}{r_1}, \qquad x = 1 + (1 + E^2)D^2$$

See Figure II-5. A graph of F_{12} for configuration P-5 is given in Figure II-19.

Configuration P-6—Reference (1)

Figure II-6 shows a differential area dA_1 and a plane disc A_2, the planes of dA_1 and A_2 intersecting at an angle of 90°. The centers of A_2 and dA_1 lie in a plane that is perpendicular to the two planes.

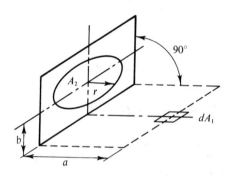

Figure II-6.

$$F_{12} = \frac{D}{2}\left[\frac{1 + R^2 + D^2}{\sqrt{(1 + R^2 + D^2)^2 - 4R^2}} - 1\right]$$

where $R = r/b$ and $D = a/b$

Configuration P-7—Reference (1)

In Figure II-7 is a differential area dA_1 and a right circular cylinder A_2 of length l. The normal to dA_1 passes through the center of one end of the cylinder and is perpendicular to the axis of the cylinder.

$$F_{12} = \frac{1}{\pi D} \tan^{-1}\left(\frac{L}{\sqrt{D^2 - 1}}\right)$$
$$+ \frac{L}{\pi}\left[\frac{A - 2D}{D\sqrt{AB}} \tan^{-1}\sqrt{\frac{A(D - 1)}{B(D + 1)}} - \frac{1}{D}\tan^{-1}\sqrt{\frac{D - 1}{D + 1}}\right]$$

where

$$D = \frac{d}{r}, \qquad L = \frac{l}{r}, \qquad A = (D + 1)^2 + L^2, \qquad B = (D - 1)^2 + L^2$$

A Graph of F_{12} for P-7 is given in Figure II-20.

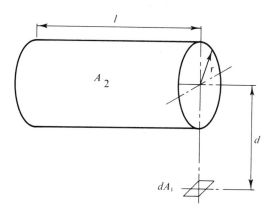

Figure II-7.

Configuration P-8—Reference (1)

A differential area dA_1, and a trapezoid formed by a rectangular plane intersecting the plane of dA_1 at an angle of ϕ, and a right triangle with its vertical leg on the edge away from dA_1 are shown in Figure II-8.

$$F_{12} = \frac{1}{2\pi} \left(\tan^{-1}\left(\frac{1}{L}\right) + \frac{N\cos\phi - L}{A} \left\{ \tan^{-1}\left[\frac{(K^2+1) + K(N - L\cos\phi)}{A}\right] \right. \right.$$

$$\left. - \tan^{-1}\left[\frac{K(N - L\cos\phi)}{A}\right] \right\} + \frac{\cos\phi}{B}\left[\tan^{-1}\left(\frac{L\cos\phi}{B}\right) \right.$$

$$\left. \left. + \tan^{-1}\left(\frac{N - L\cos\phi + K}{B}\right) \right] \right)$$

where

$$N = \frac{a}{b}, \qquad L = \frac{c}{b}, \qquad \theta = \tan^{-1} K$$

$$A = \sqrt{(K^2 + 1) L^2 \sin^2\phi + (N - L\cos\phi)^2}$$

$$B = \sqrt{1 + L^2 \sin^2\phi}$$

The graph of F_{12} for configuration P-8 is given in Figure II-21.

Configuration P-9—Reference (1)

Configuration P-9 has the same geometry as P-8 with the triangle reversed.

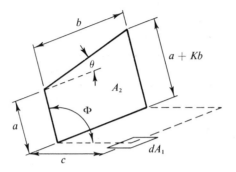

Figure II-8.

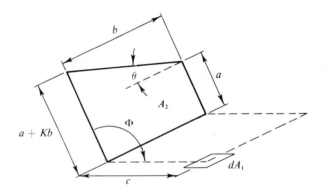

Figure II-9.

$$F_{12} = \frac{1}{2\pi} \left\{ \left\{ \tan^{-1}\left(\frac{1}{L}\right) + \frac{\cos\phi}{B}\left[\tan^{-1}\left(\frac{N - L\cos\phi}{B}\right) + \tan^{-1}\left(\frac{L\cos\phi}{B}\right)\right] \right.\right.$$
$$+ \frac{(N + K)\cos\phi - L}{A}\left\{\tan^{-1}\left[\frac{1 - K(N - L\cos\phi)}{A}\right]\right.$$
$$\left.\left.\left. + \tan^{-1}\left[\frac{K(N + K - L\cos\phi)}{A}\right]\right\} \right\} \right\}$$

where

$$N = \frac{a}{b}, \qquad L = \frac{c}{b}, \qquad \theta = \tan^{-1}(K)$$
$$A = \sqrt{(K^2 + 1)L^2 \sin^2\phi + (N + K - L\cos\phi)^2}$$

$$B = \sqrt{1 + L^2 \sin^2 \phi}$$

See Figure II-9. The graph of F_{12} for configuration P-9 is given in Figure II-22.

Configuration L-1—Reference (1)

A strip of differential width dA_1 and a plane rectangle A_2 parallel to the plane of dA_1 are in Figure II-10. Here, dA_1 is opposite one edge of A_2.

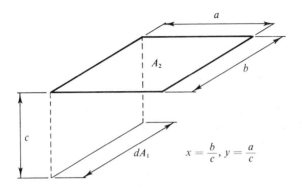

Figure II-10.

$$F_{12} = \frac{1}{\pi x} \left[\sqrt{1 + x^2} \tan^{-1} \left(\frac{y}{\sqrt{1 + x^2}} \right) \right.$$
$$\left. - \tan^{-1} y + \frac{xy}{\sqrt{1 + y^2}} \tan^{-1} \left(\frac{x}{\sqrt{1 + y^2}} \right) \right]$$

The graph of F_{12} for configuration L-1 is given in Figure II-23.

Configuration A-1—Reference (1)

Identical, parallel, directly opposed rectangles A_1 and A_2 are shown in Figure II-11.

$$*F_{12} = \frac{[(x^2 + 1 - 1)/x] \, [(y^2 + 1 - 1)/y]}{1 - [0.23/(x^2 + y^2 + 1)]}$$

The graph of F_{12} for configuration A-1 is given in Figure II-24.

---

*This formulation is an approximation to the analytical expression given by Hamilton and Morgan and actually gives more accurate results in certain regimes. Developed by F. E. Merliss, University of Oklahoma.

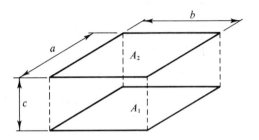

Figure II-11.

Configuration A-2—Reference (1)

Two rectangles A_1 and A_2 with one common edge and included angle Φ between the two planes comprise this configuration shown in Figure II-12. For $\Phi = 90°$,

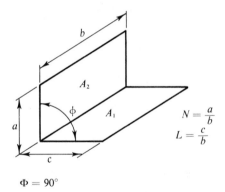

$$N = \frac{a}{b}$$

$$L = \frac{c}{b}$$

$\Phi = 90°$

Figure II-12.

$$F_{12} = \frac{1}{\pi L}\left\{\left\{L\tan^{-1}\left(\frac{1}{L}\right) + N\tan^{-1}\left(\frac{1}{N}\right) - \sqrt{N^2 + L^2}\tan^{-1}\left(\frac{1}{\sqrt{N^2 + L^2}}\right)\right.\right.$$
$$+ \frac{1}{4}\log_e\left\{\left[\frac{(1 + L^2)(1 + N^2)}{(1 + N^2 + L^2)}\right]\left[\frac{L^2(1 + L^2 + N^2)}{(1 + L^2)(L^2 + N^2)}\right]\right.$$
$$\left.\left.\left.\times\left[\frac{N^2(1 + L^2 + N^2)}{(1 + N^2)(L^2 + N^2)}\right]\right\}\right\}\right\}$$

The graph of F_{12} for configuration A-2 is given in Figure II-25.

Configuration A-3—Reference (1)

Parallel, directly-opposed, plane-circular discs comprise this configuration as shown in Figure II-13.

$$E = \frac{r_2}{d}, \qquad D\frac{d}{r_1}$$

$$F_{12} = \tfrac{1}{2}[x - \sqrt{x^2 - 4E^2D^2}]$$

where

$$x = 1 - (1 + E^2)D^2$$

The graph of F_{12} for configuration A-3 is given in Figure II-26.

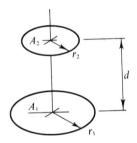

Figure II-13.

Configuration P-10—Reference (2)

A differential area dA_1 and a sphere with geometry as shown in Figure II-14 make up this configuration.

Case I: $\theta + \phi \leq \pi/2$

$$F_{12} = \frac{\cos \theta}{H^2}$$

Case II: $(\pi/2) - \phi < \theta \leq \pi/2$ (See Figure II-15)

$$F_{12} = \frac{2}{\pi} \left\{ \left\{ \frac{\pi}{4} - \frac{\sin^{-1}}{2} \left[\frac{(H^2 - 1)^{1/2}}{H \sin \theta} \right] \right. \right.$$
$$+ \frac{1}{2H^2} \{\cos \theta \cos^{-1}[- (H^2 - 1)^{1/2} \cot \theta]$$
$$- (H^2 - 1)^{1/2} [(1 - H^2) \cos^2 \theta]^{1/2}\} \right\}$$

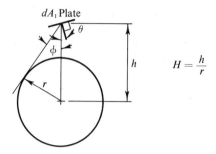

Figure II-14.

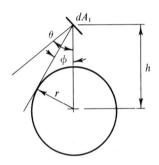

Figure II-15.

The graph of F_{12} for configuration P-10, Case II is given in Figure II-27.

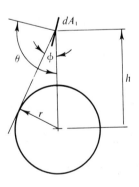

Figure II-16.

Case III: $\pi/2 < \theta \leq (\pi/2) + \phi$ (See Figure II-16)

$$F_{12} = \frac{2}{\pi} \left\{ \left\{ \frac{\pi}{4} - \frac{\sin^{-1}}{2} \left[\frac{(H^2 - 1)^{1/2}}{H \sin \theta} \right] \right. \right.$$
$$+ \frac{1}{2H^2} \left\{ \cos \theta \cos^{-1} \left[-(H^2 - 1)^{1/2} \cot \theta \right] \right.$$
$$\left. \left. - (H^2 - 1)^{1/2} \left[(1 - H^2) \cos^2 \theta \right]^{1/2} \right\} \right\}$$

The graph of F_{12} for configuration P-10, Case III is given in Figure II-28.

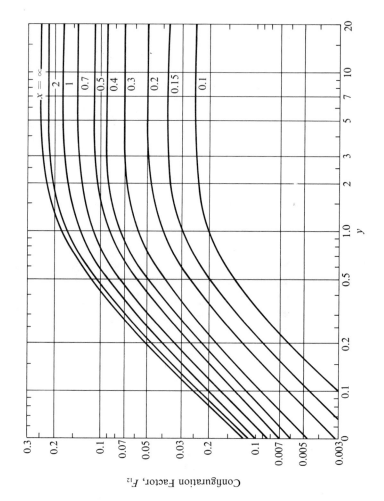

Figure II-17. Configuration-factor curves for configuration P-1 (1).

242

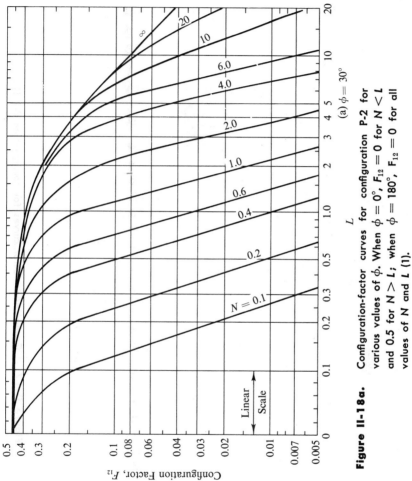

Figure II-18a. Configuration-factor curves for configuration P-2 for various values of ϕ. When $\phi = 0°$, $F_{12} = 0$ for $N < L$ and 0.5 for $N > L$; when $\phi = 180°$, $F_{12} = 0$ for all values of N and L (1).

(a) $\phi = 30°$

Configuration Factor, F_{12}

L

243

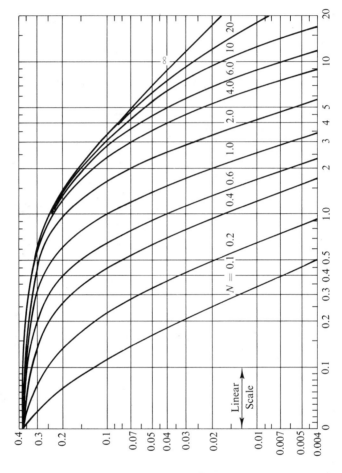

Figure II-18b. Reference (1).

244

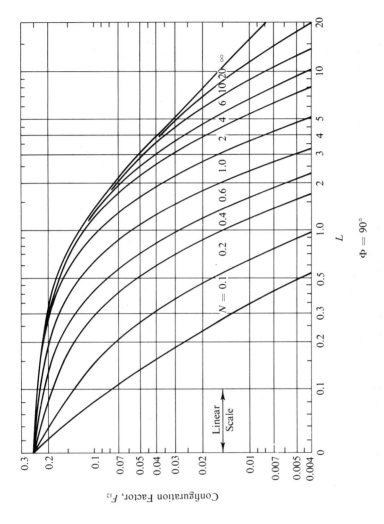

Figure II-18c. Reference (1).

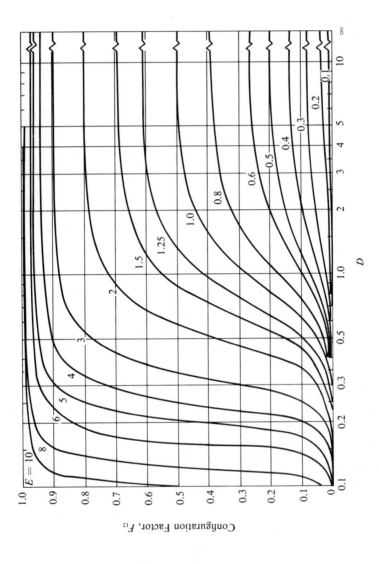

Figure II-19. Configuration-factor curves for configuration P-5 (I).

246

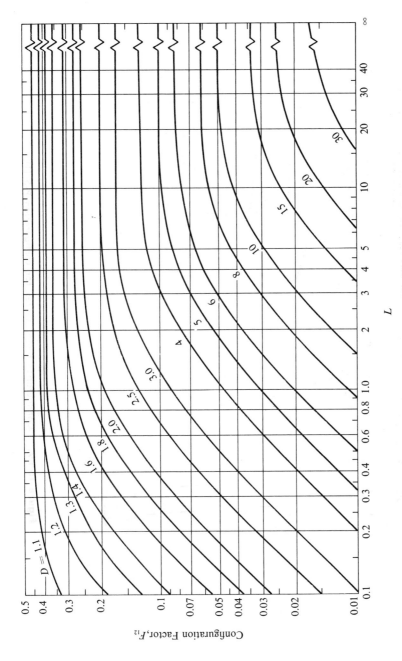

Figure II-20. Configuration-factor curves for configuration P-7 (1).

247

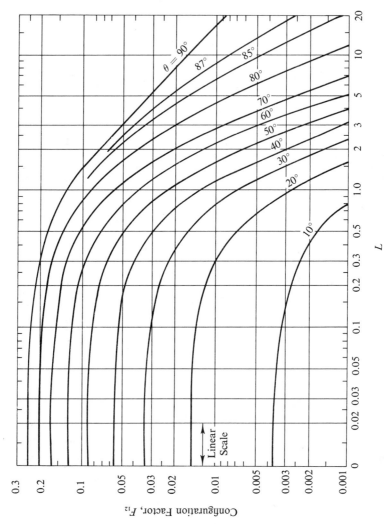

Figure II-21. Configuration-factor curves for configuration P-8 with $\phi = 90°$ (1).

248

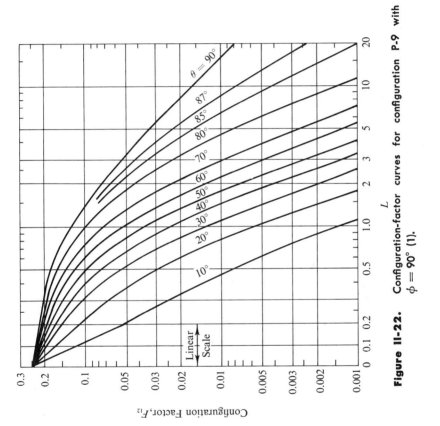

Figure II-22. Configuration-factor curves for configuration P-9 with $\phi = 90°$ (1).

249

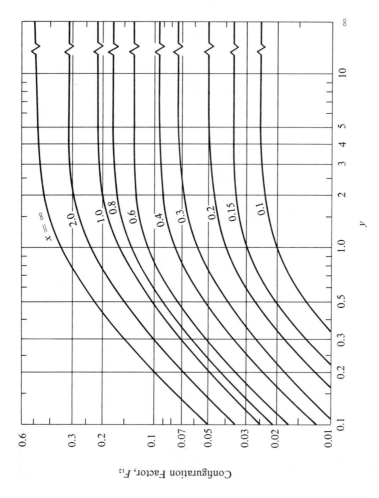

Figure II-23. Configuration-factor curves for configuration L-1 (1).

250

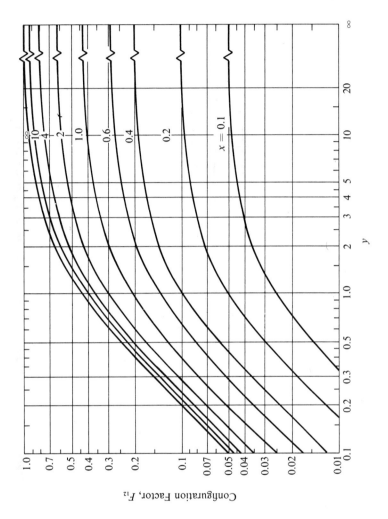

Figure II-24. Configuration-factor curves for configuration A-1 (1).

251

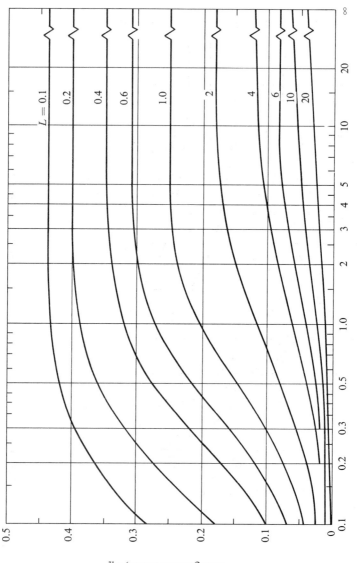

Figure II-25. Configuration-factor curves for configuration A-2 (1).

(c) $\theta = 90°$

252

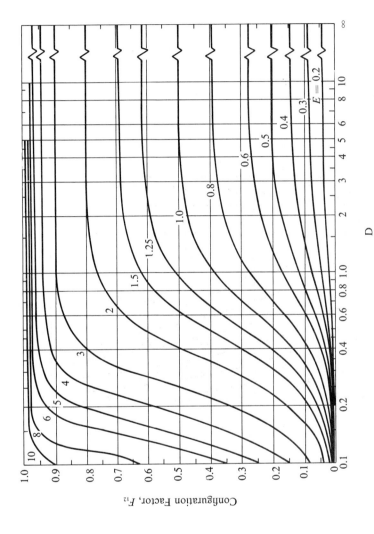

Figure II-26. Configuration-factor curves for configuration A-3 (1).

253

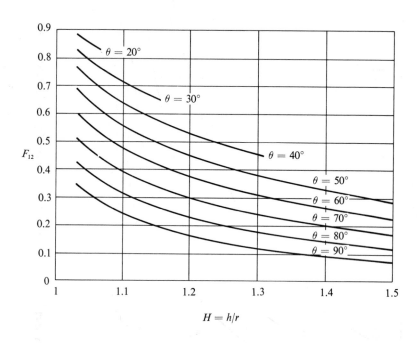

Figure II-27. Configuration-factor curves for configuration P-10, Case II (3).

254

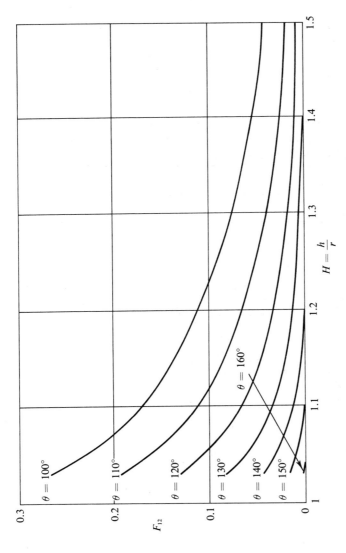

Figure II-28. Configuration-factor curves for configuration P-10, Case III (3).

255

References

1. Hamilton, D. C., and Morgan, W. R., *Radiant Interchange Configuration Factors*, NACA TN 2836, December 1952.
2. Buschman, A. J., and Pittman, C. M., *Configuration Factors for Exchange of Radiant Energy Between Axisymmetrical Sections of Cylinders, Cones, and Hemispheres and Their Bases*, NASA TN D-944, October, 1961.
3. Cunningham, F. G., "Power Input to a Small Flat Plate From a Diffusely Radiating Sphere, With Applications to Earth Satellites", NASA TN D-710, August, 1961.

Review of Matrices

A matrix note such as $[a_{ij}]$, represents a rectangular array of numbers that are subject to certain rules of operation.

$$[a_{ij}] = \begin{bmatrix} a_{11} & a_{12} & a_{13} & \cdots & a_{1n} \\ a_{21} & a_{22} & a_{23} & \cdots & a_{2n} \\ a_{31} & a_{32} & a_{33} & \cdots & a_{3n} \\ \cdot & \cdot & \cdot & \cdot & \cdot \\ \cdot & \cdot & \cdot & \cdot & \cdot \\ a_{m1} & a_{m2} & a_{m3} & \cdots & a_{mn} \end{bmatrix} \qquad \textbf{(III-1)}$$

A matrix of m rows and n columns is an $m \times n$ matrix. When $n = m$, the matrix is said to be a *square matrix;* if $n = 1$, the matrix is a *column matrix*.

The numbers or functions a_{ij} are the elements of the matrix. In a square matrix, the elements $a_{11}, a_{22}, a_{33}, \ldots, a_{mn}$ that run diagonally from the upper left to the lower right corner of the matrix are called the *diagonal elements*. Other elements are off-diagonal elements. The "identity matrix" is defined as *a square matrix* with *diagonal elements that are all equal to unity and with off-diagonal elements that are all zero.* The following is an example of an identity matrix.

$$I = \begin{bmatrix} 1 & 0 & 0 & 0 & 0 & 0 \\ 0 & 1 & 0 & 0 & 0 & 0 \\ 0 & 0 & 1 & 0 & 0 & 0 \\ 0 & 0 & 0 & 1 & 0 & 0 \\ 0 & 0 & 0 & 0 & 1 & 0 \\ 0 & 0 & 0 & 0 & 0 & 1 \end{bmatrix}$$

(III-2)

Sums of Matrices

Two matrices may be added or subtracted if the number of rows in the two matrices are equal and if the number of columns are equal so that for each element in one matrix there is a corresponding element in the other matrix. The matrix representing the sum will have elements equal to the sum of the corresponding elements of the addends. In such a case, the two matrices are said to be *conformable for addition.* An example of matrix addition is

$$\begin{bmatrix} a_{11} & a_{12} & a_{13} \\ a_{21} & a_{22} & a_{23} \\ a_{31} & a_{32} & a_{33} \\ a_{41} & a_{42} & a_{43} \end{bmatrix} + \begin{bmatrix} b_{11} & b_{12} & b_{13} \\ b_{21} & b_{22} & b_{23} \\ b_{31} & b_{32} & b_{33} \\ b_{41} & b_{42} & b_{43} \end{bmatrix} = \begin{bmatrix} a_{11}+b_{11} & a_{12}+b_{12} & a_{13}+b_{13} \\ a_{21}+b_{21} & a_{22}+b_{22} & a_{23}+b_{23} \\ a_{31}+b_{31} & a_{32}+b_{32} & a_{33}+b_{33} \\ a_{41}+b_{41} & a_{42}+b_{42} & a_{43}+b_{43} \end{bmatrix}$$

(III-3)

Matrix Multiplication

The product AB of matrix A and matrix B is defined only when the number of columns in matrix A equals the number of rows in matrix B. The multiplication results in a matrix with elements that are the sums of the products of the elements of each row in matrix A and corresponding elements of each column in matrix B. An example of matrix multiplication is

$$\begin{bmatrix} a_{11} & a_{12} & a_{13} \\ a_{21} & a_{22} & a_{23} \\ a_{31} & a_{32} & a_{33} \\ a_{41} & a_{42} & a_{43} \end{bmatrix} \cdot \begin{bmatrix} b_{11} & b_{12} \\ b_{21} & b_{22} \\ b_{31} & b_{32} \end{bmatrix}$$

$$= \begin{bmatrix} a_{11}b_{11}+a_{12}b_{21}+a_{13}b_{31} & a_{11}b_{12}+a_{12}b_{22}+a_{13}b_{32} \\ a_{21}b_{11}+a_{22}b_{21}+a_{23}b_{22} & a_{21}b_{12}+a_{22}b_{22}+a_{23}b_{32} \\ a_{31}b_{11}+a_{32}b_{21}+a_{33}b_{31} & a_{31}b_{12}+a_{32}b_{22}+a_{33}b_{32} \\ a_{41}b_{11}+a_{42}b_{21}+a_{43}b_{31} & a_{41}b_{12}+a_{42}b_{22}+a_{43}b_{32} \end{bmatrix}$$

(III-4)

It can be seen that the resulting matrix has the same number of rows as matrix A and the same number of columns as matrix B. When the product above is defined, matrix A is said to be conformable to B for multiplication.

Some rules for multiplication are listed below. Assuming that A, B, and C are conformable for the indicated sums and products, the following must hold.

$$
\begin{array}{lll}
(1) & A(B + C) = AB + AC & \\
(2) & (A + B)C = AC + BC & \\
(3) & A(BC) = (AB)C & \\
(4) & AB \neq BA & \text{in general} \\
(5) & AB = 0 & \text{does not necessarily imply } A = 0 \text{ or } B = 0 \\
(6) & AB = AC & \text{does not necessarily imply that } B = C
\end{array}
$$

(III-5)

The Inverse of a Matrix

If the product of two square matrices is equal to the identity matrix, then each of the matrices may be said to be the *inverse* of the other. For example, if

$$[a_{ij}][b_{ij}] = [I]$$

then

$$[b_{ij}] = [a_{ij}]^{-1} \quad \text{and} \quad [a_{ij}] = [b_{ij}]^{-1} \tag{III-6}$$

Finding the inverse of a matrix is a key step in the solution of a system of linear algebraic equations. In most practical problems this will be accomplished through the use of a subroutine from the library of the digital computer. The reader is referred to books on numerical analysis for detailed procedures.

Solution of Simultaneous Linear Algebraic Equations

Following the rules of matrix addition and multiplication, the following set of simultaneous equations may be represented by the matrix equation that follows.

$$
\begin{aligned}
a_{11}x_1 + a_{12}x_2 + a_{13}x_3 + a_{14}x_4 &= C_1 \\
a_{21}x_1 + a_{22}x_2 + a_{23}x_3 + a_{24}x_4 &= C_2 \\
a_{31}x_1 + a_{32}x_2 + a_{33}x_3 + a_{34}x_4 &= C_3 \\
a_{41}x_1 + a_{42}x_2 + a_{43}x_3 + a_{44}x_4 &= C_4
\end{aligned}
$$

(III-7)

$$
\begin{bmatrix}
a_{11} & a_{21} & a_{31} & a_{41} \\
a_{12} & a_{22} & a_{32} & a_{42} \\
a_{13} & a_{23} & a_{33} & a_{43} \\
a_{14} & a_{24} & a_{34} & a_{44}
\end{bmatrix}
\begin{bmatrix}
x_1 \\
x_2 \\
x_3 \\
x_4
\end{bmatrix}
=
\begin{bmatrix}
C_1 \\
C_2 \\
C_3 \\
C_4
\end{bmatrix}
$$

or

$$[a_{ij}][x_j] = [C_j] \qquad \text{(III-8)}$$

Multiplication of both sides of this equation by the inverse of the coefficient matrix results in the solution

$$[x_j] = [a_{ij}]^{-1}[C_j] \qquad \text{(III-9)}$$

Thus, the inverse of the coefficient matrix provides a solution to the set of equations.

Eigenvalues and Eigenvectors of a Matrix

If λ is an unknown constant in the following set of equations, then there must exist a set of values for λ for which a nontrivial solution may be found.

$$\begin{bmatrix} \lambda - a_{11} & -a_{12} & \cdots & -a_{1n} \\ -a_{21} & \lambda - a_{22} & \cdots & -a_{2n} \\ \cdots & \cdots & \cdots & \cdots \\ -a_{n1} & -a_{n2} & \cdots & \lambda - a_{nn} \end{bmatrix} \begin{bmatrix} x_1 \\ x_2 \\ \vdots \\ x_n \end{bmatrix} = 0 \qquad \text{(III-10)}$$

The nontrivial solution exists only when the determinant of the coefficient matrix is equal to zero.

$$\begin{bmatrix} \lambda - a_{11} & -a_{12} & \cdots & -a_{1n} \\ -a_{21} & \lambda - a_{22} & \cdots & -a_{2n} \\ \cdots & \cdots & \cdots & \cdots \\ -a_{n1} & -a_{n2} & \cdots & \lambda - a_{nn} \end{bmatrix} = 0 \qquad \text{(III-11)}$$

The expanded determinant may be expressed as a polynomial in λ of order n.

$$\lambda^n + A_1\lambda^{n-1} + A_2\lambda^{n-2} + \cdots A_n = 0 \qquad \text{(III-12)}$$

The roots of this polynomial are the values of λ for which nontrivial solutions of the homogeneous set of equations exist. These are called *Eigenvalues*. For each λ there exists a set of values for the column matrix $[x_1]$. These are called the *Eigenvectors* of the matrix.

Problems involving the solution of a set of homogeneous differential equations such as a multidegree of freedom vibration problem result in matrices of the type shown above. The Eigenvalues correspond to the square of the natural frequencies in such problems.

APPENDIX IV

Quadrature Formulae*

---

* Appendix IV has been selected from *Handbook of Mathematical Functions*, National Bureau of Standards Applied Mathematics Series No. 55, edited by M. Abramowitz and I. A. Stegun. June 1964.

Abscissas and Weight Factors for Gaussian Integration

$$\int_{-1}^{+1} f(x)\, dx \approx \sum_{i=1}^{n} w_i f(x_i)$$

Abscissas = $\pm x_i$ (Zeros of Legendre Polynomials)   Weight Factors = w_i

$\pm x_i$	w_i
n = 2	
0.57735 02691 89626	1.00000 00000 00000
n = 3	
0.00000 00000 00000	0.88888 88888 88889
0.77459 66692 41483	0.55555 55555 55556
n = 4	
0.33998 10435 84856	0.65214 51548 62546
0.86113 63115 94053	0.34785 48451 37454
n = 5	
0.00000 00000 00000	0.56888 88888 88889
0.53846 93101 05683	0.47862 86704 99366
0.90617 98459 38664	0.23692 68850 56189
n = 6	
0.23861 91860 83197	0.46791 39345 72691
0.66120 93864 66265	0.36076 15730 48139
0.93246 95142 03152	0.17132 44923 79170
n = 7	
0.00000 00000 00000	0.41795 91836 73469
0.40584 51513 77397	0.38183 00505 05119
0.74153 11855 99394	0.27970 53914 89277
0.94910 79123 42759	0.12948 49661 68870

$\pm x_i$	w_i
n = 8	
0.18343 46424 95650	0.36268 37833 78362
0.52553 24099 16329	0.31370 66458 77887
0.79666 64774 13627	0.22238 10344 53374
0.96028 98564 97536	0.10122 85362 90376
n = 9	
0.00000 00000 00000	0.33023 93550 01260
0.32425 34234 03809	0.31234 70770 40003
0.61337 14327 00590	0.26061 06964 02935
0.83603 11073 26636	0.18064 81606 94857
0.96816 02395 07626	0.08127 43883 61574
n = 10	
0.14887 43389 81631	0.29552 42247 14753
0.43339 53941 29247	0.26926 67193 09996
0.67940 95682 99024	0.21908 63625 15982
0.86506 33666 88985	0.14945 13491 50581
0.97390 65285 17172	0.06667 13443 08688
n = 12	
0.12523 34085 11469	0.24914 70458 13403
0.36783 14989 98180	0.23349 25365 38355
0.58731 79542 86617	0.20316 74267 23066
0.76990 26741 94305	0.16007 83285 43346
0.90411 72563 70475	0.10693 93259 95318
0.98156 06342 46719	0.04717 53363 86512

$\pm x_i$	w_i
0.09501 25098 37637 440185	0.18945 06104 55068 496285
0.28160 35507 79258 913230	0.18260 34150 44923 588867
0.45801 67776 57227 386342	0.16915 65193 95002 538189
0.61787 62444 62643 748447	0.14959 59888 16576 732081
0.75540 44083 55003 033895	0.12462 89712 55533 872052
0.86563 12023 87831 743880	0.09515 85116 82492 784810
0.94457 50230 73232 576078	0.06225 35239 38647 892863
0.98940 09349 91649 932596	0.02715 24594 11754 094852

$\pm x_i$	w_i
0.07652 65211 33497 333755	0.15275 33871 30725 850698
0.22778 58511 41645 078080	0.14917 29864 72603 746788
0.37370 60887 15419 560673	0.14209 61093 18382 051329
0.51086 70019 50827 098004	0.13168 86384 49176 626898
0.63605 36807 26515 025453	0.11819 45319 61518 417312
0.74633 19064 60150 792614	0.10193 01198 17240 435037
0.83911 69718 22218 823395	0.08327 67415 76704 748725
0.91223 44282 51325 905868	0.06267 20483 34109 063570
0.96397 19272 77913 791268	0.04060 14298 00386 941331
0.99312 85991 85094 924786	0.01761 40071 39152 118312

$\pm x_i$	w_i
0.06405 68928 62605 626085	0.12793 81953 46752 156974
0.19111 88674 73616 309159	0.12583 74563 46828 296121
0.31504 26796 96163 374387	0.12167 04729 27803 391204
0.43379 35076 26045 138487	0.11550 56680 53725 601353
0.54542 14713 88839 535658	0.10744 42701 15965 634783
0.64809 36519 36975 569252	0.09761 86521 04113 888270
0.74012 41915 78554 364244	0.08619 01615 31953 275917
0.82000 19859 73902 921954	0.07334 64814 11080 305734
0.88641 55270 04401 034213	0.05929 85849 15436 780746
0.93827 45520 02732 758524	0.04427 74388 17419 806169
0.97472 85559 71309 498198	0.02853 13886 28933 663181
0.99518 72199 97021 360180	0.01234 12297 99987 199547

Abscissas and Weight Factors for Gaussian Integration of Moments

$$\int_0^1 x^k f(x)\,dx \approx \sum_{i=1}^n w_i f(x_i)$$

Abscissas = x_i Weight Factors = w_i

n	$k=0$ x_i	w_i	$k=1$ x_i	w_i	$k=2$ x_i	w_i
1	0.50000 00000	1.00000 00000	0.66666 66667	0.50000 00000	0.75000 00000	0.33333 33333
2	0.21132 48654	0.50000 00000	0.35505 10257	0.18195 86183	0.45584 81560	0.10078 58821
	0.78867 51346	0.50000 00000	0.84494 89743	0.31804 13817	0.87748 51773	0.23254 74513
3	0.11270 16654	0.27777 77778	0.21234 05382	0.06982 69799	0.29499 77901	0.02995 07030
	0.50000 00000	0.44444 44444	0.59053 31356	0.22924 11064	0.65299 62340	0.14624 62693
	0.88729 83346	0.27777 77778	0.91141 20405	0.20093 19137	0.92700 59759	0.15713 63611
4	0.06943 18442	0.17392 74226	0.13975 98643	0.03118 09710	0.20414 85821	0.01035 22408
	0.33000 94782	0.32607 25774	0.41640 95676	0.12984 75476	0.48295 27049	0.06863 38872
	0.66999 05218	0.32607 25774	0.72315 69864	0.20346 45680	0.76139 92624	0.14345 87898
	0.93056 81558	0.17392 74226	0.94289 58039	0.13550 69134	0.95149 94506	0.11088 84156
5	0.04691 00770	0.11846 34425	0.09853 50858	0.01574 79145	0.14894 57871	0.00411 38252
	0.23076 53449	0.23931 43352	0.30453 57266	0.07390 88701	0.36566 65274	0.03205 56007
	0.50000 00000	0.28444 44444	0.56202 51898	0.14638 69871	0.61011 36129	0.08920 01612
	0.76923 46551	0.23931 43352	0.80198 65821	0.16717 46381	0.82651 96792	0.12619 89619
	0.95308 99230	0.11846 34425	0.96019 01429	0.09678 15902	0.96542 10601	0.08176 47843

6	0.0337652429	0.0856622462	0.0730543287	0.0087383018	0.1131943838	0.0018310758
	0.1693953068	0.1803807865	0.2307661380	0.0439551656	0.2843188727	0.0157202972
	0.3806904070	0.2339569673	0.4413284812	0.0986611509	0.4909635868	0.0512895711
	0.6193095930	0.2339569673	0.6630153097	0.1407925538	0.6975630820	0.0945771867
	0.8306046932	0.1803807865	0.8519214003	0.1355424972	0.8684360583	0.1073764997
	0.9662347571	0.0856622462	0.9706835728	0.0723103307	0.9740954449	0.0625387027
7	0.0254460438	0.0647424831	0.0562625605	0.0052143622	0.0888168334	0.0008926880
	0.1292344072	0.1398526957	0.1802406917	0.0274083567	0.2264827534	0.0081629256
	0.2970774243	0.1909150253	0.3526247171	0.0663846965	0.3999784867	0.0294222113
	0.5000000000	0.2089795918	0.5471536263	0.1071250657	0.5859978554	0.0631463787
	0.7029225757	0.1909150253	0.7342101772	0.1273908973	0.7594458740	0.0917338033
	0.8707655928	0.1398526957	0.8853209468	0.1105092582	0.8969109709	0.0906988246
	0.9745539562	0.0647424831	0.9775206136	0.0559673634	0.9798672262	0.0492765018
8	0.0198550718	0.0506142681	0.0446339553	0.0032951914	0.0714910350	0.0004685178
	0.1016667613	0.1111905172	0.1443662570	0.0178429027	0.1842282964	0.0044745217
	0.2372337950	0.1568533229	0.2868247571	0.0454393195	0.3304477282	0.0172468638
	0.4082826788	0.1813418917	0.4548133152	0.0791995995	0.4944029218	0.0408144264
	0.5917173212	0.1813418917	0.6280678354	0.1060473594	0.6583480085	0.0684471834
	0.7627662050	0.1568533229	0.7856915206	0.1125057995	0.8045248315	0.0852847692
	0.8983332387	0.1111905172	0.9086763921	0.0911190236	0.9170993825	0.0768180933
	0.9801449282	0.0506142681	0.9822200849	0.0445508044	0.9839022404	0.0397789578

Abscissas and Weight Factors for Laguerre Integration

$$\int_0^\infty e^{-x} f(x)\, dx \approx \sum_{i=1}^{n} w_i f(x_i)$$

Abscissas $= x_i$ (Zeros of Laguerre Polynomials)

x_i			w_i		$w_i e^{x_i}$	
			$n = 2$			
0.58578	64376	27	$(-1)8.53553$	390593	1.53332	603312
3.41421	35623	73	$(-1)1.46446$	609407	4.45095	733505
			$n = 3$			
0.41577	45567	83	$(-1)7.11093$	009929	1.07769	285927
2.29428	03602	79	$(-1)2.78517$	733569	2.76214	296190
6.28994	50829	37	$(-2)1.03892$	565016	5.60109	462543
			$n = 4$			
0.32254	76896	19	$(-1)6.03154$	104342	0.83273	91238 38
1.74576	11011	58	$(-1)3.57418$	692438	2.04810	243845
4.53662	02969	21	$(-2)3.88879$	085150	3.63114	630582
9.39507	09123	01	$(-4)5.39294$	705561	6.48714	508441
			$n = 5$			
0.26356	03197	18	$(-1)5.21755$	610583	0.67909	40422 08
1.41340	30591	07	$(-1)3.98666$	811083	1.63848	787360
3.59642	57710	41	$(-2)7.59424$	496817	2.76944	324237
7.08581	00058	59	$(-3)3.61175$	867992	4.31565	690092
12.64080	08442	76	$(-5)2.33699$	723858	7.21918	635435
			$n = 6$			
0.22284	66041	79	$(-1)4.58964$	673950	0.57353	55074 23
1.18893	21016	73	$(-1)4.17000$	830772	1.36925	259071
2.99273	63260	59	$(-1)1.13373$	382074	2.26068	459338
5.77514	35691	05	$(-2)1.03991$	974531	3.35052	458236
9.83746	74183	83	$(-4)2.61017$	202815	4.88682	680021
15.98287	39806	02	$(-7)8.98547$	906430	7.84901	594560
			$n = 7$			
0.19304	36765	60	$(-1)4.09318$	951701	0.49647	75975 40
1.02666	48953	39	$(-1)4.21831$	277862	1.17764	306086
2.56787	67449	51	$(-1)1.47126$	348658	1.91824	978166
4.90035	30845	26	$(-2)2.06335$	144687	2.77184	863623
8.18215	34445	63	$(-3)1.07401$	014328	3.84124	912249
12.73418	02917	98	$(-5)1.58654$	643486	5.38067	820792
19.39572	78622	63	$(-8)3.17031$	547900	8.40543	248683
			$n = 8$			
0.17027	96323	05	$(-1)3.69188$	589342	0.43772	34104 93
0.90370	17767	99	$(-1)4.18786$	780814	1.03386	934767
2.25108	66298	66	$(-1)1.75794$	986637	1.66970	976566
4.26670	01702	88	$(-2)3.33434$	922612	2.37692	470176
7.04590	54023	93	$(-3)2.79453$	623523	3.20854	091335
10.75851	60101	81	$(-5)9.07650$	877336	4.26857	551083
15.74067	86412	78	$(-7)8.48574$	671627	5.81808	336867
22.86313	17368	89	$(-9)1.04800$	117487	8.90622	621529

Abscissas and Weight Factors for Laguerre Integration

$$\int_0^\infty g(x)\,dx \approx \sum_{i=1}^n w_i e^{x_i} g(x_i)$$

Weight Factors $= w_i$

x_i			w_i		$w_i e^{x_i}$	
			$n = 9$			
0.15232	22277	32	(− 1)3.36126	421798	0.39143	11243 16
0.80722	00227	42	(− 1)4.11213	980424	0.92180	50285 29
2.00513	51556	19	(− 1)1.99287	525371	1.48012	790994
3.78347	39733	31	(− 2)4.74605	627657	2.08677	080755
6.20495	67778	77	(− 3)5.59962	661079	2.77292	138971
9.37298	52516	88	(− 4)3.05249	767093	3.59162	606809
13.46623	69110	92	(− 6)6.59212	302608	4.64876	600214
18.83359	77889	92	(− 8)4.11076	933035	6.21227	541975
26.37407	18909	27	(−11)3.29087	403035	9.36321	823771
			$n = 10$			
0.13779	34705	40	(− 1)3.08441	115765	0.35400	97386 07
0.72945	45495	03	(− 1)4.01119	929155	0.83190	23010 44
1.80834	29017	40	(− 1)2.18068	287612	1.33028	856175
3.40143	36978	55	(− 2)6.20874	560987	1.86306	390311
5.55249	61400	64	(− 3)9.50151	697518	2.45025	555808
8.33015	27467	64	(− 4)7.53008	388588	3.12276	415514
11.84378	58379	00	(− 5)2.82592	334960	3.93415	269556
16.27925	78313	78	(− 7)4.24931	398496	4.99241	487219
21.99658	58119	81	(− 9)1.83956	482398	6.57220	248513
29.92069	70122	74	(−13)9.91182	721961	9.78469	584037
			$n = 12$			
0.11572	21173	58	(− 1)2.64731	371055	0.29720	96360 44
0.61175	74845	15	(− 1)3.77759	275873	0.69646	29804 31
1.51261	02697	76	(− 1)2.44082	011320	1.10778	139462
2.83375	13377	44	(− 2)9.04492	222117	1.53846	423904
4.59922	76394	18	(− 2)2.01023	811546	1.99832	760627
6.84452	54531	15	(− 3)2.66397	354187	2.50074	576910
9.62131	68424	57	(− 4)2.03231	592663	3.06532	151828
13.00605	49933	06	(− 6)8.36505	585682	3.72328	911078
17.11685	51874	62	(− 7)1.66849	387654	4.52981	402998
22.15109	03793	97	(− 9)1.34239	103052	5.59725	846184
28.48796	72509	84	(−12)3.06160	163504	7.21299	546093
37.09912	10444	67	(−16)8.14807	746743	10.54383	74619
			$n = 15$			
0.09330	78120	17	(− 1)2.18234	885940	0.23957	81703 11
0.49269	17403	02	(− 1)3.42210	177923	0.56010	08427 93
1.21559	54120	71	(− 1)2.63027	577942	0.88700	82629 19
2.26994	95262	04	(− 1)1.26425	818106	1.22366	440215
3.66762	27217	51	(− 2)4.02068	649210	1.57444	872163
5.42533	66274	14	(− 3)8.56387	780361	1.94475	197653
7.56591	62266	13	(− 3)1.21243	614721	2.34150	205664
10.12022	85680	19	(− 4)1.11674	392344	2.77404	192683
13.13028	24821	76	(− 6)6.45992	676202	3.25564	334640
16.65440	77083	30	(− 7)2.22631	690710	3.80631	171423
20.77647	88994	49	(− 9)4.22743	038498	4.45847	775384
25.62389	42267	29	(−11)3.92189	726704	5.27001	778443
31.40751	91697	54	(−13)1.45651	526407	6.35956	346973
38.53068	33064	86	(−16)1.48302	705111	8.03178	763212
48.02608	55726	86	(−20)1.60059	490621	11.52777	21009

The Method of Averaging
Functional Corrections

A method for speeding the convergence of iterations in the method of solving integral equations by successive approximations has been developed in Russia by Yu D. Sokolov. This has been called the *method of averaging functional corrections* and is reported along with many applications by A. Y. Luchka (1). By way of illustration, consider the linear Fredholm integral equation of the second kind that occurs in radiative heat-transfer computations and has been considered before in Chapter 4

$$u(x) = f(x) + \lambda \int_a^b K(x, t)u(t)\, dt \qquad \text{(V-1)}$$

As a first approximation, the average value α_1 of $u(t)$ over the interval $a \le t \le b$ is substituted.

$$u_1(x) = f(x) + \alpha_1 \lambda \int_a^b K(x, t)\, dt \qquad \text{(V-2)}$$

$$\alpha_1 = \frac{1}{b-a} \int_a^b u_1(t)\,dt \qquad \text{(V-3)}$$

Now α_1 may be determined by substituting Equation (V-2) into Equation (V-3).

$$\alpha_1 = \frac{1}{D(\lambda)} \int_a^b f(x)\,dx \qquad \text{(V-4)}$$

where

$$D(\lambda) = (b-a) - \lambda \int_a^b \int_a^b K(x,t)\,dt\,dx \qquad \text{(V-5)}$$

It can be seen that in the radiosity equation for evacuated enclosures, the development of the lumped-parameter method was equivalent to this first approximation.

For the second approximation a correction is made to the first approximation as follows:

$$u_2(x) = f(x) + \lambda \int_a^b K(x,t)\,[u_1(t) + \alpha_2]\,dt \qquad \text{(V-6)}$$

where α_2 is the average difference between $u_1(t)$ and $u_2(t)$.

$$\alpha_2 = \frac{1}{b-a} \int_a^b [u_2(t) - u_1(t)]\,dt \qquad \text{(V-7)}$$

Now substituting **V-6** and **V-2** into **V-7** leads to the following expression for α_2.

$$\alpha_2 = \frac{\lambda}{D(\lambda)} \int_a^b \int_a^b K(x,t)\,[u_1(t) - \alpha_1]\,dt\,dx \qquad \text{(V-8)}$$

For the nth approximation we have

$$u_n(x) = f(x) + \lambda \int_a^b K(x,t)\,[u_{n-1}(t) + \alpha_n]\,dt \qquad \text{(V-9)}$$

where

$$\alpha_n = \frac{1}{b-a} \int_a^b [u_n(x) - u_{n-1}(x)]\,dx \qquad \text{(V-10)}$$

Upon combining (V-9) and (V-10) we obtain the following expression for α_n.

$$\alpha_n = \frac{\lambda}{D(\lambda)} \int_a^b \int_a^b K(x,t)\,[u_{n-1}(t) - u_{n-2}(t) - \alpha_{n-1}]\,dt\,dx \qquad \text{(V-11)}$$

*Example.** Let us now apply this method to the solution of the radiosity equation, (4-91), that was solved by two different approximate methods in Chapter 4.*

---

*This example has been prepared by Mr. Al Crosbie, Graduate Student at Purdue University.

$$B(x) = 1 + \frac{\rho H^2}{2} \int_{-1/2}^{1/2} B(y) \frac{1}{[(y-x)^2 + H^2]^{3/2}} dy \qquad \text{(4-91)}$$

Applying Sokolov's method of averaging functional corrections, the first approximation is

$$B_1(x) = 1 + \frac{\rho H^2}{2} \alpha_1 \int_{-1/2}^{1/2} \frac{dy}{[(y-x)^2 + H^2]^{3/2}} \qquad \text{(V-12)}$$

where

$$\alpha_1 = \int_{-1/2}^{1/2} B_1(x) \, dx \qquad \text{(V-13)}$$

Substituting $B_1(x)$ from Equation (V-2) into Equation (V-3), the following expression for α_1 is found.

$$\alpha_1 = 1 + \frac{\rho H^2}{2} \alpha_1 \int_{-1/2}^{1/2} \int_{-1/2}^{1/2} \frac{dy \, dx}{[(y-x)^2 + H^2]^{3/2}} \qquad \text{(V-14)}$$

Solving for α_1 we find

$$\alpha_1 = \frac{1}{1 - (\rho H^2 / 2) \int_{-1/2}^{1/2} \int_{-1/2}^{1/2} dy dx / [(y-x)^2 + H^2]^{3/2}} \qquad \text{(V-15)}$$

Noting the value of the integral, the equation is

$$\int_{-1/2}^{1/2} \int_{-1/2}^{1/2} \frac{dy dx}{[(y-x)^2 + H^2]^{3/2}} = \frac{2[(1 + H^2)^{1/2} - H]}{H^2} \qquad \text{(V-16)}$$

Substituting this back into (V-12) results in Equation (V-17).

$$B_1(x) = 1 + \alpha_1 \frac{\rho}{2} \left\{ \frac{\frac{1}{2} - x}{[(\frac{1}{2} - x)^2 + H^2]^{1/2}} + \frac{\frac{1}{2} + x}{[(\frac{1}{2} + x)^2 + H^2]^{1/2}} \right\} \qquad \text{(V-17)}$$

where

$$\alpha_1 = \frac{1}{(1 - \rho)[(1 + H^2)^{1/2} - H]} \qquad \text{(V-18)}$$

Over-all heat transfer may be computed by application of (4-13).

$$\frac{Q/L}{\epsilon \sigma T^4} = \frac{1}{\rho} \left[1 - \epsilon \int_{-1/2}^{1/2} B_1(x) \, dx \right]$$

$$= \frac{1 - \epsilon - \frac{1}{2} H^2 \rho \epsilon \alpha_1 \int_{-1/2}^{1/2} \int_{-1/2}^{1/2} [(y-x)^2 + H^2]^{-3/2} \, dx dy}{\rho}$$

$$= 1 - \epsilon \alpha_1 F \qquad \text{(V-19)}$$

where

$$F = \frac{1}{2} H^2 \int_{-1/2}^{1/2} \int_{-1/2}^{1/2} [(y-x)^2 + H^2]^{3/2} \, dy dx$$
$$= (1 + H^2)^{1/2} - H \qquad \text{(V-20)}$$

Thus, from Equation (V-5)

$$\alpha_1 = \frac{1}{1 - \rho F} \tag{V-21}$$

Therefore,

$$\frac{Q/L}{\epsilon \sigma T^4} = 1 - \frac{\epsilon F}{1 - \rho F} = \frac{(1 - F)}{1 - \rho F} \tag{V-22}$$

Thus, the first approximation corresponds to the two-zone, lumped-system approximation. For $\rho = 0.9$, $H = 0.5$

$$\left(\frac{Q/L}{\epsilon \sigma T^4}\right) = 0.86073$$

The *second approximation* gives

$$B_2(x) = 1 + \frac{\rho H^2}{2} \int_{-1/2}^{1/2} \frac{B_1(x) + \alpha_2}{[(y - x)^2 + H^2]^{3/2}} \, dy \tag{V-23}$$

where

$$\alpha_2 = \int_{-1/2}^{1/2} [B_2(x) - B_1(x)] \, dx = \int_{-1/2}^{1/2} B_1(x) \, dx - \alpha_1 \tag{V-24}$$

Substituting the expression for $B_2(x)$ into the definition for α_1, we obtain

$$\alpha_2 = 1 + \frac{\rho H^2}{2} \int_{-1/2}^{1/2} \int_{-1/2}^{1/2} \frac{B_1(x) \, dy dx}{[(y - x)^2 + H^2]^{3/2}}$$
$$+ \frac{\rho H^2}{2} \alpha_2 \int_{-1/2}^{1/2} \int_{-1/2}^{1/2} \frac{dy dx}{[(y - x)^2 + H^2]^{3/2}} - \alpha_1 \tag{V-25}$$

Thus,

$$\alpha_2 = \frac{1 + (\rho H^2/2) \int_{-1/2}^{1/2} \{B_1(x) \, dy dx/[(y - x)^2 + H^2]^{3/2}\} - \alpha_1}{1 - (\rho H^2/2) \int_{-1/2}^{1/2} \int_{-1/2}^{1/2} dy dx/[(y - x)^2 + H^2]^{3/2}} \tag{V-26}$$

$$\alpha_2 = \alpha_1 \left\{ 1 - \alpha_1 + (\rho H^2/2) \int_{-1/2}^{1/2} \int_{-1/2}^{1/2} \frac{B_1(x) \, dy dx}{[(y - x)^2 + H^2]^{3/2}} \right\} \tag{V-27}$$

Numerical integration is normally expedient for the higher approximations and has been utilized in computing the table of values on the next page.

$$\left(\frac{Q/L}{\epsilon \sigma T^4}\right)_{\text{Exact}} = 0.85759$$

Thus, it can be seen that the method of averaging functional corrections converges much more rapidly than the method of successive substitutions for this problem. The former does have the disadvantage that each successive substitution involves more computation than the less sophisticated method.

Some Results

$\rho = 0.9$	$H = 0.5$	$x = 0$
Iteration Number	$B(x)$ Successive Approximations	$B(x)$ Averaging Functional Corrections
0	1	
1	1.63640	2.43407
2	2.00360	2.48018
33	2.21219	2.48459
4	2.33043	2.48501
5	2.39744	2.48505
6	2.43541	2.48506
7	2.45692	
8	2.46911	
9	2.47602	
10	2.47994	
11	2.48215	
12	2.48341	
13	2.48412	
14	2.48453	
15	2.48476	
16	2.48489	
17	2.48496	
18	2.48500	
19	2.48502	
20	2.48504	
21	2.48505	
22	2.48505	

References

1. A. Yu. Luchka, *The Method of Averaging Functional Corrections: Theory and Applications*, Academic Press, New York, 1965.

APPENDIX **VI**

The Monte Carlo Method*

As the name implies, Monte Carlo methods are based on the theory of probability and statistics. The method is normally applied to problems where the events that occur at a given location are known, but where the inter-relations between happenings at various locations are described by complex equations that cannot be readily solved. To apply the Monte Carlo method, one creates a mathematical model of the problem, specifying all of the events that can occur, the sequence in which they occur, and the probability distributions for their occurrence. He then performs a statistically significant number of trials of the model and analyzes the results.

Monte Carlo methods have been applied to neutron diffusion problems for many years. [See Kahn (1)]. These have only recently been applied to any great extent in radiative transfer problems. See References (2) through (7). An excellent discussion of Monte Carlo methods in radiant heat

*This section has been prepared by Mr. Leo W. Stockham, Graduate Student, University of Oklahoma.

exchange has been given by Howell (8). The intent of the present discussion is to provide an elementary understanding of the fundamentals.

It will become apparent in what follows that one of the prerequisites for application of the Monte Carlo method is the ability to generate random numbers. For the pruposes of this discussion the term random number will be understood to mean *a number between zero and one that is a member of a set of numbers uniformly distributed over this interval.* That is, if one plots a large number of random numbers as points on a line between zero and one and then subdivides the interval into equal subintervals, no matter how small, every subinterval will contain about the same number of points. Note the emphasis on "large number of." If only a few random numbers are plotted there is no implication at all that they will be evenly spaced on the line.

A discussion of the theory of random number generation is beyond the scope of this presentation. Suffice it to say that a theory exists and that simple computer programs have been written that will provide suitable random numbers. See References (9) through (12).

As a simple illustration of the application of the Monte Carlo method, consider calculating the area A under the curve $y = x^2$ in the xy plane for $0 \le x \le 1$. Figure VI-1 depicts the problem.

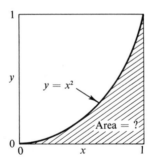

Figure VI-1.

Following the steps indicated above, the first consideration is to create a model of the problem. A suitable model here is to consider the area $0 \le y \le 1, 0 \le x \le 1$ analogous to a dart board and to have a computer "throw darts" under the following restrictions.

1. Every dart thrown must hit the dart board.
2. A dart is equally likely to hit any point on the board.
3. A large number of darts will be thrown.

In this model a dart either hits within the area A or it does not. The probability that a dart will hit in A is just the ratio of the area A to the total area of the board. Hence,

$$P(A) = \frac{A}{AT} \qquad \text{(VI-1)}$$

The probability that a dart hits in A can also be calculated, after a large number of throws, as the ratio of the number of hits in A to the total number of throws. Hence,

$$P(A) = \frac{\text{Hits in } A}{\text{Total throws}} \qquad \text{(VI-2)}$$

Combining (VI-1) and (VI-2),

$$A = AT \frac{\text{Hits in } A}{\text{Total throws}} \qquad \text{(VI-3)}$$

To accomplish the dart throwing, and calculate the answer, a computer is used as follows:

1. Set $x = Rx$, $Rx \equiv$ Random number for x $y = Ry$, $Ry \equiv$ Random number for y
2. Calculate $y = Rx^2$
3. If $Ry \leq Rx^2$ record a hit, otherwise a miss.
4. After completing a large number of throws, calculate A from Equation (VI-3).

Step 1 provides a uniform distribution of coordinate points (x, y) representing the locations where darts hit the board. Step 2 calculates the height of the boundary of A at the randomly chosen x coordinate. Step 3 compares the randomly chosen y coordinate with the boundary of A, and determines whether the point lies within A. Step 4 completes the problem by calculating the area of A.

This problem can be much more easily solved by elementary means, and the application of Monte Carlo methods would be an inefficient means of solution. Nevertheless, the problem serves well as a vehicle for illustrating the method.

In the illustration just concluded it was necessary to generate random values for x and y, both of which were uniformly distributed. In more complex applications, one may want to generate random values for variables which are not uniformly distributed. As an example one might wish to generate values for x conforming to the distribution illustrated in Figure VI-2.

Here we seek to choose values of x such that the fraction of values of x chosen between x and $x + \Delta x$ will be proportional to the area under the curve between x and $x + \Delta x$.

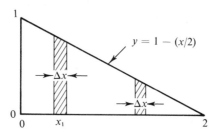

Figure VI-2.

For example we must choose more values between x_1 and $x_1 + \Delta x$ than between x_2 and $x_2 + \Delta x$. This can be accomplished in the following way.

1. Set $x = 2Rx$, $y = Ry$ **(VI-4)**
2. Calculating $y = 1 - (x/2) = 1 - Rx$
3. If $Ry \leq 1 - Rx$, use x, otherwise discard it.

Step 1 provides a uniform distribution of coordinate points over the whole of the area $0 \leq y \leq 1$, $0 \leq x \leq 2$. Step 2 calculates the y value of the curve above a randomly selected value of x. Step 3 compares the calculated y with the randomly selected value of y and determines whether or not the corresponding value of x should be used. If one were to plot all of the randomly selected points ($y = Ry$, $x = 2Rx$), they would be uniformly distributed over the area $0 \leq y \leq 1$, $0 \leq x \leq 2$. The x values used would be those values of X for which the point (x, y) is below $y = 1 - (x/2)$. The rest would be discarded. The number of values of x taken in any interval between x and $x + \Delta x$ would be proportional to the fraction of the total area under the curve that lies between x and $x + \Delta x$.

One should note that this procedure makes rather inefficient use of random numbers. The object was to generate random values for x conforming to a desired distribution. The procedure above generates two random numbers to determine each point (x, y), discards half of the points completely, and only makes use of the random value for x of the points it keeps. Hence it selects for values of x only one-fourth of the random numbers generated. For other distributions it will discard a different proportion but will never use more than half of the numbers generated.

A method that uses all of the random numbers generated can be derived from the theory of probability. Only some definitions and results will be given here. See (2), (8), (13), (14) for further information.

A function $f(x)$ is called the *probability density function* for x if

$$f(x) \geq 0 \qquad -\infty \leq x \leq \infty \qquad \text{(VI-5)}$$

and

$$\int_{-\infty}^{\infty} f(x)\,dx = 1$$

The integral of a probability density function from $-\infty$ to x is called the *probability distribution function.*

$$F(x) = \int_{-\infty}^{x} f(t)\,dt \qquad \text{(VI-6)}$$

The probability density function can be satisfied by setting $F(x) = R$, where R is a uniformly-distributed random number on the interval 0 to 1.

In the previous example, the function

$$f(x) = 1 - \frac{x}{2} \qquad 0 \leq x \leq 2$$
$$= 0 \qquad\qquad \text{for all other } x \qquad \text{(VI-7)}$$

is a probability density function for x since $f(x) \geq 0$ and

$$\int_{-\infty}^{\infty} f(x)dx = \int_{0}^{2}\left(1 - \frac{x}{2}\right)dx = \left[x - \frac{x^2}{4}\right]_{0}^{1} = 1 \qquad \text{(VI-8)}$$

(If the integral were not unity the probability density function could be obtained from the given function by dividing by the value of the integral.)

In this case we can select values of x that will satisfy $f(x)$ by setting $F(x)$ equal to random numbers and solving for x. Hence,

$$F(x) = R = x - \frac{x^2}{4} \qquad \text{(VI-9)}$$

which gives

$$x = 2 \pm 2(1 - R)^{1/2} \qquad \text{(VI-10)}$$

and since $0 \leq x \leq 2$, we take

$$x = 2 - 2(1 - R)^{1/2} \qquad \text{(VI-11)}$$

The choice of the method used in selecting values of x depends on the specific distribution function. While the latter method makes use of all the random numbers generated, it may be that solving $F(x) = R$ for x will consume more computer time than will the generating of additional random numbers. In such cases, the former method would be more attractive.

As an example of a typical decision arising in a radiant heat-transfer application of Monte Carlo, consider the selection of the coordinates of the emission point for a photon in a homogeneous, isothermal, cylinder of gas. Assume that the emission is equally likely at any point in the cylin-

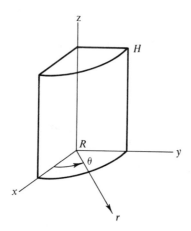

Figure VI-3.

der. Figure VI-3 shows the coordinate system for a cylinder of radius R and height H.

The probability that emission will occur in any given volume element is equal to the volume of the element divided by the volume of the cylinder. Hence,

$$PE = \frac{r\, d\theta dr dz}{\pi R^2 H} \qquad \text{(VI-12)}$$

Noting that

$$PE \geq 0$$

and

$$\int_0^H \int_0^R \int_0^{2\pi} \frac{r\, d\theta dr dz}{\pi R^2 H} = 1 \qquad \text{(VI-13)}$$

we conclude that $PE = f(r, \theta, z)\, d\theta dr dz$ where $f(f, \theta, z)$ is the joint probability density function. Since $r\, d\theta dr dz / \pi R^2 H$ can be written

$$\left(\frac{\partial r}{R^2} dr\right)\left(\frac{d\theta}{2\pi}\right)\left(\frac{dz}{H}\right)$$

we conclude that r, θ, z are independent in the probability sense and that

$$f(r) = \frac{\partial r}{R^2}$$
$$f(\theta) = \tfrac{1}{2}\pi \qquad \text{(VI-14)}$$
$$f(z) = \frac{1}{H}$$

Remembering that we can satisfy these probability density functions by setting the corresponding distribution functions equal to random numbers and solving for the value of the variable, we take

$$F(r) = \int_0^r \frac{2r}{R^2}\, dr = \frac{r^2}{R^2} = Rr$$

$$F(\theta) = \int_0^\theta \frac{d\theta}{2\pi} \quad = \frac{\theta}{2\pi} = R\theta \tag{VI-15}$$

$$F(z) = \int_0^z \frac{dz}{H} \quad = \frac{z}{H} = Rz$$

or

$$r = R\sqrt{Rr}$$

$$\theta = 2\pi R\theta \tag{VI-16}$$

$$z = HRz$$

The typical decision discussed above corresponds to one step in a Monte Carlo solution. In a complete problem, one is faced with similar decisions for such things as emission direction, frequency of radiation, probable path length, and where and when an individual particle history will terminate. Finally, after following a large number of particles, one must still decide what significance to attach to the results.

There is no cookbook that specifies when and how one should apply Monte Carlo methods to various problems. The decision to do so is probably as much a function of the decision maker as it is of the problem. Nevertheless, above some nebulous minimum standard of complexity one can probably do better with Monte Carlo than with other techniques. It can be said in general that the complexity of a Monte Carlo solution increases directly with the complexity of the problem, whereas the complexity of solutions using simultaneous equations and matrices increases roughly with its square. Computer times are relatively long for Monte Carlo solutions because the accuracy of the solution depends on the number of trials of the model and is never very good until the number of trials becomes large. Thus, for simple problems elementary methods are often vastly superior. However, the answer obtained from a well-designed Monte Carlo solution, regardless of the problem complexity, tends to the exact answer as the number of trials becomes very large. Hence Monte Carlo is often more accurate than approximate methods when applied to complex problems and may be applied to problems too complex to tackle by other means.

References

1. Kahn, H., *Random Sampling (Monte Carlo) Techniques in Neutron Attenuation Problems*—I and II, Nucleonics, May and June 1950.

2. Howell, J. R. and Perlmutter, M., "Monte Carlo Solution of Thermal

Transfer Through Radiant Media Between Gray Walls," *Journal of Heat Transfer*, Vol. 86, Series C, No. 1 (February 1964).

3. Howell, J. R. and Perlmutter, M., "Radiant Transfer Through a Gray Gas Between Concentric Cylinders Using Monte Carlo," *Journal of Heat Transfer*, Vol. 86, Series C, No. 2 (May 1964).

4. Howell, J. R. and Perlmutter, M., "Monte Carlo Solution of Radiant Heat Transfer in a Nongrey Nonisothermal Gas with Temperature Dependent Properties," *A.I. Ch.E. Journal*, Vol. 10, No. 4 (July 1964).

5. Polgar, L. G. and Howell, J. R., *Directional Thermal-Radiative Properties of Conical Cavities*, NASA TN D–2904, June 1965.

6. Corlett, R. C., "Direct Monte Carle Calculation of Radiative Heat Transfer in Vacuum," *Journal of Heat Transfer*, Vol. 88, Series C, No. 4 (November 1966).

7. Fleck, J. A., Jr., *The Calculation of Nonlinear Radiation Transport by a Monte Carlo Method*, Methods in Computational Physics, Vol. 1, Academic Press, New York, 1963.

8. Howell, J. R., *Caclulation of Radiant Heat Exchange by the Monte Carlo Method*, NASA TMX–52101, 1965.

9. Kuo, S. S., *Numerical Methods and Computers*, Addison-Wesley, Reading, Mass., 1965.

10. Coveyou, R. R., *Serial Correlation in the Generation of Pseudo-Random Numbers*, J. Assoc. Comput. Mach., Vol. 7, No. 1 (1960).

11. Rotenberg, A., *A New Pseudo-Random Number Generator*, J. Assoc. Comput. Mach., Vol. 7, No. 1 (1960).

12. Page, E. S., *Pseudo-Random Elements for Computers*, Applied Statistics, Vol. 8, No. 2 (1956).

13. Mood, A. M. and Graybill, F. A., *Introduction to the Theory of Statistics*, McGraw-Hill Book Company, New York, 1963.

14. Parzen, E., *Modern Probability Threoy and Its Applications*, John Wiley & Sons, Inc., New York, 1960.

Author Index

Abramowitz, M., 166, 173

Beattie, J. F., 143, 162, 195, 199
Beckmann, P., 51, 56
Belcher, R. L., 165, 173
Best, G., 183, 184, 199
Bevans, J. T., 133, 134, 138, 185, 187, 199
Birkebak, R. C., 51, 56
Blanton, R. W., 102, 111
Blau, H., 174, 198
Branstetter, J. R., 105, 111
Burch, D. L., 133, 138
Buschman, A. J., 256

Cess, R. D., 170, 172, 173
Chandrasekhar, S., 137, 158, 160, 162
Chasmar, R. D., 175, 177, 178, 179, 182, 198
Chu, C. M., 142, 160, 161, 162

Churchill, S. W., 142, 160, 161, 162
Clark, C. C., 142, 161
Clauss, F. J., 174, 183, 186, 198
Coffin, C. L., 183, 184, 199
Cohen, E. S., 130, 138
Condon, E. V., 37
Corlett, R. C., 280
Courant, R., 85, 110
Coveyou, R. R., 280
Crosbie, A. L., 269
Cunningham, F. G., 256

Deem, H. W., 48, 56, 229
Deirmendjian, D., 143, 162
Dewitt, D. P., 191, 199
Drake, R. M., 65, 110
Drude, P., 37
Dunkle, R. V., 39, 56, 133, 134, 138, 187
Dunn, S. T., 191, 199

281

Subject Index